Gaia Herbs Farm valley. 200 pristine acres of certified organic farmland. Ric Scalzo conducts a tour of the farm facilities.

Skullcap growing inside the cultivation greenhouses at Gaia Herbs Farm prior to transplantation into the farm fields.

The 3 stages of development of certified organic Echinacea on Gaia Herbs Farm.

Certified organic Valerian in full bloom.

Certified organic California Poppy blooming in summer on Gaia Herbs Farm.

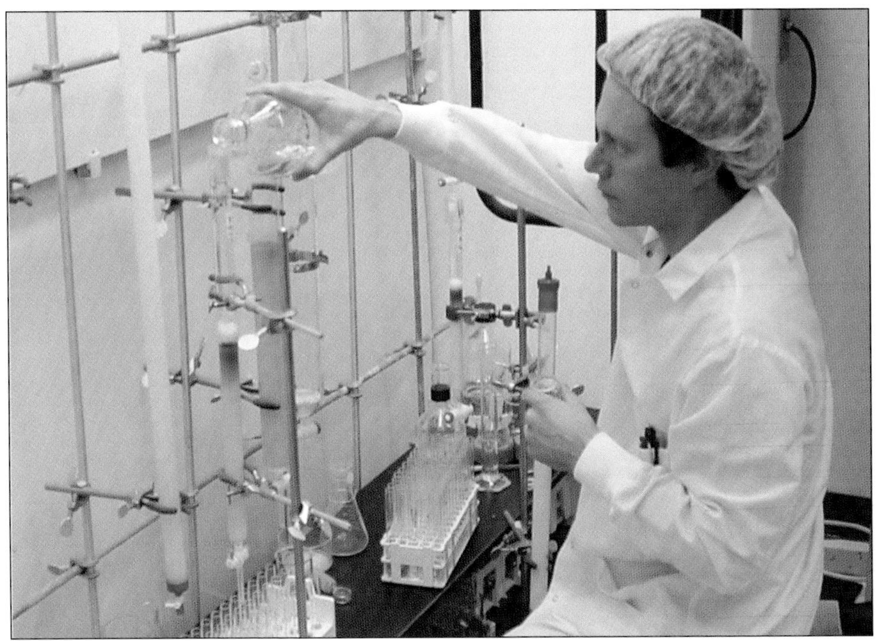

Dr. Jeremy Stewart separates constituants for identification using a column extractor.

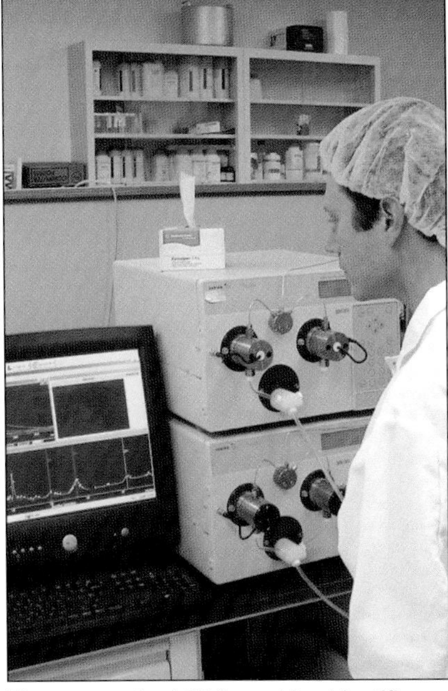

The preparative HPLC machine identifies specific marker compounds within various herbal extracts.

Large capacity low heat vacuum roto-evaporation unit concentrates large batches of extract.

Highly concentrated liquid herbal extract is encapsulated into vegetarian capsules with this machinery, producing up to 40,000 Liquid Phyto-Caps™ per hour.

The new Liquid Phyto-Caps™ are automatically sealed and carefully inspected.

Terry oversees the automated bottling and labeling of Liquid Phyto-Caps™ at their final stage of production.

Medicines from the Earth

Table of Contents

Easy Look-up Guide by Topic

ADRENAL

ANTIOXIDANTS

BACK AND JOINT MOBILITY

BLOOD SUGAR SUPPORT

CARDIOVASCULAR HEALTH

CIRCULATORY FUNCTION

CHOLESTEROL

Gaia Herbs Liquid Phyto-Caps™

SINGLE HERBS AND FORMULAS

ADRENAL HEALTH

Supports Healthy
Adrenal Function*

ALCOHOL-FREE CONCENTRATED EXTRACTS OF:

FORMULA	MG EXTRACT PER 2 CAPSULES
Rhodiola root (*Rhodiola rosea*)	200 mg
Ashwagandha root and leaf (*Withania somnifera*)*	100 mg
Schizandra berry (*Schizandra chinensis*)	100 mg
Wild Oats (*Avena sativa*)	100 mg
Holy Basil E.T.O.H. (*Ocimum sanctum*)	100 mg
Holy Basil Supercritical Extract (*Ocimum sanctum*)	50 mg

*Ingredient is protected under US Patent Nos. 6,153,198 and 6,713,092

STANDARDIZED TO FULL SPECTRUM ACTIVITY PROFILE

Withanolide glycosides (from Ashwagandha)	8 mg
Rosavins (from Rhodiola root)	6 mg
Salidrosides (from Rhodiola root)	1.6 mg

DOSAGE
Liquid Phyto-Caps: 2 capsules, 2 times daily

DURATION OF USE
3 months

BEST TAKEN
After meals, with warm water

DESCRIPTION OF FORMULA

Adrenal Health enhances the body's physiologic response to stress. Stress is defined as any situation or condition that causes undue physical, emotional and/or mental strain on the body. When one experiences stress, in any form, the adrenal glands secrete specific hormones that have a profound effect on the body.

*THIS STATEMENT HAS NOT BEEN EVALUATED BY THE FOOD AND DRUG ADMINISTRATION. THIS PRODUCT IS NOT INTENDED TO DIAGNOSE, TREAT, CURE OR PREVENT ANY DISEASE.

One can imagine the adrenal glands as little "hats" that sit on top of the kidneys. These hats secrete hormones such as cortisol and DHEA in response to stress. Over time, as one experiences stress on a daily basis, the adrenal glands can function less optimally, secreting unhealthy levels of these stress-related hormones. Overworking of the adrenal glands can lead to something called adrenal stress. Nervousness, poor memory, difficulty with concentration and decision-making, cravings for sweets, weight gain and compromised sleep are all associated with failure to maintain healthy levels of these two hormones.

The Adrenal Health formula can have a profound influence on the body, helping to maintain a healthy response to stress by supporting the adrenal glands and nourishing the nervous system. Select herbs within the formula contain compounds recognized for their ability to support the health and function of the adrenal glands and maintaining normal secretion levels of key stress-related hormones such as cortisol.*

Rhodiola rosea root supports the functioning of the adrenal glands and encourages a healthy response to physical, emotional and mental stress by normalizing cortisol levels and other stress-related hormones. If used regularly, it enhances the body's natural resistance and adaptation to stressful influences. Rhodiola rosea root is classified as an adaptogen, which represents a class of herbs that help the body adapt to stresses of various kinds. In order to achieve this classification, a plant must be harmless and must have a normalizing, broad-spectrum action that supports homeostasis, particularly when under stressful influences.*

Ashwaghanda, often referred to as "Indian Ginseng," is a common herb used in Ayurvedic medicine (from India) to support mental and physical vitality and stamina. It contains steroidal compounds and additional chemical constituents that advance the body's natural resistance and adaptation to stressful influences. Ashwaghanda also supports mental endurance, promotes total metabolic efficiency and encourages an overall sense of well-being.*

Schizandra berries provide powerful antioxidant protection, particularly from free radicals and other toxins in the environment that may cause cellular damage. Regarded as a popular adaptogenic agent, schizandra berries are unique in that they hold a remarkable blend of five distinct flavor properties collectively serving to promote overall health and vitality. Namely, bitter, sweet, sour, salty and hot. Schizandra berries function to enhance the body's natural resistance and adaptation to stressful influences, support mental endurance and promote overall metabolic efficiency.*

Wild Oats milky seed contains numerous compounds that promote a vital nervous system while working to ease temporary nervous stress, weakness, and exhaustion.*

Holy Basil has long been used in Ayurvedic medicine to support a healthy response to stress, nourish the mind and elevate the spirit. Revered by Ayurvedic practitioners as "the incomparable one," this herb's documented actions on the

*THIS STATEMENT HAS NOT BEEN EVALUATED BY THE FOOD AND DRUG ADMINISTRATION.
THIS PRODUCT IS NOT INTENDED TO DIAGNOSE, TREAT, CURE OR PREVENT ANY DISEASE.

body date back thousands of years. Today, we know that holy basil contains a variety of constituents, including eugenol, camphor, caryophyllene, Ursolic acid, luteolin and apigenin that function collectively to normalize stress hormones and enhance adrenal function. The properties inherent in this herb make it ideally suited for helping to support a healthy adrenal system and stress response.*

COMPLEMENTARY PHYTO-CAPS/LIQUID FORMULAS/LIQUID EXTRACTS

Rhodiola Rosea Liquid Phyto-Caps™, Astragalus Supreme Liquid Phyto-Caps™

SAFETY EVALUATION/CONTRAINDICATIONS

Before using this product, talk with your healthcare professional if you suffer from a medical condition. Please visit www.gaiaherbs.com to obtain information regarding potential contraindications and/or side effects that may be associated with herbs found in this formula.*

KNOWN DRUG INTERACTIONS

Before using this product, talk with your healthcare professional if you take any medications. Please visit www.gaiaherbs.com to obtain information regarding any possible drug interactions that may be associated with herbs found in this formula.*

REFERENCES

Brown RP, Gerbarg PL, Ramazanov Z. Rhodiola rosea: a phytomedicinal overview. Herbalgram 2002;56:40–52.

Chiu PY et al. In vivo antioxidant action of a lignan-enriched extract of Schisandra fruit and an anthraquinone-containing extract of Polygonum root in comparison with schisandrin B and emodin. Planta Med. 2002 Nov;68(11):951-6.

Darbinyan V et al. Rhodiola rosea in stress induced fatigue - a double blind cross-over study of a standardized extract SHR-5 with a repeated low-dose regimen on the mental performance of healthy physicians during night duty. Phytomedicine 2000;7(5):365-71.

Darbinyan V, Kteyan A, Panossian A, et al. Rhodiola rosea in stress induced fatigue - a double blind cross-over study of a standardized extract SHR-5 with a repeated low-dose regimen on the mental performance of healthy physicians during night duty. Phytomedicine 2000;7(5):365-71.

Davis JM et al. Effects of oat beta-glucan on innate immunity and infection after exercise stress. Med Sci Sports Exerc. 2004 Aug;36(8):1321-7.

Dhuley JN.Adaptogenic and cardioprotective action of ashwagandha in rats and frogs. J Ethnopharmacol. 2000 Apr;70(1):57-63.

Hoffmann D. Oats. http://www.healthy.net/scr/Article.asp?Id=1592 [Accessed March2, 2005].

Kelly GS. Rhodiola rosea: a possible plant adaptogen. Altern Med Rev 2001;6:293-302.

Kucinskaite A, Briedis V, Savickas A.[Experimental analysis of therapeutic properties of Rhodiola rosea L. and its possible application in medicine].[Article in Lithuanian]. Medicina (Kaunas). 2004;40(7):614-9.

Maslova LV et al. [The cardioprotective and antiadrenergic activity of an extract of Rhodiola rosea in stress]. [Article in Russian]. Eksp Klin Farmakol 1994;57(6):61-3.

Petkov VD et al. Effects of alcohol aqueous extract from Rhodiola rosea L. roots on learning and memory. Acta Physiol Pharmacol Bulg 1986;12(1):3-16.

Spasov AA et al. A double-blind, placebo-controlled pilot study of the stimulating and adaptogenic effect of Rhodiola rosea SHR-5 extract on the fatigue of students caused by stress during an examination period with a repeated low-dose regimen. Phytomedicine 2000;7(2):85-89.

Vats V, Yadav SP, Grover JK. Ethanolic extract of Ocimum sanctum leaves partially attenuates streptozotocin-induced alterations in glycogen content and carbohydrate metabolism in rats. Ethnopharmacol. 2004 Jan;90(1):155-60.

ALLER-LEAF

Supports Healthy Functioning of the Upper Respiratory System*

ALCOHOL-FREE CONCENTRATED EXTRACTS OF:

FORMULA	MG PER 2 CAPSULES
Turmeric rhizome (*Curcuma longa*)	132 mg
Eyebright herb (*Euphrasia officinalis*)	132 mg
Nettle leaf (*Urtica dioica*)	106 mg
Bayberry bark (*Myrica cerifera*)	100 mg
Chinese Skullcap root (*Scutellaria baicalensis*)	36 mg
Goldenseal rhizome (*Hydrastis canadensis*)	16 mg
Yarrow flower (*Achillea millefolium*)	14 mg
Feverfew tops (*Tanacetum parthenium*)	8 mg

DOSAGE

Liquid Phyto-Caps: 2 capsules, 2-3 times daily

DURATION OF USE

2 or more months

BEST TAKEN

Between meals with a small amount of warm water

DESCRIPTION OF FORMULA

Aller-Leaf is a unique formula specifically designed to both support the health of the respiratory mucous membranes, and support the body's immune response to poor nutrition, indoor and outdoor air pollution, pollen and other toxins, and environmental insults. Its component herbs support immunologic balance and mucous membrane health.*

Turmeric rhizome contains a variety of constituents known as curcuminoids that are responsible for turmeric's characteristic yellow color. These compounds also offer health-giving properties, as they provide the mucous membranes of the respiratory tract with antioxidant protection from free radicals and pollutants in our environment. Additionally, turmeric works synergistically with Nettle leaf in this formula to ensure the maintenance of acceptable levels of histamine in the body. The properties inherent in this herb make it ideally suited for helping support a healthy immune and respiratory system response.*

Eyebright herb is a European herb traditionally used for maintaining the healthy function of the sinuses. While researchers have not studied this herb for this purpose, we do know that Eyebright contains tannin and caffeic acid constituents that function to support the health of respiratory mucous membranes and maintain healthy levels of mucous excretions.*

Nettle leaf was traditionally used as a nutritive food. It represents a concentrated source of health-giving factors, including vitamin C, carotene and calcium that are important supporters of the immune and respiratory systems. Carotene in particular helps to nourish the lining of the respiratory tract and the mucous membranes, while calcium is essential for the proper functioning of certain immune-related white blood cells. Nettle leaf also contains flavonoids such as quercitin, kaempferol, and rutin that help to maintain healthy levels of histamine in the body. Histamine release is associated with response to environmental insult. Nettle leaf helps to maintain your body's defense system and increase histamine efficiency.*

Bayberry bark contains tannin components, which are traditionally used to help maintain healthy mucous membranes, particularly in the respiratory tract.*

Chinese Skullcap root contains many important flavonoid constituents such as baicalin, scutellarein, wogonin and baicalein. Some of these flavonoids are of particular interest to researchers looking for herbs that maintain healthy fluid balance in the body. Further, these constituents provide potent antioxidant protection against free radicals that challenge the lining of the respiratory tract.*

Goldenseal root has long been used as a Native American remedy for helping maintain normal respiratory mucosal function. While research is lacking on the use of this root as a whole, two of its main constituents, berberine and hydrastine, have been studied extensively. These alkaloids aid in the proper maintenance of mucous membranes, and in strengthening immune system health.*

Yarrow flowers contain many health-giving constituents including amino acids, folic acid, caffeic acid, salicylic acid, alkaloids and flavonoids that all work synergistically to support the health of the respiratory mucous membranes and protect them from effects of free radicals and other toxic elements in our environment. These flowers also help to support the body's immune system response.*

Feverfew leaf promotes the healthy metabolism and activity of prostaglandins, leukotrienes, platelets and serotonin. Further, feverfew contains melatonin, a hormone that may play a role in encouraging a healthy sleep cycle and promoting a healthy response to stressors that cause occasional temporary pain.*

COMPLEMENTARY PHYTO-CAPS/LIQUID FORMULAS/LIQUID EXTRACTS

Infla-Profen Liquid Phyto-Caps™, Breathe Naturally

SAFETY EVALUATION/CONTRAINDICATIONS

This formula should be avoided in pregnancy and lactation. It may occasionally cause gastrointestinal upset if taken away from food. It may increase one's sensitivity to sunlight and cause loosening of stools, which is normal and will tend to pass with time. Use with caution if you are allergic to the Astercaceae/

Compositae (includes daisies, marigolds, ragweeds and others) family. If you experience fast or irregular breathing, itching, skin rash or hives, seek medical attention promptly. Also, use with caution and seek the advice of a qualified healthcare professional if you have heart disease, congestive heart failure, diabetes, gallstones, stomach ulcer or other stomach disorder, a kidney disorder, or high/low blood pressure.*

KNOWN DRUG INTERACTIONS

Take one half hour before or an hour after taking any medicine due to the potential interaction caused by tannins contained in Aller-Leaf. This formula should be used with caution in combination with drugs that inhibit blood clotting and platelet aggregation including but not limited to warfarin (Coumadin®) due to its vitamin K content. Additionally, this formula may interact with antihypertension and antidiabetic medications. There is also a possibility that this formula might cause further drowsiness if taken with a medication that causes drowsiness. The herbs in this formula have not been studied extensively to determine their interactions with other medications. Before using this formula, talk with your healthcare professional if you take any medications.*

REFERENCES

Arora RB, Basu N, Kapoor V, Jain AP. Anti-inflammatory studies on Curcuma longa (turmeric). Ind J Med Res 1971;59:1289–95.

Blumenthal M, et al. ed. The Complete German Commission E Monographs: Therapeutic Guide to Herbal Medicines. Trans. S. Klein. Boston, MA: American Botanical Council, 1998.

Brinker F. Herb Contraindications and Drug Interactions. 2nd ed. Sandy, OR: Eclectic Medical Publications, 1998.

Gao Z, Huang K, Yang X, Xu H. Free radical scavenging and antioxidant activities of flavonoids extracted from the radix of Scutellaria baicalensis Georgi. Biochim Biophys Acta 1999;1472:643-50.

Gruenwald J, et al. PDR for Herbal Medicines. 1st ed. Montvale, NJ: Medical Economics Company, Inc., 1998.

Hoffman D. The Herbal Handbook: A User's Guide to Medical Herbalism. Rochester, VT: Healing Arts Press, 1988, 136–7.

Huang KC. The pharmacology of Chinese herbs. 2nd ed. New York, NY: CRC Press LLC. 1999;385-6, 400-1.

Leung AY, Foster S. Encyclopedia of Common Natural Ingredients Used in Food, Drugs and Cosmetics. 2nd ed. New York, NY: John Wiley & Sons, 1996.

Lloyd JU, Lloyd CG. Drugs and Medicines of North America vol 1--Ranunculaceae. Cincinnati, Robert Clarke & Co, 1884-1885.

McGuffin M, et al., ed. American Herbal Products Association's Botanical Safety Handbook. Boca Raton, FL: CRC Press, 1997.

Nadkarni AK, Nadkarni KM. Indian Materia Medica vol 1. Bombay: Popular Prakashan, 1976:35-7.

Newall CA, Anderson LA, Philpson JD. Herbal Medicine: A Guide for Healthcare Professionals. London, UK: The Pharmaceutical Press, 1996.

Nordstrom DC, Honkanen VE, Nasu Y, et al. Alpha-linolenic acid in the treatment of rheumatoid arthritis. A double-blind, placebo-controlled and randomized study: flaxseed vs. safflower seed. Rheumatol Int

*THIS STATEMENT HAS NOT BEEN EVALUATED BY THE FOOD AND DRUG ADMINISTRATION.
THIS PRODUCT IS NOT INTENDED TO DIAGNOSE, TREAT, CURE OR PREVENT ANY DISEASE.

1995;14(6):231-4.

Ramirez-Boscá A, Soler A, Gutierrez MAC, et al. Antioxidant Curcuma extracts decrease the blood lipid peroxide levels of human subjects. Age 1995;18:167-9.

Tillotson AK, Tillotson NSH, Abel R. The One Earth Herbal Sourcebook. New York: Kensington Publishing.

Wichtl MW. Herbal Drugs and Phytopharmaceuticals. Ed. N.M. Bisset. Stuttgart: Medpharm GmbH Scientific Publishers, 1994.

ANTI-OXIDANT SUPREME

Whole-Body Plant Anti-Oxidant*

ALCOHOL-FREE CONCENTRATED EXTRACTS OF:

FORMULA	MG EXTRACT PER 2 CAPSULES
Hawthorn berry, Solid Extract (*Crataegus spp.*)	100 mg
Green Tea leaf (*Camellia sinensis*)	100 mg
Bilberry berry (*Vaccinium myrtillus*)	50 mg
Ginkgo leaf (*Ginkgo biloba*)	20 mg
Prickly Ash bark (*Xanthoxylum clava-herculis*)	8 mg
Rosemary leaf, Supercritical CO_2 Extract (*Rosmarinus* off.)	8 mg
Astaxanthin	2 mg

STANDARDIZED TO FULL SPECTRUM ACTIVITY PROFILE

Anthocyanidins (from Bilberry)	12.5 mg
Polyphenols (from Green Tea)	80 mg

DOSAGE

1 capsule 2 times daily

DURATION OF USE

3-4 months or longer

BEST TAKEN

Between meals, with warm water

THE STORY OF FREE RADICALS

Free radicals, which are atoms that have an unpaired electron, are both essential to life and harmful. The body produces oxygen free radicals as a natural part of making energy (in the form of ATP) in most cells. Because making energy and thus free radicals cannot be avoided, the body has evolved a variety of defenses against free radicals known as antioxidants. These quench or neutralize the free radicals after they are produced, allowing cells to make ATP energy without building up toxic levels of free radicals. Natural antioxidants include such familiar substances as vitamin C, vitamin E and coenzyme Q10. Some less familiar natural antioxidants include superoxide dismutase and catalase. The problem with free radicals arises when the body comes under assault above and beyond the normal metabolic process. Since the air, water, and food all contain significant sources of free radicals, the body now has to quench these or face cellular damage and disease. Additionally, chronic inflammation causes a great increase in free radicals because immune cells use free radicals to try to control the inflammation. White blood cells are very active; requiring and producing a lot of energy and free radicals. Fortunately plants contain numerous types of antioxidants that can bolster the body's defenses against free radicals.

Hawthorn berry has a long history of use for supporting normal heart function and structure. The usefulness of Hawthorn for supporting heart health concerns is supported by research. Modern research has also indicated that Hawthorn has potent antioxidant activity, in particular protecting collagen and the cardiovascular system. Hawthorn is widely recommended by clinicians with extensive experience in its use for long term intake to obtain optimal benefits for heart health.*

Green Tea contains polyphenols and flavonoids that give it strong antioxidant activity. Green tea is considered to be partly responsible for the low incidence of free radical-related conditions in Japan, China, and other places where it is widely consumed as a beverage.*

Bilberry contains proanthocyanidin molecules that are established as strong antioxidants. Bilberry has shown the strongest affinity for the eyes, blood vessels, heart, and connective tissue (collagen). It also protects the digestive tract and the skin. Bilberry can strengthen the blood-brain barrier and other blood vessels. Bilberry and its close cousin blueberry are used traditionally as food and to support digestive health.*

Ginkgo leaf is a modern antioxidant phenomenon. The nuts were used traditionally but the leaves only rarely. A great wealth of studies in the past 50 years have documented the antioxidant activity of this versatile herb. Ginkgo's antioxidant effects appear to be most pronounced in the brain, nerves, and cardiovascular system. In addition to quenching the common oxygen free radicals, Ginkgo is also shown to eliminate excessive nitric oxide, another type of free radical.*

Prickly Ash bark is considered a circulatory stimulant and nerve tonic in traditional cultures. It may accomplish some of its actions by being antioxidant, and it theoretically helps distribute other antioxidants throughout the body by increasing circulation.*

Rosemary leaf has been demonstrated in studies to be a powerful antioxidant. Traditional reports of the benefits of rosemary include supporting cognitive abilities and poor memory ("weakness of the brain"), immune function, digestive health and circulation.*

*THIS STATEMENT HAS NOT BEEN EVALUATED BY THE FOOD AND DRUG ADMINISTRATION.
THIS PRODUCT IS NOT INTENDED TO DIAGNOSE, TREAT, CURE OR PREVENT ANY DISEASE.

Astaxanthin is the pink carotenoid that gives salmon, crabs, shrimp, and flamingos their color. This is because these animals eat microorganisms that contain large quantities of astaxanthin. Like other carotenoids, astaxanthin shows promise as a remarkably effective fat-soluble antioxidant. This may be particularly important in protecting cell membranes, which are primarily made up of fats.*

COMPLEMENTARY PHYTO-CAPS/LIQUID FORMULAS/LIQUID EXTRACTS

Vision Enhancement Liquid Phyto-Caps™

SAFETY EVALUATION/CONTRAINDICATIONS

Do not use this product during pregnancy or lactation.

KNOWN DRUG INTERACTIONS

Consult a physician if you are taking any pharmaceutical drugs. Anti-Oxidant Supreme should be used with caution when combining with aspirin, non-steroidal anti-inflammatory drugs (NSAIDs) such as ibuprofen, warfarin (Coumadin®), heparin, or any other drug that affects blood clotting.

Use of this formula should be discussed with a physician knowledgeable in herbal medicine before combining it with cancer chemotherapy or radiation therapy.

REFERENCES

Cunio L. Vaccinium myrtillus. Australian J Med Herbalism 1993;5:81-85.

Murray M. Bilberry (Vaccinium myrtillus). Am J Nat Med 1997;4:18-22.

Detre A, Jellinke H, Miskulin M, Robert AM. Studies on vascular permeability in hypertension: Action of anthocyanosides. Clin Physiol Biochem 1986;4:143-9.

Robert AM, Godeau G, Moati F, Miskulin M. Action of the anthocyanosides of Vaccinium myrtillis [sic] on the permeability of the blood brain barrier. J Med 1977;8:321-32.

Reuter HD. Crataegus (hawthorn): A botanical cardiac agent. Z Phytother 1994;15:73-81. Reprinted in Q Rev Nat Med 1995;summer:107-17.

Murray MT, Pizzorno JE Jr. Crataegus oxyacantha (hawthorn). In: Pizzorno JE Jr, Murray MT (eds) Textbook of Natural Medicine vol 1. Edinburgh: Churchill Livingstone, 1990:683-7.

Squires R. Ginkgo biloba. ATOMS (Austral Trad Med Soc) 1995; Autumn:9-14.

Yan LJ, Droy-Lefaix MT, Packer L. Ginkgo biloba extract (EGb 761) protects human low density lipoproteins against oxidative modification mediated by copper. Biochem Biophys Res Comm 1995;212:360-6.

Haramaki N, Aggarwal S, Kawabata T, et al. Effects of natural antioxidant Ginkgo biloba extract (EGB 761) on myocardial ischemia-reperfusion injury. Free Rad Biol Med 1994;16:780-94.

Oken BS, Storzbach DM, Kaye JA. The efficacy of Ginkgo biloba on cognitive function in Alzheimer disease. Arch Neurol 1998;55:1409-15.

Peters H, Kieser M, Hölscher U. Demonstration of the efficacy of Ginkgo biloba special extract EGb 761_ on intermittent claudication--a placebo controlled, double-blind multicenter trial. Vasa 1998;27:106-10 [in German].

Marcocci L, Maguire JJ, Droy-Lefaix MT, et al. The nitric oxide-scavenging properties of Ginkgo biloba extract EGb 761. Biochem Biophys Res Commun 1994;201:748-55.

Brown MD. Review of green tea's role in cancer prevention. Alt Med Rev 1999;4(5):360-

Katiyar SK, Agarwal R, Mukhtar H. Inhibition of spontaneous and photo-enhanced lipid peroxidation in mouse epidermal microsomes by epicatechin derivatives from green tea. Cancer Lett 1994;79:61-66.

Imai K, Nakachi K. Cross sectional study of effects of drinking green tea on cardiovascular and liver diseases. BMJ 1995;310:693-6.

Ho CT, Ferraro T, Chen QY, et al. Phytochemicals in teas and rosemary and their cancer-preventive properties. In: Ho CT, Osawa T, Huang MT, Rosen RT (eds) Food Phytochemicals for Cancer Prevention II: Teas, Spices and Herbs. Washington, DC: American Chemical Society, 1994:2-19.

Grieve M. A Modern Herbal vol 2. New York: Dover, 1971.

Maher TJ. Astaxanthin continuing education module. Boulder, CO: New Hope Institute of Retailing, 2000.

Kurashige M, Okimasu M, Utsumi K. Inhibition of oxidative injury of biological membranes by astaxanthin. Physiol Chem Phys Med NMR 1990;22:27-38.

Nuttall SL, Kendall MJ, Bombardelli E, Morazzoni P. An evaluation of the antioxidant activity of a standardized grape seed extract, Leucoselect_. J Clin Pharm Ther 1998;23:385-9.

Bombardelli E, Morazzoni P. Vitis vinifera L. Fitoterapia 1995;66:291-317.

Hoffmann D. The Complete Illustrated Herbal. New York: Barnes & Noble Books, 1996:82.

Naguib Y. Antioxidants: A technical overview. Nutraceuticals World 1999;March/April:40-42, 44.

Murray MT. Flavonoids: Tissue-specific antioxidants. Gaia Symposium Proceedings on Naturopathic Herbal Wisdom, 1994:107-10.

Brown MD. Review of green tea's role in cancer prevention. Alt Med Rev 1999;4(5):360-70.

Oyama Y, Fuchs PA, Katayama N, Noda K. Myricetin and quercetin, the flavonoid constituents of Ginkgo biloba extract, greatly reduced oxidative metabolism in both resting and Ca2+-loaded brain neurons. Brain Res 1994;635:125-9.

Age-Related Macular Degeneration Study Group. Multicenter ophthalmic and nutritional age-related macular degeneration study--part 2: Antioxidant intervention and conclusions. J Am Optometric Assoc 1996;67:30-49.

Emerit I, Oganesian N, Sarkisian T, et al. Clastogenic factors in the plasma of Chernobyl accident recovery workers: Anticlastogenic effect of Ginkgo biloba extract. Rad Res 1995;144:198-205

ASTRAGALUS SUPREME

Supports
Healthy Immune Function*

ALCOHOL-FREE CONCENTRATED EXTRACTS OF:

FORMULA	MG EXTRACT PER 2 CAPSULES
Chinese Astragalus root (*Astragalus membranaceus*)	380 mg
Chinese Schizandra berry (*Schizandra chinensis*)	370 mg
Chinese Ligustrum berry (*Ligustrum lucidum*)	120 mg

STANDARDIZED TO FULL SPECTRUM ACTIVITY PROFILE

Total Astragalosides	1.0 mg
Total Schizandrins	7.0 mg

DOSAGE
2 caps 2 times daily

DURATION OF USE
4-6 months

BEST TAKEN
Between meals, with warm water

DEEP IMMUNE SUPPORT

The immune system is a complex and sophisticated system. It involves two general types of response. First, there are the non-specific defenses of the immune system. Phagocytosis (ingesting) of foreign matter by white blood cells and macrophages is a primary non-specific defense. The second type of defense is known as acquired immunity. This is where the body develops specific antibodies. B-cells and T-cells assist in the large scale attack against specific pathogens (such as bacteria). The second sort is sometimes referred to as the deep immune system.

Not only is the immune system intricate in its own right, but it is tied to all other systems of the body in one way or another. Numerous factors such as hormones, nutrition, and stress management affect immune function. The complex nature of plants seems suited to the complex nature of the immune response. Plants can have a profound effect on immune function.

A properly functioning immune system is clearly important for health and vitality. Astragalus Supreme is formulated to support deep immunity*. It does this both directly by helping maintain immune function and indirectly by supporting liver and adrenal function and providing nutrients.

*THIS STATEMENT HAS NOT BEEN EVALUATED BY THE FOOD AND DRUG ADMINISTRATION.
THIS PRODUCT IS NOT INTENDED TO DIAGNOSE, TREAT, CURE OR PREVENT ANY DISEASE.

Astragalus root is a favorite herb in Traditional Chinese Medicine. A long history of use centers on tonic properties used to build strength in states of deficiency. Astragalus also has a traditional reputation for promoting elimination processes. There is a great deal of research interest in Astragalus, which contains a fascinating array of constituents including flavonoids, saponins, polysaccharides, free amino acids, essential fatty acids and trace minerals. The polysaccharides are of particular interest for their immune stimulating properties. Astragalus appears to be ideal for immune support. It is shown to affect non-specific defenses such as promoting macrophage and monocyte function as well as interferon activity. It also supports deep immune function by promoting natural killer cell and T-cell function. It appears especially effective when immune function is stressed by environmental or endogenous challenges.*

Schizandra berries are considered balanced and tonic in Traditional Chinese Herbalism. Their reputation for balance is signified by their name "five flavored berries", promoting the Traditional Chinese concept that each flavor represents an action. In many ways, Schizandra is similar to Astragalus. It enjoys both a long history of use and a great deal of research. Like Astragalus, Schizandra is traditionally considered a tonic with building properties and supportive to elimination systems. It is considered adaptogenic as well, meaning that it non-specifically increases the body's ability to handle stress of varying types. The research tends to focus on antioxidant and liver supportive properties. Fractions of Schizandra are shown to support the function of the liver's metabolic enzyme pathways, including hepatic glutathione, cytochrome P-450, and protein synthesis. Other fractions decrease lipid peroxidation (anti-oxidant), glutamic oxaleacetic transaminase, total bilirubin and total cholesterol. The combination of Schizandra's many constituents results in powerful liver support that indirectly promotes immune function. The liver is responsible for metabolizing the immune complexes that contain ingested pathogens. The liver supportive and adaptogenic qualities of Schizandra work with Astragalus to support the overall goal of this formula.*

Ligustrum fruits round out Astragalus Supreme, bringing about a balance of their own. This is another favorite tonic from the Chinese herbal tradition. It is used to nourish and tone both kidney and liver. There is less research completed on Ligustrum berries, but preliminary results indicate immune support is likely. It appears as though immunomodulary activity includes an effect on phagocyte, killer cell and/or T-cell activity. It also appears that Ligustrum fruits contain significant anti-oxidant activity.*

COMPLEMENTARY PHYTO-CAPS/LIQUID FORMULAS/LIQUID EXTRACTS
Anti-Oxidant Supreme Liquid Phyto-Caps™, Ginseng Schizandra Supreme

SAFETY EVALUATION/CONTRAINDICATIONS
Do not use this product during pregnancy or lactation.

*THIS STATEMENT HAS NOT BEEN EVALUATED BY THE FOOD AND DRUG ADMINISTRATION.
THIS PRODUCT IS NOT INTENDED TO DIAGNOSE, TREAT, CURE OR PREVENT ANY DISEASE.

KNOWN DRUG INTERACTIONS

Consult a physician if you are using any pharmaceutical drugs.

REFERENCES:

Pizzorno J and Murray M. Textbook of Natural Medicine,Vol 1. Edinburgh; Churchill Livingstone, 1999.

Rittenhouse JR, Lui PD, Lau BH. Chinese medicinal herbs reverse macrophage suppression induced by urological tumors. Journal of Urology. 1991; 146(2): 486-90.

Zhao KS, Mancini C, Doria G. Enhancement of the immune response in mice by Astragalus membranaceus extract. Immunopharmacology. 1990; 20 (3): 225-33.

Sun Y, et al. Immune Restoration and/or Augmentation of Local Graft Versus Host Reaction by Traditional Chinese Medicinal Herbs. Cancer. 1983; 52(1): 70-73.

Chu DT, Wong WL, Mavligit GM. Immunotherapy with Chinese medicinal herbs. II. Reversal of cyclophosphamide-induced immune suppression by administration of fractionated Astragalus membranaceus in vivo. J Clin Lab Immunol. 1988 Mar; 25(3): 125-9.

Yeung H. Handbook of Chinese Herbs and Formulas. Inst of Chinese Med. 1985; Vol I: 529.

Upton R ed. Schixandra berry (Schizandra chinensis): Analytical, quality control and therapeutic monograph. Santa Cruz: American Herbal Pharmacopoeia and Therapeutic Compendium, 1999.

Wagner H, Hikino H, Farnsworth N. Economic and Medicinal Plant Research Vol 2. London: Academic Press, 1988.

Ko KM, et al. Effect of a Lignan-Enriched Fructus Schizandrae Extract on Hepatic Glutathione Status in Rats: Protection against Carbon Tetrachloride Toxicity. Planta Medica; 61: 134-37.

Tang W and Eisenbrand G. Chinese Drugs of Plant Origin: Chemistry, Pharmacology, and Use in Traditional and Modern Medicine. Berlin; Springer-Verlag, 1992.

Leung A and Foster S. Encyclopedia of Common Natural Ingredients. NY: Wiley, 1996.

Bensky D and Gamble A. Chinese Herbal Medicine: Materia Medica. Seattle: Eastland, 1986.

Halstead B and Hood L. Bulletin of the Oriental Healing Arts Institute of USA. Special Issue: Natural Methods to Enhance Immunity. 1984; 9 (8): 391-394.

Wang Y, et al. Phytochemicals potentiate interleukin-2 generated lymphokine-activated killer cell cytotoxicity against murine renal vell carcinoma. Mol Biother. 1992; 4(3): 143-6.

Yim TK, et al. Hepatoporotective action of an oleanolic acid-enriched extract of Ligustrum lucidum fruits is mediated through an enhancement on hepatic glutathione regeneration capacity in mice. Phytotherapy Res. 2001 Nov; 15(7): 589-92.

He ZD, et al. Antioxidative glucosides from the fruits of Ligustrum lucidum. Chem Pharm Bull. 2001 Jun; 49(6): 780-4.

BLACK COHOSH

Supports Healthy Function of the Hormonal System*

ALCOHOL-FREE CONCENTRATED EXTRACTS OF:

FORMULA	MG PER 2 CAPSULES
Black Cohosh root (*Actaea racemosa*)	80 mg

WHOLE PLANT STANDARDIZATION PROCESS™ PROFILE

Triterpene Glycosides	4 mg

DOSAGE
1 Liquid Phyto-Cap 2 times daily.

DURATION OF USE
3 months, or on an as-needed basis.

BEST TAKEN
Between meals, with a small amount of warm water.

HISTORY

A plant native to the eastern part of North America, black cohosh was used by Native Americans to help relieve female symptoms commonly associated with hormonal fluctuations. This prized herb was the main constituent in Lydia Pinkham's well-known "Vegetable Compound," a popular concoction drunk by women in the 1800's to relieve hormone-related symptoms and more specifically, for "all those painful complaints and weaknesses so common to our best female population." Women now use black cohosh to support healthy hormone balance during menopause and reduce the number of hot flashes they endure.*

Black cohosh contains many substances that play a role in its overall effect in alleviating symptoms associated with menopause including phytosterin; isoferulic acid; fukinolic acid; caffeic acid, salicylic acid; sugars; tannins; long-chain fatty acids; and triterpene glycosides, including acetin and 27-deoxyacetin. Of primary importance are the triterpene glycosides. The majority of clinical trials published to date on the effects of black cohosh have focused on an extract standardized based on the triterpene glycosides, indicating the clinical importance of maintaining sufficient levels of this constituent in a black cohosh herbal preparation.*

The bioactivity profile for Black Cohosh Liquid Phyto-Caps demonstrates an impressive 4 milligrams of the active triterpene glycosides per serving. Further,

*THIS STATEMENT HAS NOT BEEN EVALUATED BY THE FOOD AND DRUG ADMINISTRATION.
THIS PRODUCT IS NOT INTENDED TO DIAGNOSE, TREAT, CURE OR PREVENT ANY DISEASE.

this product is standardized to its active constituents using the Whole Plant Standardization Process' which ensures that it maintains a full spectrum of the phytochemicals found in the herb while maintaining the exact concentration of the scientifically validated marker compound, the triterpene glycosides.*

HORMONE REPLACEMENT THERAPY AND MENOPAUSE

As a woman ages, she will naturally approach menopause and the cessation of ovarian function which is a time when black cohosh can become increasingly helpful to women. Menopause is not a disease. It is a natural transition in a woman's life, with black cohosh, a natural product, helping to ease the effects of this transition. Some women experience negative symptoms when they are going through menopause. For example, women can experience:

Hot flashes
Headaches
Depression
Lack of concentration
Anxiety
Vertigo
Joint pain
Hair loss, and
Sleep disturbances

BLACK COHOSH, MENOPAUSE AND HORMONE BALANCE

Clearly, women need options to support this natural transition in their lives and to reduce the number of hot flashes they experience. Black cohosh offers scientifically supported assistance to women looking for a way to alleviate symptoms normally associated with menopause.*

As women reach menopause, their bodies naturally secrete higher levels of luteinizing hormone (LH) and produce lower levels of estrogen. This is primarily due to a diminishing of the communication between the ovaries and the pituitary gland. Consequently, women experience hot flashes. Black cohosh helps to bring back hormonal balance and normalize levels of LH.*

Likewise, black cohosh supports healthy menstruation and eases the effects of natural hormone fluctuations associated with the menstrual cycle.*

COMPLEMENTARY PHYTO-CAPS/LIQUID FORMULAS/LIQUID EXTRACTS

Phyto-Estrogen Liquid Phyto-Caps™, Vitex-Alfalfa Supreme, Dong Quai Supreme

SAFETY EVALUATION/CONTRAINDICATIONS

Do not use during pregnancy or lactation. Women with hormone sensitive conditions such as breast, uterine or ovarian cancer, endometriosis, and uterine fibroids should consult a qualified healthcare professional before using this product due to its potential estrogenic effects. Occasional gastrointestinal discomfort may occur with this product.*

KNOWN DRUG INTERACTIONS

While there are no well-known drug interactions, concurrent use with hormone replacement therapy is not recommended due to possible potentiation of estrogen effects. Black cohosh may have synergistic effects with tamoxifen. Before using this product, talk with your healthcare professional if you take any medications.*

REFERENCES

Blumenthal M, et al. ed. The Complete German Commission E Monographs: Therapeutic Guide to Herbal Medicines. Trans. S. Klein. Boston, MA: American Botanical Council, 1998.

Düker EM, Kopanski L, Jarry H, Wuttke W. Effects of extracts from Cimicifuga racemosa on gonadotropin release in menopausal women and ovariectomized rats. Planta Med 1991;57:420–4.

Foster S. Herbs for Your Health. Loveland, CO: Interweave Press; 1996: 12–3.

Haas,J. Kaplan,C., Gerstenberger,E., Kerlikowske,K. Changes in the use of postmenopausal hormone therapy after the publication of clinical trial results. Ann Intern Med 2004; 140: 184 -88.

Jarry H, et al. The endocrine effects of constituents of Cimicifuga racemosa. 2. in vitro binding of constituents to estrogen receptors. Planta Med 1985;4:316-19.

Jarry H, Harnischfeger G. Studies on endocrine effects of the contents of Cimicifuga racemosa. 1. Influence on the serum concentration of pituitary hormones in ovariectomized rats. Planta Med 1985;51:46–9.

Leung AY, Foster S. Encyclopedia of Common Natural Ingredients Used in Food, Drugs, and Cosmetics, 2d ed. New York: John Wiley & Sons: 1996: 88–9.

Loser B, Kruse SO, Melzig MF, Nahrstedt A. Inhibition of neutrophil elastase activity by cinnamic acid derivatives from Cimicifuga racemosa. Planta Med 2000;66:751-3.

Warnecke G. Using phyto-treatment to influence menopause symptoms. Med Welt 1985;36:871–4.

Women's Health Initiative Trial. JAMA 2002; 288:321-33.

BLACK ELDERBERRY

Ultimate Support for Healthy Immune Function*

ALCOHOL FREE CONCENTRATED EXTRACT OF:

BLACK ELDERBERRY	MG EXTRACT PER 2 CAPS
(*Sambucus nigra*)	800 mg

DOSAGE
2 Liquid Phyto-Caps, 3 times daily

DURATION OF USE
2-3 months

BEST TAKEN
Between meals, with warm water

HISTORY

Primarily found in Europe and North America, black elderberries have long been used in traditional cultures to support immune function. Elderberries have also traditionally been used as a food, popular even today for making wine and as a flavoring agent.*

BLACK ELDERBERRY AND THE IMMUNE SYSTEM

Black elderberries encourage a healthy immune reaction against undesired organisms that induce flu-like symptoms. Black elderberry's antioxidant and immune-enhancing properties may specifically have a beneficial effect on the body's normal response to influenza viruses A and B.*

A number of research studies have examined the constituents of black elderberries, with one group of active compounds, the flavonoids, receiving considerable attention. Of particular interest are the anthocyanidin flavonoids that have been shown to enhance immune system function and offer significant antioxidant protection.*

Fittingly, black elderberry's antioxidant properties support immune system function by advancing the body's natural resistance and adaptation to stressful influences that make one more susceptible to suffering from influenza. In addition to supporting normal defense systems against select viruses, the anthocyanins and other flavonoids found in black elderberries function to protect the body from the damaging effects of free radicals. Collectively, the actions of these berries serve to promote optimal immune system function.*

COMPLEMENTARY PHYTO-CAPS/LIQUID FORMULAS/LIQUID EXTRACTS

Echinacea Supreme Liquid Phyto-Caps™, Echinacea/Goldenseal Supreme Liquid Phyto-Caps™, Oil of Oregano Liquid Phyto-Caps™, Olive Leaf Liquid Phyto-Caps™, Quick Defense Liquid Phyto-Caps™, Whole Body Defense Liquid Phyto-Caps™

SAFETY EVALUATION/CONTRAINDICATIONS

Do not use during pregnancy or lactation.*

KNOWN DRUG INTERACTIONS

Black elderberries have not been studied extensively to determine their interactions with other medications. Before using this formula, talk with your healthcare professional if you take any medications.*

REFERENCES

Duke JA. CRC Handbook of Medicinal Herbs. Boca Raton, FL: CRC Press, 1985, 423.

Foster S. 101 Medicinal Plants. Loveland, CO: Interweave Press, 1998, 72–3.

Gruenwald J, Brendler T, Jaenicke C, et al. (eds). PDR for Herbal Medicines. Montvale, NJ: Medical Economics, 1998, 1116–7.

Mascolo N, Autore G, Capasso G, et al. Biological screening of Italian medicinal plants for anti-inflammatory activity. Phytother Res 1987;1:28–31.

Newall C, Anderson L, Phillipson J. Herbal Medicines: A Guide for Health-Care Professionals. London: The Pharmaceutical Press, 1996, 104–5.

Van Damme EJ, Roy S, Barre A, et al. The major elderberry (Sambucus nigra) fruit protein is a lectin derived from a truncated type 2 ribosome-inactivating protein. Plant J 1997;12(6):1251-60.

Youdim KA, Martin A, Joseph JA. Incorporation of the elderberry anthocyanins by endothelial cells increases protection against oxidative stress. Free Radical Biol Med 2000;29:51–60.

Zakay-Rones Z, Varsano N, Zlotnik M, et al. Inhibition of several strains of influenza virus in vitro and reduction of symptoms by an elderberry extract (Sambucus nigra L.) during an outbreak of influenza B Panama. J Alt Compl Med 1995;1:361–9.

*THIS STATEMENT HAS NOT BEEN EVALUATED BY THE FOOD AND DRUG ADMINISTRATION. THIS PRODUCT IS NOT INTENDED TO DIAGNOSE, TREAT, CURE OR PREVENT ANY DISEASE.

CHOLESTEROL VITAL MAINTENANCE

Helps Retain Healthy Cholesterol Levels*

ALCOHOL FREE CONCENTRATED EXTRACT OF:

FORMULA	MG EXTRACT PER 2 CAPSULES
Pantethine	200 mg
Artichoke leaf (*Cynara scolymus*)	200 mg
Coleus root (*Coleus forskholii*)	160 mg
Guggulu resin (*Commiphora mukul*)	150 mg
Arjuna bark (*Terminalia arjuna*)	100 mg
Wild Yam rhizome (*Dioscorea villosa*)	22 mg
Policosanol	8 mg
Greater Celandine tops & roots (*Chelidonium majus*)	8 mg

DOSAGE

Liquid Phyto-Caps: 2 capsules, 2 times daily

DURATION OF USE

6-12 months (Do Not Use for more than 3 months consecutively)

BEST TAKEN

Between meals with a small amount of warm water

DESCRIPTION OF FORMULA

The Cholesterol Vital Maintenance formula includes herbs and nutrients that function synergistically to help preserve the healthy metabolism of cholesterol, particularly in the liver. Cholesterol Vital Maintenance also protects low-density lipoprotein (LDL) cholesterol from the damaging effects of free radicals. Adopting a healthy lifestyle that includes a daily exercise regimen and a diet high in unprocessed foods (fresh vegetables, fruits and whole grains), will optimize the effects of Cholesterol Vital Maintenance in maintaining a vibrant cardiovascular system.*

Pantethine is a form of vitamin B5 that helps to maintain normal LDL and HDL cholesterol levels within a normal range.*

Artichoke leaf contains bitter compounds known as caffeoylquinic acids that have multiple beneficial effects on cholesterol metabolism. Artichoke reduces the formation of cholesterol in the liver, promotes the excretion of cholesterol through the bile and protects cholesterol from the damaging effects of free radicals. Collectively, the actions of this leaf serve to promote optimal levels of cholesterol in the body and help to maintain healthy heart function.*

Coleus Forskohlii root contains forskolin, a compound that works directly on the heart muscle and on blood vessels to optimize blood flow throughout the cardiovascular system. Forskolin also helps to maintain healthy fat metabolism.*

Guggulu extract is a resinous derivative of a close relative of myrrh that comes from India. Guggulu extract helps to maintain normal cholesterol and triglyceride levels by optimizing cholesterol metabolism in the liver, promoting the excretion of cholesterol through the bile, and protecting LDL cholesterol from the damaging effects of free radical oxidation.*

Arjuna herb is derived from the bark of a tree, which contains several important constituents, including gallic acid and ethyl gallate. These elements help to maintain a healthy heart. Likewise, several studies suggest that, when used alone or in conjunction with conventional heart medications, Arjuna helps preserve the proper functioning of the cardiovascular system, and fittingly, the bark is traditionally used in Ayurvedic medicine (from India) to rejuvenate the heart.*

Wild Yam root contains diosgenin, a constituent that preserves the proper flow of bile, particularly in the presence of estrogen, a hormone that can sometimes reduce the flow. Consequently, this root promotes the normal excretion of cholesterol through the bile.*

Policosanol (sometimes called octacosanol) is a wax found in Saccharum officinarum (sugar cane). Policosanol helps to maintain a healthy balance between LDL and HDL cholesterol by promoting the proper metabolism of cholesterol in the liver. Accordingly, policosanol plays an important role in maintaining a healthy cardiovascular system.*

Greater Celandine herb is traditionally regarded as an herb that helps to support the healthy flow of bile. More research is warranted to validate its use in promoting heart health.*

COMPLEMENTARY PHYTO-CAPS/LIQUID FORMULAS/LIQUID EXTRACTS

Cholesterol Vital Maintenance Liquid Phyto-Caps™, Hawthorn Supreme Liquid Phyto-Caps™.

SAFETY EVALUATION/CONTRAINDICATIONS

This formula should be avoided in pregnancy and lactation. It may occasionally cause an upset stomach, in which case it should be taken with food. It may cause loosening of stools, which is normal and will tend to pass with time. Use with caution if you are allergic to the daisy or chrysanthemum family. If you experience fast or irregular breathing, itching, skin rash or hives, seek medical attention promptly. Also, use with caution and seek the advice of a qualified healthcare professional if you have liver disease, hemophilia or a stomach or intestinal blockage. **Do not use for more than three consecutive months.***

*THIS STATEMENT HAS NOT BEEN EVALUATED BY THE FOOD AND DRUG ADMINISTRATION. THIS PRODUCT IS NOT INTENDED TO DIAGNOSE, TREAT, CURE OR PREVENT ANY DISEASE.

KNOWN DRUG INTERACTIONS

This formula should be used with caution in combination with drugs that inhibit blood clotting and platelet aggregation including but not limited to warfarin (Coumadin®), heparin, clopidogrel (Plavix®), pentoxifylline (Trental®), and aspirin. Additionally, this formula may interact with antihistamine and antihypertention medications. Some of the herbs in this formula have not been studied extensively to determine their interactions with other medications. Before using this formula, talk with your healthcare professional if you take any medications.*

REFERENCES

Accatino L, Pizarro M, Solis N, Koenig CS. Effects of diosgenin, a plant-derived steroid, on bile secretion and hepatocellular cholestasis induced by estrogens in the rat. Hepatology 1998;28(1):129-40.

Araghiniknam M, Chung S, Nelson-White T, et al. Antioxidant activity of dioscorea and dehydroepiandrosterone (DHEA) in older humans. Life Sci 1996;59(11):PL147-57.

Batista J, Stüsser R, Penichet M, et al. Doppler-ultrasound pilot study of the effects of long-term policosanol therapy on carotid-vertebral atherosclerosis. Curr Ther Res 1995;56:906–914.

Baumann JC, Heintze K, Muth HW. Clinico-experimental studies on the secretion of bile, pancreatic and gastric juice under the influence of phytocholagogous agents of a suspension of Carduus marianus, Chelidonium and Curcuma. Arzneim Forsch 1971;21:98-101.

Benítez M, Romero C, Más R, et al. A comparative study of policosanol versus pravastatin in patients with type II hypercholesterolemia. Curr Ther Res 1997;58:859-867.

Bharani A, Ganguly A, Bhargava KD. Salutary effect of Terminalia Arjuna in patients with severe refractory heart failure. Int J Cardiol 1995;49(3):191-9.

Blumenthal M, et al. ed. The Complete German Commission E Monographs: Therapeutic Guide to Herbal Medicines. Trans. S. Klein. Boston, MA: American Botanical Council, 1998.

Castaño G, Canetti M, Moreira M, et al. Efficacy and tolerability of policosanol in elderly patients with type II hypercholesterolemia: a 12-month study. Curr Ther Res 1995;56:819-828.

Chander R, Khanna AK, Kapoor NK. Lipid lowering activity of guggulsterone from Commiphora mukul in hyperlipidaemic rats. Phytother Res 1996;10:508-11.

Dwivedi S, Agarwal MP. Antianginal and cardioprotective effects of Terminalia arjuna, an indigenous drug, in coronary artery disease. J Assoc Physicians India 1994;42(4):287-9.

Englisch W, Beckers C, Unkauf M, et al. Efficacy of artichoke dry extract in patients with hyperlipoproteinemia. Arzneim Forsch 2000;50:260-5.

Felter HW, Lloyd JU. King's American Dispensatory 2 vols., 18th ed. Portland OR: Eclectic Medical Publications, 1898, 1983.

Hoffman BB, Chang H, Reaven GM. Stimulation and inhibition of lipolysis in isolated rat adipocytes: Evidence for age-related changes in responses to forskolin and PGE1. Horm Metabol Res 1987;19:358-360.

Kelly GS. Pantethine: A review of its biochemistry and therapeutic applications. Alt Med Rev 1997;2(5):365-77.

Kraft K. Artichoke leaf extract--recent findings reflecting effects on lipid metabolism, liver and gastrointestinal tracts. Phytomedicine 1997;4:370-8.

Menéndez R, Arruzazabala L, Más R, et al. Cholesterol-lowering effect of policosanol on rabbits with hypercholesterolaemia induced by a wheat starch-casein diet. Br J Nutr 1997;77:923–932.

Ram A, Lauria P, Gupta R, et al. Hypocholesterolaemic effects of Terminalia arjuna tree bark. J Ethnopharmacol 1997;55(3):165-9.

Satyavati GV. Guggulipid: A promising hypolipidemic agent from gum guggul (Commiphora wightii). Econ Med Plant Res 1991;5:47-82.

Shaila HP, Udupa SL, Udupa AL. Hypolipidemic activity of three indigenous drugs in experimentally induced atherosclerosis. Int J Cardiol 1998;67(2):119-214.

Singh K, Chander R, Kapoor NK. Guggulsterone, a potent hypolipidaemic, prevents oxidation of low density lipoprotein. Phytother Res 1997;11:291-4.

Snow JM. Coleus forskohlii Willd (Lamiaceae). Prot J Botan Med 1995;Autumn:39-42.

Thakur CP, Thakur B, Singh S, et al. The Ayurvedic medicines Haritaki, Amala and Bahira reduce cholesterol-induced atherosclerosis in rabbits. Int J Cardiol 1988;21(2):167-75.

CINNAMON BARK

Supports Healthy Blood Sugar Levels*

ALCOHOL-FREE CONCENTRATED EXTRACTS OF:

FORMULA	MG EXTRACT PER 2 CAPSULES
Cinnamon bark, Supercritical CO_2 Extract (*Cinnamomum aromaticum*)	50 mg
Cinnamon bark, ETOH Extract (*Cinnamomum burmanii*)	200 mg

STANDARDIZED TO FULL SPECTRUM ACTIVITY PROFILE

Total Cinnamaldehydes	33.75 mg
Total Phenols	45 mg

DOSAGE

Liquid Phyto-Caps: 1 capsule, 2 times daily

DURATION OF USE

3 months

BEST TAKEN

After meals, with a small amount of warm water

HISTORY

Cinnamon Bark has been used throughout history, and across most cultures, as a culinary spice, for herbal bath decoctions and as a food remedy to maintain healthy blood sugar balance. Cinnamon contains the constituent, cinnamaldehyde, found in the volatile oil fraction of the plant. Cinnamaldehyde has potent antioxidant actions, protecting cells from oxidative damage, and supporting healthy fat and cholesterol balance within the normal range. Cinnamon bark also contains

*THIS STATEMENT HAS NOT BEEN EVALUATED BY THE FOOD AND DRUG ADMINISTRATION.
THIS PRODUCT IS NOT INTENDED TO DIAGNOSE, TREAT, CURE OR PREVENT ANY DISEASE.

polyphenolic polymers that support healthy insulin and blood glucose balance within the normal range, and promote healthy blood flow.*

Cinnamon bark studies show favorable results for its efficacy in promoting healthy blood sugar levels by maintaining a normal range, and protecting cells from oxidative damage. Maintaining a healthy blood sugar level is critical to promoting optimal health and is associated with healthy vision, heart/circulation, kidneys and a healthy nervous system.*

Cinnamon bark also supports the liver and pancreas and promotes the healthy functioning of insulin and other glucose-regulating factors in the body.*

Beyond its well-documented actions in enhancing blood glucose metabolism, numerous studies have demonstrated cinnamon bark extract's ability to promote healthy lipid metabolism, by providing antioxidant protection and by maintaining a healthy glycemic response. In one clinical trial, researchers reported that cinnamon bark supplementation not only promoted healthy glucose balance, but also demonstrated a statistically significant action on supporting healthy lipid and triglyceride balance.*

There is a well recognized connection between an excess of free radicals in the body (also known as oxidative stress) and healthy cholesterol balance. Cinnamon bark extract has demonstrated particular benefit for promoting healthy cholesterol balance within the normal range by providing antioxidant support during lipid metabolism.*

Cinnamon Bark also provides assistance in maintaining a natural balance between free radicals (necessary for the healthy functioning of the body) and an excess of free radicals. We are exposed to free radicals daily, in our external environment (our food, air and water supply) and our internal environment (a result of normal biological processes). Research demonstrates that consuming antioxidants, such as cinnamon bark, is one of the most powerful methods we know of to help neutralize the actions of too many free radicals in our body. While free radicals are part of normal human body function, too many free radicals can cause cellular damage.*

COMPLEMENTARY PHYTO-CAPS/LIQUID FORMULAS/LIQUID EXTRACTS

Glycemic Health Liquid Phyto-Caps™, Adrenal Health Liquid Phyto-Caps™

SAFETY EVALUATION/CONTRAINDICATIONS

Before using this product, talk with your healthcare professional if you suffer from a medical condition. Please visit www.gaiaherbs.com to obtain information regarding potential contraindications and/or side effects that may be associated with the herbal extract found in this product.*

KNOWN DRUG INTERACTIONS

Before using this product, talk with your healthcare professional if you take any medications. Please visit www.gaiaherbs.com to obtain information regarding any possible drug interactions that may be associated with the herbal extract found in this product.*

REFERENCES

Khan A, et al. Cinnamon improves glucose and lipids of people with type 2 diabetes. Diabetes Care. 2003 Dec;26(12):3215-8.

Anderson RA, et al. Isolation and characterization of polyphenol type-A polymers from cinnamon with insulin-like biological activity. J Agric Food Chem. 2004 Jan 14;52(1):65-70.

Broadhurst CL, Polansky MM, Anderson RA. Insulin-like biological activity of culinary and medicinal plant aqueous extracts in vitro. J Agric Food Chem. 2000 Mar;48(3):849-52.

CRANBERRY CONCENTRATE

Supports Healthy Functioning of the Urinary System*

ALCOHOL-FREE CONCENTRATED EXTRACTS OF:

FORMULA	MG PER 2 CAPSULES
Cranberry fruit (*Vaccinium macrocarpon*)	400 mg

STANDARDIZED TO FULL SPECTRUM ACTIVITY PROFILE

BIOACTIVITY PER 2 CAPSULES	MG ACTIVITY
Quinic acids (from Cranberry)	60 mg

DOSAGE

1 Liquid Phyto-Cap 2 times daily.

DURATION OF USE

3 weeks and then as needed

BEST TAKEN

After meals, with a small amount of warm water.

Cranberry's historical use as a powerful functional food has now gained support from scientific data. Cranberry Liquid Phyto-Cap™ combines medicinal grade cranberries with state-of-the-art extraction techniques to provide a concentrated extract for overall urinary health.

HISTORY

Originally named "crane berries" in reference to the large birds that regularly eat them, the cranberry shrub grows in watery bogs and has been a celebrated part of medical and culinary history. Its use among the Iroquois as a blood purifier is well documented throughout early American history though the cranberry is most celebrated for its role in the first American "Thanksgiving". Playing a large

*THIS STATEMENT HAS NOT BEEN EVALUATED BY THE FOOD AND DRUG ADMINISTRATION. THIS PRODUCT IS NOT INTENDED TO DIAGNOSE, TREAT, CURE OR PREVENT ANY DISEASE.

role in the history of the early colonist, Native American tribes taught colonist the method by which to sweeten this unusually bitter fruit as well as techniques to preserve them for use during the long winter months.

MECHANISM OF ACTION

The cranberry is a close relative to other well documented functional food such as the blueberry, and bilberry. As such, the cranberry fruit is high in antioxidants, particularly in a compound called proanthocyanidins also called "PAC's". The "PAC's" are potent antioxidants that scavenge for damaging particles in the body known as "free radicals". Although free radicals are a normal by-product of our metabolism, in excess amounts they can negatively alter cell membranes and even cause cell death. The potent and highly absorbable antioxidants found in cranberry can help to neutralize free radicals before they cause irreparable damage. "PAC's" are primarily responsible for the deep red color found in the skins of the various fruits which is probably why most dark fruits and vegetables are so healthy. Cranberries are also a rich source of bioactive source of vitamin C which supports the overall immune system.

URINARY TRACT HEALTH

Specifically, science turned its focus on cranberry by the early 1920's when it became apparent that it contained healthful aspects with regards to urinary health. Initially, scientists theorized that eating cranberries may make the urine more acidic and therefore create a hostile environment to bacteria living in the urinary tract. Yet, modern science has shed new light on this theory. It seems that "PAC's" play a significant role in the overall wellness of the urinary tract. In fact, some research has suggested that "PAC's" may help support the body's ability to prevent microorganisms from attaching to the cell wall of the urinary canal. This aspect of activity has been shown to be an effective technique to maintain normal bacterial levels in the urinary tract and support overall urinary health. Unfortunately, in order to get optimum amounts of "PAC's" into the urinary tract a person would have to drink an extensive amount of cranberry juice. In light of this dilemma, Gaia Herbs has created a technique by which to concentrate cranberry extract and deliver them in a vegetarian Liquid Phyto-Cap™ allowing for optimum dosage without the bitter taste or the unnecessary sugar.

SAFETY EVALUATION/CONTRAINDICATIONS

Do not use during pregnancy or lactation.

KNOWN DRUG INTERACTIONS

Consult a physician if you are taking any pharmaceutical drugs.

REFERENCES

Bruyere F. Use of cranberry in chronic urinary tract infections. Med Mal Infect. 2006 Jul;36(7):358-63. Epub 2006 Jul 18. Review [French].

Howell AB, Vorsa N, Der Maderosian A. Inhibition of the adherence of P-Fimbriated *E. coli* to uroepithelial – all surfaces by proanthocyanidin extracts fro cranberries. New Engl J Med 1998; 339:1005-6.

Liu Y, Black MA, Caron L, Camesano TA. Role of cranberry juice on molecular-scale surface characteristics and adhesion behavior of Escherichia coli. Biotech Bioeng. 2006 Feb 5;93(2):297-305.

Mills S, Bone K. The Essential Guide to Herbal Safety. St. Louis MO : Elsevier, Inc, 2005.

Zafiri D, Ofek I, et al. Inhibitory activity of cranberry juice on adherence of type 1 and type P fimbriated *E. Coli* to eukaryotic cells. Antimicrob Agents Chemother 1989; 33: 92-98.

DIET-SLIM

Ultimate Support for Weight Loss*

ALCOHOL-FREE CONCENTRATED EXTRACTS OF:

FORMULA	MG EXTRACT PER 3 CAPSULES
Garcinia fruit (*Garcinia cambogia*)	300 mg
Green Tea leaf (*Camellia sinensis*)	225 mg
Coleus root (*Coleus forskohlii*)	138 mg
Turmeric rhizome (*Curcuma longa*)	90 mg
Elder berry (*Sambucus* spp.)	90 mg
Yohimbe bark (*Corynanthe yohimbe*)	60 mg
Bitter Orange peel (*Citrus aurantium*)	57 mg
Gymnema leaf (*Gymnema sylvestre*)	51 mg
Bladderwrack fronds (*Fucus vesiculosis*)	27 mg
Ginger Rhizome, (*Zingiber officinale*) Supercritical CO_2 Extract	12 mg

STANDARDIZED TO FULL SPECTRUM ACTIVITY PROFILE

Hydroxycitric acid (from Garcinia)	135 mg
Polyphenols (from Green Tea)	120 mg

DOSAGE

Liquid Phyto-Caps: 1 capsule, 3 times daily

DURATION OF USE

3-4 months

BEST TAKEN

Between meals with a small amount of warm water

Note: Dietary and lifestyle adjustments must be made in conjunction with this formula's use. *The 3 Season Diet* by Dr. John Douillard, D.C., Ph.D. is recommended reading.

*THIS STATEMENT HAS NOT BEEN EVALUATED BY THE FOOD AND DRUG ADMINISTRATION. THIS PRODUCT IS NOT INTENDED TO DIAGNOSE, TREAT, CURE OR PREVENT ANY DISEASE.

THE METABOLISM OF WEIGHT LOSS

This formula helps to correct fat cell metabolism by promoting a state of fat utilization rather than storage. It is particularly useful for what is known as the classic 'Venus' body type, where fat storage is concentrated around the hips, thighs and buttocks. Likewise, for individuals who lose weight only to have it return, this formula is of particular benefit.

The primary focus of this formula is to establish a metabolic environment where breakdown and utilization of fat (adrenergic-receptor mediated lipolysis) is enhanced due to an increase of available cAMP. Two primary adrenergic receptors control lipolysis (beta-1 and alpha-2 type). The beta-1 receptor is coupled positively to adenylate cyclase, whereas the alpha-2 sites are negatively coupled to the enzyme. The underlying strategy of this botanical formula utilizes these receptors. The approach is three-fold:

1. To block the alpha-2 adrenergic sites - thereby reducing their impact of decreasing cyclic AMP
2. Activate beta-1 sites to encourage the formation of cyclic AMP
3. Prevent the breakdown of cyclic AMP via phosphodiesterase inhibition

In summary, this compound serves to elevate intra-cellular cyclic AMP levels via those receptor-dependent and independent mechanisms associated with forskolin (from Coleus forskohlii). Additionally, the inhibition of the phosphodiesterase regulated hydrolysis of the cyclic AMP nucleotide to its ester group allows cAMP to be more available. This strategy results in a net increase of cyclic AMP and an associated increase in lipolysis, or the conversion of triglycerides into fatty acids and glycerols. This is the form of fat that is utilized rather than stored.

Other strategies of this important formula are to:

- Enhance thermogenesis (heat production), thereby promoting fat metabolism
- Balance sugar metabolism, thereby correcting food cravings
- Promote healthy liver metabolism, thereby supporting healthy detoxification and elimination patterns.

Diet-Slim thus increases function at the cellular level of numerous processes involved with weight management. It is the combination of these factors which makes Diet-Slim so effective.

Garcinia-Malabar Tamarind is a natural source of hydroxycitric acid (HCA). HCA is known to cause an increase in fat metabolism, possibly via its influence on liver function.*

Green Tea has traditionally been used to support mental function, promote digestion, reduce flatulence, and to regulate body temperature. It is used here for the effect of several of its components to stimulate lipolysis by preventing the breakdown of cyclic AMP. Cyclic AMP affects hormonal messages within a fat cell. This 'message' helps to amplify the response of a fat cell to adrenaline, the

*THIS STATEMENT HAS NOT BEEN EVALUATED BY THE FOOD AND DRUG ADMINISTRATION.
THIS PRODUCT IS NOT INTENDED TO DIAGNOSE, TREAT, CURE OR PREVENT ANY DISEASE.

hormone that tells it to burn fat. Green Tea is also valuable here as an established antioxidant and as a moderate stimulant, further assisting the underlying function of the formula.*

Coleus Forskohlii is perhaps Green Tea's best friend when it comes to weight-loss. As mentioned above, utilization of fat is in part controlled by the hormone adrenaline, along with its capacity to form cyclic AMP inside a fat cell. Green Tea and Coleus both modify the fat burning affect of adrenaline (via modification of beta-1 adrenergic-receptor cAMP expression). Forskolin, one of the main active molecules in Coleus, also plays a role by promoting a healthy nervous state and supporting thyroid hormone production, making it particularly well suited for weight management.*

Turmeric rhizome serves this formula through its outstanding antioxidant and liver supportive effects. Normalizing liver function during weight management is highly desirable. The liver is actively involved in regulating blood sugar availability, and metabolism of the 3-ketosteroids, a group of hormones which affect fat metabolism.*

Elderberries bring a number of desirable qualities to this formula. They are recognized to promote healthy elimination patterns and support the liver. Via these actions, Elderberry promotes the removal of cellular wastes and helps to correct general metabolism.*

Yohimbe has been included in this formula specifically for its ability to redirect adrenaline toward the receptors on fat cells that burn fat (Beta-1), and by blocking those receptors which result in fat storage (Alpha-2).*

Bitter Orange is used for weight loss due to its purported thermogenic effects.*

Gymnema leaf is a digestive or stomach tonic with well-known support to the urinary system. It has been reported to "maintain sugar levels within their normal range". Gymnema is also known as gur-mur (which literally means sugar destroying) because of its noted ability to abolish the taste of sugar.

Bladderwrack fronds have been widely used for weight management. Such benefit quite possibly results from its supportive effect on thyroid function. Bladderwrack fronds must be harvested however from pristine water, as they are known to absorb toxic waste metals from polluted waters.*

Ginger rhizome addresses healthy digestion and works as an antioxidant. In addition to these benefits, Ginger is useful here as a support to the circulatory system, helping to deliver the entire formula throughout the body.*

COMPLEMENTARY PHYTO-CAPS/LIQUID FORMULAS/LIQUID EXTRACTS
Supreme Cleanse Kit

KNOWN DRUG INTERACTIONS

Consult a physician if you are taking any prescription drugs.

SAFETY EVALUTATION / CONTRAINDICATIONS

Do not take during pregnancy and lactation.

REFERENCES

Snow JM. Camellia sinensis (L.) Kuntze (Theaceae). The Protocol Journal of Botanical Medicine. 1995;1(2):47-51.

Fredholm BB, Lindgren E. The effect of alkylxanthines and other phosphodiesterase inhibitors on adenosine-receptor mediated decrease in lipolysis and cyclic AMP accumulation in rat fat cells. Acta Pharmacol Toxicol (Copenh).1984; 54(1):64-71.

McCarty MF, Gustin JC. Pyruvate and hydroxycitrate/carnitine may synergize to promote reverse electron transport in hepatocyte mitochondria, effectively 'uncoupling' the oxidation of fatty acids. Med Hypothese. 1999;52(5):407-16

Murray M. The unique pharmacology of Coleus Forskohlii. The American Journal of Natural Medicine. 1994; 1(3):10-13.

Anonymous. Elderberry. The Lawrence Review of Natural Products.1992; Jul.

Kapoor LD. Handbook of Ayurvedic Medicinal Plants. Florida. CRC Press; 1990.

Snow JM. Curcuma longa L. (Zingiberaceae). The Protocol Journal of Botanical Medicine. 1995;1(2):43-46.

Mitchell W. Foundations of Natural Therapeutics – Biochemical Apologetics of Naturopathic Medicine. Tempe, Arizona. Southwest College Press. 1997.

Mills S, Bone K. Principles and Practice of Phytotherapy: Modern Herbal Medicine. Churchill Livingstone, London: 2000.

Galitzky J, et. al. Thermogenic and lipolytic effect of yohimbine in the dog. Br J Pharmacol. 1991; 104(2): 514-18.

Berlan M, et. al. Plasma catecholamine levels and lipid mobilization induced by yohimbine in obese and non-obese women. Int J Obes. 1991; 15(5): 305-15.

Galitzky J, et. al. Alpha 2-antagonist compounds and lipid mobilization: evidence for a lipid mobilizing effect of oral yohimbine in healthy male volunteers. Eur J Clin Invest. 1988; 18(6): 587-94.

Boehringer Ingelheim. Consumer Health Care News-Orange aid in weight loss. Online. Internet. [3/7/02]. Available WW: http://www.boehringer-ingelheim.ca/selfmed/02.07.00.htm

ECHINACEA/GOLDENSEAL SUPREME

Ultimate Support for Healthy Immune Function*

ALCOHOL-FREE CONCENTRATED EXTRACTS OF:

FORMULA	MG EXTRACT PER 2 CAPSULES
Echinacea purpurea root	44 mg
Echinacea purpurea aerial parts	44 mg
St. John's Wort flower buds (*Hypericum perforatum*)	40 mg
Goldenseal root (*Hydrastis canadensis*)	40 mg
Echinacea angustifolia root	36 mg
Barberry root (*Berberis vulgaris*)	30 mg
Oregon Grape root (*Berberis aquifolium*)	30 mg
Echinacea purpurea seed	8 mg

STANDARDIZED TO FULL SPECTRUM ACTIVITY PROFILE

Total isobutylamides (from Echinacea)	1.52 mg
Total alkaloids	10.0 mg

DOSAGE

Liquid Phyto-Caps: 1 capsule every 2 hours at the onset of cold or flu

DURATION OF USE

A maximum of 5 days.

Note: Although there are conflicting beliefs surrounding the negative impact of using berberine-containing plants, it is suggested that you follow the use of this formula with probiotic treatment (*L. acidophilus*, *L. bifidus*, etc.). If Crohn's disease is present, please consult a licensed health-care professional before commencing probiotic use.

BEST TAKEN

Between meals, with warm water

ANCIENT PLANTS IN MODERN TIMES

This formula supports the immune system during times of stress. Echinacea/Goldenseal Supreme is particularly useful where support for respiratory health is indicated. As you can see from the traditional use of this compound's ingredients (described below), it has been formulated to be broad acting in such situations.

*THIS STATEMENT HAS NOT BEEN EVALUATED BY THE FOOD AND DRUG ADMINISTRATION. THIS PRODUCT IS NOT INTENDED TO DIAGNOSE, TREAT, CURE OR PREVENT ANY DISEASE.

It has been said that Native Americans used Echinacea to treat more conditions than any other remedy. The Eclectic medical doctors, from the first half of the last century, also praised Echinacea for its benefits to the respiratory tract. Today, modern science is beginning to support much of its established traditional use, by showing that extracts of Echinacea spp. have the ability to strengthen immune function. Research has further shown that alcohol/water extracts of Echinacea significantly enhance natural killer cell function, and have phagocytic and metabolic influence on macrophages. This simply means that Echinacea has the potential to non-specifically activate your immune system. In other words, it helps your body respond when needed. Almost any alterative formula that focuses on enhancing the immune system could well benefit from this powerful botanical.*

St. John's Wort flower buds have been used traditionally for more than 2,000 years. It is utilized here for its harmonizing effect with anxiety and nervous system health.*

Goldenseal rhizome and root is native to North America. It has traditionally been used to soothe the mucous membranes. Like several other ingredients of this formula (i.e., Oregon Grape root and Barberry root), Goldenseal contains the immunostimulatory alkaloid, berberine.*

Barberry root is a bitter tonic that pharmacologically shares many properties with Goldenseal and Oregon Grape root. As one may expect of plants with closely related chemistry, the traditional use of Barberry is also similar to other berberine containing plants.*

Oregon Grape root has a history of traditional use closely resembling that of Goldenseal. Oregon Grape has distinguished itself, however, by its effect with simple acne.*

COMPLEMENTARY PHYTO-CAPS/LIQUID FORMULAS/LIQUID EXTRACTS

Yarrow, Elder flowers, Peppermint, Ginger Liquid Phyto-Caps™, Sage, and Boneset. Also, Composition Essence, Quick Defense Liquid Phyto-Caps™, Respiratory Defense Liquid Phyto-Caps™

SAFETY EVALUATION/CONTRAINDICATIONS

Do not use this product during pregnancy or lactation.

KNOWN DRUG INTERACTIONS

Consult a physician if you are taking any prescription drugs.

REFERENCES

Murray M. The healing power of herbs - The enlightened persons guide to the wonders of medicinal plants. Rocklin, Ca. Prima publishing; 1995.

Bauer R, Wagner H. Echinacea species as potential immunostimulatory drugs. Economic and Medicinal Plant Research. San Diego: Academic press Ltd.; 1991.

Schranner I, Wurdinger M, et al. Modification of avian humoral immunoreactions by Influx and Echinacea angustifolia extract. Zentralbl Veterinarmed (B) 1989; 36.

Balch JF, Balch PA. Prescription for Nutritional Healing. New York; Avery Publishing

ECHINACEA SUPREME

Ultimate Support for Healthy Immune Function*

ALCOHOL-FREE CONCENTRATED EXTRACTS OF:

FORMULA	MG EXTRACT PER 2 CAPSULES
Echinacea purpurea aerial parts	120 mg
Echinacea purpurea root	72 mg
Echinacea angustifolia root	72 mg
Echinacea purpurea seed	3 mg

STANDARDIZED TO FULL SPECTRUM ACTIVITY PROFILE

Total isobutylamides	4.4 mg

DOSAGE

Liquid Phyto-Caps: 1 capsule every 2 hours at the onset of cold or flu

DURATION OF USE

5-10 days

BEST TAKEN

Between meals, with warm water

ACTIVATE YOUR IMMUNE SYSTEM

Echinacea Supreme is an alterative formula that is useful when immune support is necessary. Echinacea is an immune-stimulant, whose properties have been widely reported. The many actions of this formula make it an appropriate choice for encouraging healthy immune function, especially when respiratory support is needed.

Note: In the context of this formula, Echinacea angustifolia and Echinacea purpurea will be discussed together. While there are certainly several distinct differences between the two species, exploration of such differences will only cloud the issue unnecessarily with semantics. Simply, *E. angustifolia* has a much longer documented history of traditional use, while *E. purpurea* has been the focus of more scientific research. In practice, their actions are similar. Both species are included in this formula to offer the full benefit of their collective chemistry and individual subtleties.

Echinacea - It has been said that Native Americans used Echinacea to treat more conditions than any other remedy. The Eclectic medical doctors, from the first half of the last century, also praised Echinacea for its benefits to the respiratory tract. Today, modern science is beginning to support much of its established traditional use, by showing that extracts of *Echinacea* spp. have the ability to strengthen

*THIS STATEMENT HAS NOT BEEN EVALUATED BY THE FOOD AND DRUG ADMINISTRATION. THIS PRODUCT IS NOT INTENDED TO DIAGNOSE, TREAT, CURE OR PREVENT ANY DISEASE.

immune function. Research has further shown that alcohol/water extracts of Echinacea significantly enhance natural killer cell function, and have phagocytic and metabolic influence on macrophages. This simply means that Echinacea has the potential to non-specifically activate your immune system, enhancing its ability to deal with a threat, if one should arise.*

COMPLEMENTARY PHYTO-CAPS/LIQUID FORMULAS/LIQUID EXTRACTS

Composition Essence, Black Elderberry Liquid Phyto-Caps™, Quick Defense Liquid Phyto-Caps™, Respiratory Defense Liquid Phyto-Caps™

SAFETY EVALUATION/CONTRAINDICATIONS

Do not use this product during pregnancy or lactation.

KNOWN DRUG INTERACTIONS

Consult a physician if you are taking any prescription drugs.

REFERENCES

Snow JM. Echinacea (Moench) Spp. Asteraceae. The Protocol Journal of Botanical Medicine. 1997; 2 (2): 18-24.

Bauer R, Wagner H. Echinacea species as potential immunostimulatory drugs. Economic and Medicinal Plant Research. San Diego: Academic press Ltd.; 1991.

Schranner I, Wurdinger M, et al. Modification of avian humeral immunoreactions by Influx and Echinacea angustifolia extract. Zentralbl Veterinarmed (B) 1989; 36.

Broumand N, Sahl L, Tilles JG. The in vitro effects of Echinacea and ginseng on natural killer and antibody-dependent cell cytotoxicity in healthy subjects and chronic fatigue syndrome or acquired immune-deficiency syndrome patients. Immunopharmacology. 1997; 35.

Bukovsky M, Kostalova D, Magnusova R, Vaverkova S. Testing for immunomodulating effects of ethanol-water extracts of the above ground parts of the plants Echinaceae and Rudbeckia. Cesk Farm. 1993; 42.

Witchl M. (Bisset NG, Ed.) Herbal Drugs and Phytopharmaceuticals. Medpharm, CRC Press: Boca Raton. 1994.

ELEUTHERO ROOT

(Eleutherococcus senticosus)

Ultimate Support to Enhance Energy and Stamina*

ALCOHOL-FREE CONCENTRATED EXTRACTS OF:

ELEUTHERO ROOT	MG EXTRACT PER 2 CAPS
(*Eleutherococcus senticosus*)	400 mg

STANDARDIZED TO FULL SPECTRUM ACTIVITY PROFILE

Eleutheroside B & E	3.2 mg

DOSAGE
1 liquid Phyto-Cap, 2 times daily

DURATION OF USE
4-6 months

BEST TAKEN
Between meals, with warm water

HISTORY

Eleuthero is a thorny shrub native to East Russia, Northeast China, Korea, and Japan. It is often confused with Panax Ginseng, which is in the same family (*Araliaceae*). However, these are distinctly different plants. While the herb is sometimes called Siberian Ginseng, it is not actually a ginseng. Eleuthero more accurately describes this plant, referring to its botanical identity, *Eleutherococcus senticosus*. And now Congress has legislated that the name Ginseng may be used only to describe the genus Panax.*

During the 1950's and 1960's Russian scientists began to extensively study the constituents and activities of Eleuthero. A new terminology was about to be born, as scientists studied substances that were able to bring about an "increased non-specific resistance" to an organism. These substances and the plants that contained them were called "adaptogens."*

MODEL ADAPTOGEN

An adaptogen is a substance that helps the body adapt to stresses of various kinds. In order to achieve this classification, a plant must be harmless. It must have a normalizing, broad-spectrum action that brings an organism back to homeostasis. Through Russian research, Eleuthero became the model of an adaptogen.*

Numerous clinical studies performed in Russia have documented the efficacy of Eleuthero as an adaptogen. In the late 1960's and 1970's studies were conducted in over 2,100 healthy people. These studies showed that Eleuthero increased the ability of the subjects to withstand stresses such as heat, noise, motion, exercise, and increase in workload. Subjects also experienced increases in mental alertness and work output.*

A popular general tonic, this root serves to promote health and vitality. It contains an assortment of chemical constituents that encourage a healthy brain, immune system and hormonal balance. Used regularly, it functions to enhance the body's natural resistance and adaptation to stressful influences. Likewise, Eleuthero supports mental endurance and promotes overall metabolic efficiency.*

COMPLEMENTARY PHYTO-CAPS/LIQUID FORMULAS/LIQUID EXTRACTS

Energy & Vitality Liquid Phyto-Caps™, Ginseng/Schizandra Supreme

SAFETY EVALUATION / CONTRAINDICATIONS

Do not use during pregnancy or lactation. Do not take during an acute infection or fever, or if you have a bleeding disorder. Side effects are rare but may include insomnia, swollen breasts, hypertension, irritability, anxiety, and/or a rapid heart rate. Use with caution and seek the advise of a qualified healthcare professional if you have hypertension.*

KNOWN DRUG INTERACTIONS

Eleuthero should be used with caution in combination with cholesterol-reducing drugs, drugs that inhibit blood clotting and platelet aggregation including but not limited to warfarin (Coumadin®). Eleuthero might increase the risk of digoxin (Lanoxin®) side effects. Additionally, it might interact with hormone therapies such as estradiol (Alora®, Estrace®), estrogen (Premarin®, Prempro®, Cenestin®), Demulen, Loestrin, Lo/Ovral, Alesse, Triphasil, Ortho Tri-Cyclen, and many others. This herb should also be used with caution in combination with antihypertention, antidiabetic, and antipsychotic medications, in addition to alcohol and barbiturates. Before using this herb, talk with your healthcare professional if you take any medications.*

REFERENCES

Akopov SE, Gabrielian ES. Effects of aspirin, dipyridamole, nifedipine and cavinton which act on platelet aggregation induced by different aggregating agents alone and in combination. Eur J Clin Pharmacol 1992;42(3):257-9.

Blumenthal M, et al. The Complete German Commission E Monographs: Therapeutic Guide to Herbal Medicines. Austin. American Botanical Council; 1998: 124-125.

Bohn B, et al. Flow-cytometric studies with Eleutherococcus senticosus extract as an immunomodulatory agent. Arzneimittelforschung. 1987; 37:1193-1196.

Brekhman II and Dardymov IV. New substances of plant origin which increase non-specific resistance. Annual Review of Pharmacology. 1969; 9: 419-430.

Davydov M and Krikorian AD. Eleutherococcus senticosus (rupr. & Maxim.) Maxim. (Araliaceae) as an adaptogen: a closer look. J of Ethnopharmacol. 2000; 72:345-393.

Farnsworth NR, et al. Siberian Ginseng (eleutherococcus senticosis): current status as an adaptogen. In: Wagner H, et al. Economic and Medicinal Plant Research, vol. 1. New York. Academic Press;1985: 155-215.

Fulder SJ. Ginseng and the hypothalamic-pituitary control of stress. Am J Chin Med. 1981 sum; 9(2): 112-8.

Kamen B. Siberian Ginseng: latest research on the fabled oriental tonic herb. CT: Keats, 1988.

McRae S. Elevated serum digoxin levels in a patient taking digoxin and Siberian ginseng. CMAJ 1996;155:293-5.

Medon PJ, Ferguson PW, Watson CF. Effects of Eleutherococcus senticosus Extracts on Hexobarbital Metabolism in Vivo and in Vitro. J Ethnopharmacol. 1984;10(2):235-41.

Monakhov BV. [The effect of Eleutherococcus senticosus maxim on the therapeutic activity of cyclophosphamide, ethymide or benzotepa.] Vopr Onkol. 1967; 13(8): 94-97. [in Russian]

PDR for Herbal Medicines, 2nd ed. Montvale, NJ: Medical Economics Company; 2000:694.

Szolomicki S, Samochowiec L, Wojcicki J, Drozdzik M. The influence of active components of Eleutherococcus senticosus on cellular defense and physical fitness in man. Phytother Res 2000;14:30-5.

ENERGY & VITALITY

Ultimate Enhancement of Mental and Physical Stamina*

ALCOHOL-FREE CONCENTRATED EXTRACTS OF:

FORMULA	MG EXTRACT PER 3 CAPSULES
Green Tea leaf (*Camellia sinensis*)	90 mg
Eleuthero root (*Eleutherococcus senticosus*)	90 mg
Schizandra berry (*Schizandra chinensis*)	75 mg
Korean Ginseng root (*Panax ginseng*)	51 mg
Cola nut (*Cola nitida*)	42 mg
Ginkgo leaf (*Ginkgo biloba*)	36 mg
Licorice root (*Glycyrrhiza* spp.)	30 mg
Nettle seed (*Urtica dioica*)	6 mg
Prickly Ash bark (*Zanthoxylum clava-herculis*)	6 mg

STANDARDIZED TO FULL SPECTRUM ACTIVITY PROFILE

Polyphenols (from Green Tea)	72 mg
Ginsenosides (from Korean Ginseng)	7.5 mg
Eleutherosides B+E (from Eleuthero Root)	0.72 mg

*THIS STATEMENT HAS NOT BEEN EVALUATED BY THE FOOD AND DRUG ADMINISTRATION. THIS PRODUCT IS NOT INTENDED TO DIAGNOSE, TREAT, CURE OR PREVENT ANY DISEASE.

DOSAGE
Liquid Phyto-Caps: 1 capsule, 3 times daily

DURATION OF USE
4-6 months

BEST TAKEN
Between meals, with warm water

ABUNDANT ENERGY

This formula is useful for anyone who suffers from fading vitality and depleted energy, particularly those individuals who are constantly exposed to overwork, stressful environments or situations, and excess strain to mind or body. This formula efficiently combines herbs which are well known for their influence on energy, with those that address adrenal function, circulatory health, and non-specific resistance to stress (including oxidative / free radical stress). The result is a comprehensive approach for supporting mental and physical stamina.

Green Tea has a long history of use, dating back to around 2,700 B.C. Today, we know that Green Tea is a stimulating antioxidant. This plant supports healthy liver function in a manner that reduces free-radical damage to the liver tissue. Free-radical damage has been linked to low energy and weariness. Oxidative (free-radical) damage is also associated with decreasing intracellular levels of cyclic AMP. Green Tea increases levels of cyclic AMP. Increased levels of cAMP allow hormones to perform better, thus overall function of the body is improved. This cyclic AMP supporting effect is highly desirable in a formula that aims to enhance vital energy. Coupled with its mild stimulant influence, Green Tea proves very useful indeed.*

Eleuthero, unlike the Nettle seed discussed above, is well known and well researched as an adaptogen. Traditionally it has been regarded as a support for weariness, stress, and deficiency. Modern research has shown it to be a stimulant with powerful antioxidant and adaptogenic qualities. It is widely reported to build resistance to both physical and mental stress.*

Chinese Schizandra berry has also been used historically during physical stress. Modern research highlights its strong antioxidant and liver supportive properties,along with its capacity to improve work performance and endurance.*

Korean Ginseng belongs to a genus (a sub-group of a family) named Panax - which is derived from the word panacea - meaning 'cure-all'. The common name also honors this highly useful herb, for Ginseng means 'wonder of the world'. It has traditionally been used to increase stamina (both mental and physical). Known as an adaptogen, Panax builds resistance to stresses of both biological and physical origin. Interestingly, modern research lends support to this adaptogenic affect. This plant is the energy tonic par excellence.*

Cola nut is a caffeine containing plant that is used with nervous stress. Although many individuals may initially think of Cola nut as a stimulant, it is well respected for use during recuperation. It is said that Cola counters weariness and restores nervous integrity, making it a valuable addition to this formula.*

Some studies have suggested an effect from Gingko leaf on glucose metabolism, thereby affecting body function from the cellular level. It appears to assist glucose and ATP metabolism. This may help to explain its usefulness in cognitive function, as well as the supportive influence it seems to have on energy. As with a number of ingredients in this formula, Ginkgo is recognized as a powerful antioxidant. Its support to the circulatory system is also of benefit here.*

Licorice root is often used with physical weariness that is related to the adrenal gland. Whereas Eleuthero supports the adrenal gland's hormonal response to stress, Licorice prevents the breakdown of such hormones. This results in an overall reduction of the functional load that is placed on this important gland. Compounds isolated from licorice appear to be immuno-stimulating.*

Nettle seed has been included here solely on the basis of empirical use with mental stress. The authors have, on many occasions, used an extract of the Nettle seed to allay drowsiness, both behind the wheel and in front of the textbooks. Its affect is not as a stimulant, but as a "mental" adaptogen (enhancing resistance to mental stress). The seed of Nettle contains fatty acids associated with brain function such as Linoleic Acid, Linolenic Acid, Oleic Acid, and Palmitic Acid, which may play a part in its activity.*

Prickly Ash bark has long been used to support circulation. Its use here is to help deliver the entire formula throughout the body. It was traditionally said that Prickly Ash has the ability to 'increase tonicity and functional activity' and to 'sustain the vital force'.*

COMPLEMENTARY PHYTO-CAPS/LIQUID FORMULAS/LIQUID EXTRACTS

Eleuthero Root Liquid Phyto-Caps™, Ginseng/Schizandra Supreme

SAFETY EVALUATION/CONTRAINDICATIONS

Do not use this product during pregnancy or lactation.

KNOWN DRUG INTERACTIONS

Consult a physician if you are taking any prescription drugs.

REFERENCES

Coon N. Using plants for healing. Philadelphia, Pa. Rodale Press. 1979.

Sonnenborn U, Proppert Y. Ginseng (Panax ginseng C.A. Meyer). British Journal of Phytotherapy. 1991; 2(1) 3-14.

Bahrke MS, Morgan WP. Evaluation of the Ergonomic Properties of Ginseng. Sports Med. 1994; 18(4): 229-248.

Snow JM. Camellia sinensis (L.) Kuntze (Theaceae). The Protocol Journal of Botanical Medicine. 1995; Autumn: 47-51.

Pizzorno J, Murray M. Textbook of Natural medicine. New york. Churchill Livingstone; 1999.

Richards RS, et al. Free radicals in chronic fatigue syndrome: cause or effect? Redox Rep. 2000; 5(2-3): 146-7.

Richards RS, et al. Blood parameters indicative of oxidative stress are associated with symptom expression in chronic fatigue syndrome. Redox Rep.2000; 5(1): 35-41

Mahomed AG, et al. Anti-oxidative effects of theophylline on human neutrophils involve cyclic nucleotides and protein kinase A. Inflammation 1998; 22(6): 545-57.

Pizurki L, Polla BS. cAMP modulates stress protein synthesis in human monocytes-macrophages. J Cell Physiol 1994; 161(1): 169-77.

Yamamoto M, et al. Induction of human thioredoxin in cultured human retinal pigment epithelial cells through cyclic AMP-dependent pathway; involvement in the cytoprotective activity of prostaglandin E1. Exp Eye Res 1997; 65(5): 645-52.

Katiyar, SK, et al. Inhibition of spontaneous and photo-enhanced lipid peroxidation in mouse epidermal microsomes by epicatechin derivatives from green tea. Cancer Let. 1994; 79: 61-66.

Kahn SG, et al. Enhancement of Antioxidant and Phase II Enzymes by Oral Feeding of Green Tea Polyphenols in Drinking Water to SKH-1 Hairless Mice: Possible Role in Cancer Chemoprevention. Cancer Res. 1992; 52: 4050-2.

Tanizawa H, et al. Natural Antioxidants. I. Antioxidative Components of Tea Leaf (Thea sinensis L.) Chem Pharm Bull. 1984; 32(5): 2011-14.

Bensky D, Gamble A. Chinese Herbal Medicine: Materia Medica. Seattle: Eastland, 1986.

Tierra M. Planetary Herbology. WI: Lotus Press, 1988.

Brekhman II, Dardymov IV. New Substances of Plant Origin Which Increase Nonspecific Resistance. Ann Rev Pharmacol.1969; 9:419-430.

Werbach M, Murray M. Botanical Influences on Illness: A sourcebook of clinical research. CA: Third Line Press, 1994.

Kamen B. Siberian Ginseng: latest research on the fabled oriental tonic herb. CT: Keats, 1988.

Fulder SJ. Ginseng and the hypothalamic-pituitary control of stress. Am J Chin Med.1981; 9(2): 112-8.

Panossian AG, et al. Effects of heavy physical exercise and adaptogens on nitric oxide content in human saliva. Phytomedicine 1999;6(1):17-26.

Priest AW, Priest LR. Herbal medication. A clinical dispensary handbook. 1982.

Baschetti R. Letter: Chronic Fatigue Syndrome and Liquorice. New Zealand Med Journ. 1995; Apr:156-157.

Snow JM. Glycyrrhiza glabra L. (Leguminaceae). The Protocol Journal of Botanical Medicine. 1996; Winter:9-14.

Willard T. Wild Rose Scientific Herbal. Wild rose College of Natural Healing; Alberta; 1991.

Squires R. Ginkgo biloba. Journal of the Australian Traditional Medicine Society. 1995; Autumn:9-14.

Snow JM. Ginkgo biloba L. (Ginkgoaceae). The Protocol Journal of Botanical Medicine. 1996; 2(1):9-15

Agricultural Research Service. Dr. Duke's Phytochemical and Ethnobotanical Databases: Ethnobotanical uses Urtica dioica. Online. Internet. [7/31/00]. Available WWW: http://www.ars-grin.gov/cgi-bin/duke/ethnobot.pl

Vasseur M, et. Al. Effects of Repeated Treatments with an Extract of Ginkgo biloba (Egb 761), Bilobalide and Ginkgolide B on the Electircal Activity of Pancreatc Beta Cells of Normal or Alloxan-Diabetic Mice: an ex vivo Study with Intracellular Microelectrodes. Gen Pharmac. 1994; 25 (1): 31-46.

FENUGREEK SEED

Supports Healthy Lactation During the Breastfeeding Months*

ALCOHOL-FREE CONCENTRATED EXTRACTS OF:

FORMULA	MG PER 2 CAPSULES
Fenugreek seed (*Trigonella foenum-graecum*)	560 mg

The time-honored traditions of Traditional Chinese Medicine, Ayurveda, and Western Medicine have all held Fenugreek seeds in high regard. Fenugreek Liquid Phyto-Cap™ is formulated to support healthy lactation using organic fenugreek seeds in an alcohol-free liquid extract.

HISTORY

Fenugreek has been used throughout the ages in several cultures and was prized for its culinary and medicinal values. From the Egyptians, to the Greeks and Romans, Fenugreek was even thought to be a religious herb and was ceremoniously used in temples dedicated to Apollo the archer-god of medicine and healing. Its potent restorative attributes quickly spread through Europe and Asia where it was commonly used for blood sugar regulation, abscesses, arthritis, bronchitis, as a soothing digestive aid, and to promote lactation. The similarity between the Arabic word for fenugreek "hulba" and the Mandarin Chinese word "hu lu ba" reveal the direct transference of information across language and culture suggesting Fenugreek's popularity as an herb of commerce throughout history.

LACTATION SUPPORT AND HEALTHY CHOLESTEROL LEVELS

Fenugreek has been traditionally used for lactation, blood sugar maintenance, and cholesterol support in Western, Ayurvedic, and Chinese Medicine. Its continued popularity in India is a testament to its success. A recent survey of 662 women in western India found that 85% of women consumed fenugreek directly following child-birth to support lactation efforts.*

Scientific literature has found several components in Fenugreek that may be responsible for its effectiveness. Most notably a group of steroidal saponins found in the seed extract seem to be of medicinal value. According to the studies performed, these powerful steroidal saponins appear to act similar to human hormones and may have a direct relationship on the glands responsible for the production of milk. The steroidal saponins are also particularly involved with the inhibition of the synthesis of cholesterol and may in fact support normal cholesterol levels.*

Some initial studies have also shown that a novel amino acid (4-hyrdoxyisoleucine)

*THIS STATEMENT HAS NOT BEEN EVALUATED BY THE FOOD AND DRUG ADMINISTRATION.
THIS PRODUCT IS NOT INTENDED TO DIAGNOSE, TREAT, CURE OR PREVENT ANY DISEASE.

found in fenugreek may have direct effects on the pancreas and help promote normal levels of insulin. Scientists have not yet determined how this effect occurs but its effectiveness and safety have been well documented historically.*

Gaia Herbs utilizes only Certified Organic Fenugreek seed and carefully extracts the beneficial properties in a controlled environment to deliver a highly absorbable, highly efficacious, Liquid Phyto-Cap™ tested free of heavy-metals for your safety.

COMPLEMENTARY PHYTO-CAPS/LIQUID FORMULAS/LIQUID EXTRACTS

Lactate Support Liquid Phyto-Caps™

SAFETY EVALUATION/CONTRAINDICATIONS

Fenugreek should be avoided during pregnancy. Some observations have suggested that on rare occasions Fenugreek may cause upset stomach including distension, dyspepsia, and diarrhea. Consumption of Fenugreek may cause a 'maple-syrup' odor in some cases that may be confused with Maple Syrup Urine Disease.

KNOWN DRUG INTERACTIONS

This herb should be used with caution in combination with drugs that inhibit blood clotting and platelet aggregation including but not limited to warfarin (Coumadin®), heparin, clopidogrel (Plavix®), pentoxifylline (Trental), and asprin. Preliminary data suggests fenugreek might have additive effects with drugs that decrease blood glucose levels. Theoretically, patients who are allergic to other plants within the Fabaceae family (including soybeans, peanuts, and green peas) might also be allergic to fenugreek.

REFERENCES

Basch E, Ulbricht C, Kuo G, Szapary P, Smith M. Therapeutic applications of Fenugreek. Alt Med Rev. Feb, 2003.

Kochhar A, Nagi M. Effect of supplementation of traditional medicinal plants on blood glucose in non-insulin-dependent diabetics: a pilot study.

J Med Food. 2005 Winter; 8(4):545-9.

Mills, S, Bone, K. The Essential Guide to Herbal Safety. St. Louis MO : Elsevier, Inc, 2005.

Nick, G. Clinical Purification – A Complete Treatment and Reference Manual. Brookfield, WI : Longevity Through Prevention, 2001.

Shekelle PG, Hardy M, Morton SC, Coulter I, Venuturupalli S, Favreau J, Hilton LK. Are Ayurvedic herbs for diabetes effective? J Fam Pract. 2005 Oct;54(10):876-86. Review.

FIT FOR HEALTH™

Weight Loss Program

The Fit For Health weight loss program offers a paradigm for weight loss that draws upon fundamental principles of naturopathic medicine: 1) The healing power of nature; 2) Do no harm; and 3) Heal oneself. Implied within these principles is the concept that when given the opportunity, the body will naturally seek its balance. The strategy we use to achieve a fit and healthy body while losing weight is to facilitate weight loss through:

- Waste removal from fat tissues (Liqui-Lieve)
- Metabolic and endocrine normalization (Diet Slim)
- Improved intracellular messaging within the body (Thyroid Support)

This easy three-step rogram, accompanied by the recommended dietary and exercise routine, will facilitate weight loss in the most natural way without hardship to one's daily routines.*

Fit For Health/LIQUI-LIEVE

Promotes
Natural Excretion of Wastes*

ALCOHOL-FREE CONCENTRATED EXTRACTS OF:

FORMULA	MG EXTRACT PER 2 CAPSULES
Dandelion leaf and root (*Taraxacum officinalis*)	200 mg
Parsley seed, leaf and root (*Petroselinum crispum*)	108 mg
Juniper berry (*Juniperus communis*)	134 mg
Fenugreek seed (*Trigonella foenum-graecum*)	96 mg
Cascara Sagrada (*Rhamnus purshiana*)	72 mg
Fennel seed (*Foeniculum vulgare*)	16 mg
Bladderwrack fronds (*Fucus vesculosis*)	16 mg
Cilantro leaf (*Coriandrum sativum*)	14 mg

DOSAGE

Liquid Phyto-Caps: 2 capsules, in the A.M.

DURATION OF USE

4-6 months

BEST TAKEN

Between meals, with warm water

*THIS STATEMENT HAS NOT BEEN EVALUATED BY THE FOOD AND DRUG ADMINISTRATION.
THIS PRODUCT IS NOT INTENDED TO DIAGNOSE, TREAT, CURE OR PREVENT ANY DISEASE.

ALTERATIVE PRINCIPLES OF VITALITY

The Eclectic and Physio-medicalist practitioners of the late 19th and early 20th century refined the process for promoting the removal of cellular wastes, generating the term "alterative" to define the process. For many years the term alterative has been defined as "blood cleansing" but this is somewhat misleading. While it is true that blood does carry the metabolites of various catabolic reactions, the organs of waste removal themselves are generally targeted by the plants. Botanicals may support liver, lymphatic, kidney, gall bladder, digestive, skin and/or lung function to achieve what we refer to as alterative activity. Indeed, it is specifically the support of the normal function of organs of elimination that results in efficient removal of waste from the blood.*

Liqui-Lieve is based on these ancient principles of healing. It is designed to support the organs of elimination. Additionally, many of these herbs provide many nutrients that help to build healthy tissue and provide the building blocks of various eliminatory pathways. While these actions are generally quite gentle, they may have profound effects on health and vitality. A build-up of toxins can result in sluggishness both physically and mentally. Helping the body perform these processes can go a long way toward promoting health. Liqui-Lieve is designed to gently promote the normal excretion of waste from tissue and organs. As such, this formula can support general vitality in a significant way.*

Dandelion leaves provide a complex of tasty nutrients, enjoyed all over the world when they are young. Interestingly, the root of dandelion is renowned for its support to liver function, while the leaves target kidney function. Another aspect of Dandelion's normalizing properties is the relatively high level of potassium it contains. Kidney activity tends to deplete potassium, so Dandelion is able to support the function of the kidney while providing valuable nutrients to further support its function. The 1950's-1970's generated a great deal of European interest in research on Dandelion, especially its constituent inulin. Much of this supported the traditional uses, indicating promise for further study of this humble plant.*

Parsley seed, leaf and root also find a place in both traditional healing and the kitchen. Traditional use of seed and leaf centers mainly on digestive support and promoting liver, lung and kidney function. It therefore results in an overall boost to elimination. Parsley has a significant essential oil content believed to be at least part of the active chemical profile. However, the essential oils can be irritating in large doses, so reason is required when consuming this food. There is little scientific research on Parsley yet; some preliminary studies indicate antioxidant activity.*

Juniper berries are renowned for their effect on kidney health. Interestingly, though, they are included in the German Commission E Monographs for their use as an antispasmodic for the digestive system. Like Parsley, Juniper berries have significant essential oil content which can be irritating in large doses.*

Fenugreek seed is an ingredient of curry powder. The seed contains a demulcent activity that soothes digestion and benefits the lungs. Like other plants, this food is nutrient rich. Additionally, Fenugreek seeds contain a great deal of fiber. The fiber aids in digestive function. Rich steroidal components allow the seed to affect the structure and function of many systems in the body. Plant steroids are made from cholesterol like endogenous steroids. They tend to have a normalizing effect on structure and function. A good deal of research interest currently exists in Fenugreek. Investigations into its effect on the glucose system indicate potential for its use in normalizing blood sugar levels. While these studies are preliminary, there is plenty of good evidence on Fenugreek's role in maintaining vital health.*

Cascara Sagrada bark is a traditional Native American remedy that has become a favorite around the world. The bark must age one year or be exposed to heat and aeration to destroy free anthrones, which will cause severe vomiting. Once the anthrones are destroyed, the plant is used to promote normal bowel movements. Its reputation and an understanding of the mechanism of action have earned Cascara Sagrada a place in the German Commission E as an approved herb. It is understood that beta-glycosides are converted into anthrones in the colon by bacterial enzymes. Anthrones are the metabolites that affect bowel function. Long term use is not advised.*

Fennel seed joins the crowd of spices in this blend. It has a taste reminiscent of Licorice. It is also rich in essential oil. It enjoys a long history of use as a flavoring for everything from candy to pickles. Traditional healing use focused on its support to healthy digestion. Research on Fennel is still limited.*

Bladderwrack fronds are eaten as food especially in the Orient. This seaweed is rich in nutrients, notably absorbable iodine and mucilage. The mucilage supports healthy function in the digestive system and lungs. Bladderwrack has a reputation of supporting thyroid function, which may be associated with its iodine content. The thyroid functions to regulate body metabolism, which will have an indirect effect on every elimination system.*

Cilantro leaf falls into the category of nutrient and oil rich seeds. It possesses digestive properties similar to those of Fenugreek and Fennel seeds.

COMPLEMENTARY PHYTO-CAPS/LIQUID FORMULAS/LIQUID EXTRACTS

Cholesterol Vital Maintenance Liquid Phyto-Caps™, Diet Slim Liquid Phyto-Caps™

SAFETY EVALUATION/CONTRAINDICATIONS

Do not use during pregnancy or lactation. Contraindicated in inflammatory kidney conditions, due to essential oil content of Parsley and Juniper Berry.

"Do not use this product if you have abdominal pain or diarrhea. Discontinue use in the event of diarrhea or watery stools. Do not exceed recommended dose. Not for long-term use."

KNOWN DRUG INTERACTIONS

Please see a physician if you are taking any pharmaceutical drugs.

REFERENCES

American Herbal Products Association. Rediscovering The "Roots" of Medicine [supplement]. Herbs for Your Health. 1992; Jan/Feb, S5-S8.

Clark E. Monograph on Taraxacum officinale in A Handbook of Plant Form. Transl. Hobbs, Christopher. Portland: Eclectic Institute, 1985 (orig. 1904).

Willard T. The Wild Rose Scientific Herbal. 1991; 106-109. Wild Rose College, Canada.

Grases F, et. al. Urolithiasis and phytotherapy. Int Urol Nephrol 1994; 26(5): 507-11.

Newall C, et al. Herbal Medicines: A Guide for Health-care Practitioners. London: Pharmaceutical Press, 1996.

Trautwein EA, et. al. Dietary inulin lowers plasma cholesterol and triacylglycerol and alters biliary bile acid profile in hamsters. J Nutr. 1998 Nov; 128(11): 1937-43.

Rowland IR, et. al. Effect of Bifidobacterium longum and inulin on gut bacterial metabolism and carcinogen-induced aberrant crypt foci in rats. Carcinognesis. 1998 Feb; 19(2): 281-5.

Kleesen B, et. al. Effects of inulin and lactose on fecal microflora, microbial activity, and bowel habit in elderly constipated persons. Am J Clin Nutr. 1997 May; 65(5): 1397-402.

Nielson SE, et al. Effect of parsley (Petroselinum crispum) intake on urinary apigenin excretion, blood antioxidant enzymes and biomarkers for oxidative stress in human subjects. Br J Nutr. 1999 Jun; 81(6): 425-6.

Adzamli IK, Kim HO, and Sykes AG. Neutral complexes as oxidants for the reduced form of parsley (Petroselinum crispum) [2FE—2S] ferredoxin. Evidence for partal blocking by redox-inactive Cr (III) complexes. Biochem J. 1982, Jun; 43(2): 201-4.

Fupta A, et al. Effect of Trigonella foenum-graecum (feunugreek) seeds on glycaemic control and insulin resistance in type 2 diabetes mellitus: a double blind placebo controlled study. J Assoc Physicians India. 2001 Nov; 49: 1057-61.

Vats V, et al. Evaluation of anti-hyperglycemic and hypoglycemic effect of Trigonella foneum-graecum Linn, Ocimum sanctum Linn and Pterocarpus marsupium Linn in normal and alloxanized diabetic rats. J Ethnopharmacol. 2002 Jan; 79(1): 95-100.

Pederson M. Nutritional Herbology. IN: Whitman, 1995.

Mills S. Out of the Earth: The Essential Book of Herbal Medicine. England: Viking Group, 1991.

Fit For Health/DIET-SLIM

*Ultimate Support for Weight Loss**

ALCOHOL-FREE CONCENTRATED EXTRACTS OF:

FORMULA	MG EXTRACT PER 3 CAPSULES
Garcinia fruit (*Garcinia cambogia*)	300 mg
Green Tea leaf (*Camellia sinensis*)	225 mg
Coleus root (*Coleus forskohlii*)	138 mg
Turmeric rhizome (*Curcuma longa*)	90 mg
Elder berry (*Sambucus* spp.)	90 mg
Yohimbe bark (*Corynanthe yohimbe*)	60 mg
Bitter Orange peel (*Citrus aurantium*)	57 mg
Gymnema leaf (*Gymnema sylvestre*)	51 mg
Bladderwrack fronds (*Fucus vesiculosis*)	27 mg
Ginger rhizome, (*Zingiber officinale*) Supercritical CO_2 Extract	12 mg

STANDARDIZED TO FULL SPECTRUM ACTIVITY PROFILE

Hydroxycitric acid (from Garcinia)	135 mg
Polyphenols (from Green Tea)	120 mg

DOSAGE

Liquid Phyto-Caps: 2 capsules, mid-day

DURATION OF USE

3-4 months

BEST TAKEN

Between meals, with a small amount of warm water

Note: Dietary and lifestyle adjustments must be made in conjunction with this formula's use. *The 3 Season Diet* by Dr. John Douillard, D.C., Ph.D. is recommended reading.

THE METABOLISM OF WEIGHT LOSS

This formula helps to correct fat cell metabolism by promoting a state of fat utilization rather than storage. It is particularly useful for what is known as the classic 'Venus' body type, where fat storage is concentrated around the hips, thighs and buttocks. Likewise, for individuals who lose weight - only to have it return - this formula is of particular benefit.*

The primary focus of this formula is to establish a metabolic environment where breakdown and utilization of fat (adrenergic-receptor mediated lipolysis) is enhanced due to an increase of available cAMP. Two primary adrenergic receptors

*THIS STATEMENT HAS NOT BEEN EVALUATED BY THE FOOD AND DRUG ADMINISTRATION. THIS PRODUCT IS NOT INTENDED TO DIAGNOSE, TREAT, CURE OR PREVENT ANY DISEASE.

control lipolysis (beta-1 and alpha-2 type). The beta-1 receptor is coupled positively to adenylate cyclase, whereas the alpha-2 sites are negatively coupled to the enzyme. The underlying strategy of this botanical formula utilizes these receptors. The approach is three-fold:

1. To block the alpha-2 adrenergic sites - thereby reducing their impact of decreasing cyclic AMP
2. Activate beta-1 sites to encourage the formation of cyclic AMP
3. Prevent the breakdown of cyclic AMP via phosphodiesterase inhibition

In summary, this compound serves to elevate intra-cellular cyclic AMP levels via those receptor-dependent and independent mechanisms associated with forskolin (from Coleus forskohlii). Additionally, the inhibition of the phosphodiesterase regulated hydrolysis of the cyclic AMP nucleotide to its ester group allows cAMP to be more available. This strategy results in a net increase of cyclic AMP and an associated increase in lipolysis, or the conversion of triglycerides into fatty acids and glycerols. This is the form of fat that is utilized rather than stored.

Other strategies of this important formula are to:

- Enhance thermogenesis (heat production), thereby promoting fat metabolism
- Balance sugar metabolism, thereby correcting food cravings
- Promote healthy liver metabolism, thereby supporting healthy detoxification and elimination patterns.

Diet-Slim thus increases function at the cellular level of numerous processes involved with weight management. It is the combination of these factors which makes Diet-Slim so effective.*

Garcinia-Malabar Tamarind is a natural source of hydroxycitric acid (HCA). HCA is known to cause an increase in fat metabolism, possibly via its influence on liver function.*

Green Tea has traditionally been used to support mental function, promote digestion, reduce flatulence, and to regulate body temperature. It is used here for the effect of several of its components to stimulate lipolysis by preventing the breakdown of cyclic AMP. Cyclic AMP affects hormonal messages within a fat cell. This 'message' helps to amplify the response of a fat cell to adrenaline, the hormone that tells it to burn fat. Green Tea is also valuable here as an established antioxidant and as a moderate stimulant, further assisting the underlying function of the formula.*

Coleus Forskohlii is perhaps Green Tea's best friend when it comes to weight-loss. As mentioned above, utilization of fat is in part controlled by the hormone adrenaline, along with its capacity to form cyclic AMP inside a fat cell. Green Tea and Coleus both modify the fat burning affect of adrenaline (via modification of beta-1 adrenergic-receptor cAMP expression). Forskolin, one of the main active molecules in Coleus, also plays a role by promoting a healthy nervous state and supporting thyroid hormone production, making it particularly well suited for weight management.*

Turmeric rhizome serves this formula through its outstanding antioxidant and liver supportive effects. Normalizing liver function during weight management is highly desirable. The liver is actively involved in regulating blood sugar availability, and metabolism of the 3-ketosteroids, a group of hormones which affect fat metabolism.*

Elderberries bring a number of desirable qualities to this formula. They are recognized to promote healthy elimination patterns and support the liver. Via these actions, Elderberry promotes the removal of cellular wastes and helps to correct general metabolism.*

Yohimbe has been included in this formula specifically for its ability to redirect adrenaline toward the receptors on fat cells that burn fat (Beta-1), and by blocking those receptors which result in fat storage (Alpha-2).*

Bitter Orange is used for weight loss due to its purported thermogenic effects.*

Gymnema leaf is a digestive or stomach tonic with well-known support to the urinary system. It has been reported to "neutralize the excess sugar present in the body." Gymnema is also known as gur-mur (which literally means sugar destroying) because of its noted ability to abolish the taste of sugar.

Bladderwrack fronds have been widely used for weight management. Such benefit quite possibly results from its supportive effect on thyroid function. Bladderwrack fronds must be harvested however from pristine water, as they are known to absorb toxic waste metals from polluted waters.*

Ginger rhizome addresses healthy digestion and works as an antioxidant. In addition to these benefits, Ginger is useful here as a support to the circulatory system, helping to deliver the entire formula throughout the body.*

Note: The intention of this information is to represent the traditional use of the individual botanicals found in these formulas and to inform the reader of any evolving scientific inquiry relevant to the formula's ingredients.

COMPLEMENTARY PHYTO-CAPS/LIQUID FORMULAS/LIQUID EXTRACTS

Supreme Cleanse Kit

KNOWN DRUG INTERACTIONS

Consult a physician if you are taking any prescription drugs.

SAFETY EVALUATION/CONTRAINDICATIONS

Do not take during pregnancy and lactation.

REFERENCES

Snow JM. Camellia sinensis (L.) Kuntze (Theaceae). The Protocol Journal of Botanical Medicine. 1995;1(2):47-51.

Fredholm BB, Lindgren E. The effect of alkylxanthines and other phosphodiesterase inhibitors on adenosine-

*THIS STATEMENT HAS NOT BEEN EVALUATED BY THE FOOD AND DRUG ADMINISTRATION. THIS PRODUCT IS NOT INTENDED TO DIAGNOSE, TREAT, CURE OR PREVENT ANY DISEASE.

receptor mediated decrease in lipolysis and cyclic AMP accumulation in rat fat cells. Acta Pharmacol Toxicol (Copenh).1984; 54(1):64-71.

McCarty MF, Gustin JC. Pyruvate and hydroxycitrate/carnitine may synergize to promote reverse electron transport in hepatocyte mitochondria, effectively 'uncoupling' the oxidation of fatty acids. Med Hypothese. 1999;52(5):407-16

Murray M. The unique pharmacology of Coleus Forskohlii. The American Journal of Natural Medicine. 1994; 1(3):10-13.

Anonymous. Elderberry. The Lawrence Review of Natural Products.1992; Jul.

Kapoor LD. Handbook of Ayurvedic Medicinal Plants. Florida. CRC Press; 1990.

Snow JM. Curcuma longa L. (Zingiberaceae). The Protocol Journal of Botanical Medicine. 1995;1(2):43-46.

Mitchell W. Foundations of Natural Therapeutics – Biochemical Apologetics of Naturopathic Medicine. Tempe, Arizona. Southwest College Press. 1997.

Mills S, Bone K. Principles and Practice of Phytotherapy: Modern Herbal Medicine. Churchill Livingstone, London: 2000.

Galitzky J, et. al. Thermogenic and lipolytic effect of yohimbine in the dog. Br J Pharmacol. 1991; 104(2): 514-18.

Berlan M, et. al. Plasma catecholamine levels and lipid mobilization induced by yohimbine in obese and non-obese women. Int J Obes. 1991; 15(5): 305-15.

Galitzky J, et. al. Alpha 2-antagonist compounds and lipid mobilization: evidence for a lipid mobilizing effect of oral yohimbine in healthy male volunteers. Eur J Clin Invest. 1988; 18(6): 587-94.

Boehringer Ingelheim. Consumer Health Care News-Orange aid in weight loss. Online. Internet. [3/7/02]. Available WW: http://www.boehringer-ingelheim.ca/selfmed/02.07.00.htm

Fit For Health/THYROID SUPPORT

Ultimate Support for Metabolic Enhancement*

ALCOHOL-FREE CONCENTRATED EXTRACTS OF:

FORMULA	MG EXTRACT PER 2 CAPSULES
L-Tyrosine	300 mg
Schizandra berry (*Schizandra chinensis*)	156 mg
Coleus root (*Coleus forskholii*)	154 mg
Kelp fronds (*Laminaria digitata*)	130 mg
Ashwagandha, Av. root (*Withania somnifera*)	120 mg
Bladderwrack fronds (*Fucus vesiculosis*)	56 mg

STANDARDIZED TO FULL SPECTRUM ACTIVITY PROFILE

Iodine (from seaweed)	0.3 mg

*THIS STATEMENT HAS NOT BEEN EVALUATED BY THE FOOD AND DRUG ADMINISTRATION. THIS PRODUCT IS NOT INTENDED TO DIAGNOSE, TREAT, CURE OR PREVENT ANY DISEASE.

DOSAGE
1 Liquid Phyto-Cap, in the P.M.

DURATION OF USE
4-6 Months

BEST TAKEN
Between meals, with warm water

WHAT IS THYROID HEALTH?

The thyroid gland is one of the most important regulators of metabolism, its effect reaching throughout the body. It is in turn regulated by the two master glands of the endocrine system, the pituitary and the hypothalamus. The thyroid gland produces hormones (known as thyroid hormones) from the amino acid tyrosine and from iodine. Since the thyroid can affect practically every cell in the body in a wide variety of ways, normal thyroid function is essential to health.

Unfortunately, many people suffer from thyroid difficulties. There are two general types of low thyroid function. One can be the result of a variety of diseases. This type of hypothyroidism is diagnosed by standard laboratory tests and is treated by a physician. If clinical hypothyroidism is suspected, please consult a physician.

The second common problem is sometimes called "subclinical" low-thyroid function, though this name is misleading. The truth is that the person with this condition does have symptoms of low thyroid function. However, standard laboratory tests do not detect any difficulty with the thyroid. Thus the most appropriate name might be "sub-laboratory" low thyroid function. This type can manifest as lack of energy, inability to concentrate, mood fluctuation, dry skin and hair loss, weight gain, and many other seemingly unrelated problems. When one realizes that thyroid hormones affect every cell in the body, however, it becomes apparent that compromised function with thyroid hormones could possibly lead to effects all over the body.

The Thyroid Support formula is designed to help maintain healthy thyroid gland function and metabolism.

L-Tyrosine is a central component of thyroid hormones. Adequate tyrosine levels help maintain normal thyroid function.

Schizandra berries are unique in that they hold a remarkable blend of five distinct flavor properties. Namely, bitter, sweet, sour, salty and hot. They also contain an array of active constituents including schizandrins, schizandrols, schizandrers, schisantherins, and others, collectively referred to as lignans. These substances work together to enhance and protect overall cellular vitality. As a group, the varying actions associated with the Schizandra berry maintain healthy nerve, liver, lung and adrenal gland function. Accordingly, this berry serves as a valuable

*THIS STATEMENT HAS NOT BEEN EVALUATED BY THE FOOD AND DRUG ADMINISTRATION.
THIS PRODUCT IS NOT INTENDED TO DIAGNOSE, TREAT, CURE OR PREVENT ANY DISEASE.

general tonic that encourages overall health and stamina, and improves one's natural ability to tolerate both physical and emotional stress. Likewise, Schizandra offers antioxidant protection and enhances healthy memory, mental clarity, energy levels, coordination and endurance. In addition, Schizandra may enhance the liver's cleansing capabilities and encourage healthy hormonal metabolic efficiency.*

Coleus forskholii is a mint family herb that contains forskolin. This compound increases cyclic AMP levels within most cells. Cyclic AMP is a type of second messenger, that is, one that transmits a signal from a hormone into the cell. Of particular interest here is the fact that thyroid stimulating hormone (TSH) requires cyclic AMP to transmit its signal. TSH is the hormone produced by the pituitary gland that tells the thyroid gland to produce thyroid hormones. This might explain how people with normal TSH levels can still have symptoms of low thyroid function--there isn't enough cyclic AMP to transmit the message. Coleus may help avoid this problem, and forskolin has been shown to increase TSH activity in thyroid cells.*

Kelp is very similar to Bladderwrack in most aspects. It was used traditionally for regulation of the thyroid gland, to minimize weight gain and to promote healthy digestive and urinary system function.*

Ashwaghanda, often referred to as "Indian Ginseng," is a common herb used in Ayurvedic medicine (from India) to enhance mental and physical vitality and stamina. It contains steroidal compounds and additional chemical constituents that advance the body's natural resistance and adaptation to stressful influences. As well, Ashwaghanda supports mental endurance, promotes total metabolic efficiency and encourages an overall sense of well-being.*

Bladderwrack is a seaweed with a long history of use for maintaining thyroid function and maintaining a healthy body weight. It was also used traditionally as a nutritive tonic. The complex carbohydrates (alginates) of Bladderwrack have been studied in the laboratory and clinic and are well known for promoting proper digestive function. Bladderwrack is purported to prevent absorption of various radioactive isotopes. Bladderwrack contains a significant amount of iodine, a nutrient necessary for thyroid hormone production. Bladderwrack has not been sufficiently studied in modern research to determine its exact mechanism of action on the thyroid gland. However, animal studies suggest Bladderwrack can help maintain healthy cholesterol levels and can have profound effects on supporting the immune system. Apparently, the actions of Bladderwrack are extensive and complex.*

COMPLEMENTARY PHYTO-CAPS/LIQUID FORMULAS/LIQUID EXTRACTS

Metabolic Support Liquid Phyto-Caps™

SAFETY EVALUATION/CONTRAINDICATIONS

Do not use during pregnancy or lactation. If symptoms of excessive thyroid activity (restlessness, anxiety, palpitations, or diarrhea) occur, the formula should be discontinued and a physician should be consulted. This formula should not be used by those with Hyperthyroidism, Hashimoto's thyroiditis, or Graves' disease. Use with caution and seek the advice of a qualified healthcare professional if you high or low blood pressure. This formula may exacerbate acne due to its iodine content, and prolonged ingestion may reduce iron absorption.

KNOWN DRUG INTERACTIONS

This formula should be used with caution in combination with drugs that inhibit blood clotting and platelet aggregation including but not limited to warfarin (Coumadin®), heparin, clopidogrel (Plavix®), pentoxifylline (Trental®), and aspirin. Additionally, this formula may interact with diuretics (due to sodium content), lithium (by increasing hypothyroid effects), barbiturates and thyroid hormone therapy.

REFERENCES

Budd M. Mild hypothyroidism--the missed diagnosis. Int J Alt Compl Med 1998;16:25-27.

Ellingwood F. American Materia Medica, Pharmacognosy and Therapeutics 11th ed. Sandy, OR: Eclectic Medical Publications, 1919:382-3.

Mills SY. Out of the Earth: The Essential Book of Herbal Medicine. Middlesex, UK: Viking Arkana, 1991:514-6

Hoffmann D. The Complete Illustrated Herbal. New York: Barnes & Noble Books, 1996:94.

Felter HW. Eclectic Materia Medica, Pharmacology and Therapeutics. Sandy, OR: Eclectic Medical Publications, 1922:381.

Bruneton J. Pharmacognosy Phytochemistry Medicinal Plants. Paris: Lavoisier Publishing, 1995:44-47.

Schulick P. Herbal Therapy from the Sea. 1993.

Lamela M, Vázquez-Freire MJ, Calleja JM. Isolation and effects on serum lipid levels of polysaccharide fractions from Fucus vesiculosus. Phytother Res 1996;10(suppl):S175-6.

Willenborg DO, Parish CR. Inhibition of allergic encephalomyelitis in rats by treatment with sulfated polysaccharides. J Immunol 1988;140:3410-5.

Scudder JM. Specific Medication and Specific Medicines. Sandy, OR: Eclectic Medical Publications,1890, 1985:116.

Seamon KB, Daly JW. Forskolin: A unique diterpene activator of cAMP-generating systems. J Cyclic Nucleotide Res 1981;7:201-24.

Murray M, Pizzorno J. Encyclopedia of Natural Medicine. Rocklin, CA: Prima Publishing, 1991:386-90.

GINGER SUPREME

with supercritical extract of Turmeric

Maintains a Healthy
Inflammatory Response*

ALCOHOL-FREE CONCENTRATED EXTRACTS OF:

FORMULA	MG EXTRACT PER 1 CAPSULE
Ginger rhizome ETOH Extract (*Zingiber* off.)	100 mg
Ginger rhizome Super-Critical Extract (*Zingiber* off.)	60 mg
Turmeric rhizome Super-Critical Extract (*Curcuma longa*)	25 mg

STANDARDIZED TO FULL SPECTRUM ACTIVITY PROFILE

Total Pungent Compounds from Ginger	30 mg
Zingiberene from Ginger	14 mg

DOSAGE

Liquid Phyto-Caps: Take 1 capsule, 1-2 times daily.

DURATION OF USE

3 months

BEST TAKEN

At meals, with warm water

GINGER SUPREME WITH TURMERIC

Ginger is well known for its use as both a food and spice, but is also revered within Ayurvedic tradition as vishwabhesaj, which means the universal medicine. As such, Ginger's various pharmacological properties include promoting digestion, serving as a powerful antioxidant, supporting cardiovascular function, and promoting a proper response to environmental stress. *

This herb, which is indigenous to Asia, is a powerful botanical promoter of prostaglandins and thromboxanes, which are compounds associated with immune function. Research suggests that Ginger supports an overall normalization of the body's immune response by normalizing prostaglandin and leukotriene production.*

Although a culinary spice and primary component of curry powder, Turmeric's popularity extends far beyond everyday kitchen use to include a variety of medicinal purposes. Within Ayurvedic medicine, Turmeric is touted not only for its soothing properties, but is also traditionally recognized to support digestive and liver function. Curcuminoids, namely Curcumin, which lend this herb its typical yellow pigment, are its primary constituents. These are believed to account for this herb's powerful antioxidant effects, which in turn, generate a supportive effect to the liver. A cousin of Ginger, this powerful antioxidant aids liver function primarily by reducing the damage caused by the free-radical oxidation generated during its metabolism. By reducing stress, Turmeric supports normal function of the liver to encourage healthy glucose metabolism. This herb also enhances the proper breakdown of dietary fats.*

It is important to note that Turmeric's benefits continue beyond supporting liver function to also include assisting the body's immune system and joints. A properly functioning liver accordingly supports the immune system by breaking down immune complexes carrying ingested pathogens. Curcumin is shown to exhibit numerous effects on the inflammatory immune response, including a normalization of leukotriene formation and neutrophil response. Research has shown that by obstructing cyclooxygenase-2 (COX-2), prostaglandins, and leukotrienes, Turmeric normalizes the inflammatory cascade of the immune response.*

The combination of these two herbs encourages the availability of the body's own anti-inflammatory hormones while simultaneously supplying vast amounts of free-radical quenching anti-oxidants. These profound actions help promote the immune response and support a healthy inflammatory response. Supplementation of Ginger Supreme with Turmeric can help to maintain and support healthy joints and connective tissues and deliver antioxidant compounds that protect the body against the damaging effects of toxins and other environmental stressors. *

*Note: The intention of this information is to represent the traditional use of the individual botanicals found in these formulas and to inform the reader of any evolving scientific inquiry relevant to the formula's ingredients.

COMPLEMENTARY PHYTO-CAPS/LIQUID FORMULAS/LIQUID EXTRACTS

Turmeric Supreme Liquid Phyto-Caps™, Infla-Profen Liquid Phto-Caps™

SAFETY EVALUATION/CONTRAINDICATIONS

Before using this product, talk with your healthcare professional if you suffer from a medical condition. Please visit www.gaiaherbs.com to obtain information regarding potential contraindications and/or side effects that may be associated with herbs found in this formula.*

KNOWN DRUG INTERACTIONS

Before using this product, talk with your healthcare professional if you take any medications. Please visit www.gaiaherbs.com to obtain information regarding any possible drug interactions that may be associated with herbs found in this formula.*

REFERENCES

Araujo CC, Leon LL. Biological activities of Curcuma longa L. Mem Inst Oswaldo Cruz 2001;96:723-8.

Frondoza CG, Sohrabi A, Polotsky A, et al. An in vitro screening assay for inhibitors of proinflammatory mediators in herbal extracts using human synoviocyte cultures. In Vitro Cell Dev Biol Anim 2004;40:95-101.

Langner E, Greifenberg S, Gruenwald J. Ginger: history and use. Adv Ther 1998;15:25-44.

Zhang F, Altorki NK, Mestre JR, et al. Curcumin inhibits cyclooxygenase-2 transcription in bile acid- and phorbol ester-treated human gastrointestinal epithelial cells. Carcinogenesis 1999;20:445-51.

GINKGO LEAF

(Ginkgo biloba)

Ultimate Support to Improve Memory*

ALCOHOL-FREE CONCENTRATED EXTRACTS OF:

GINKGO LEAF	MG EXTRACT PER 2 CAPS
(*Ginkgo biloba*)	128 mg

STANDARDIZED TO FULL SPECTRUM ACTIVITY PROFILE

24% Ginkgo flavonoid glycosides (from Ginkgo)	30.8 mg

DOSAGE
1 Liquid Phyto-Cap, 2 times daily

DURATION OF USE
4-6 Months

BEST TAKEN
Between meals, with warm water

HISTORY

Ginkgo is the oldest surviving species of tree and is often referred to as "the living fossil." Fossil records indicate that it probably originated during the Permian period about 250 million years ago. The tree ranged worldwide during the Paleozoic era and went into decline before the Ice Age, eventually retreating to the mountain forests of China.

That Ginkgo is the oldest living species of its family speaks of the tree's hardiness. The first green growth to emerge in the city of Hiroshima after the atomic blast was Ginkgo. The properties of Ginkgo were first recorded around 2,800 BC. In Chinese folk medicine, the leaf was used to support the respiratory system. It's truly amazing that Ginkgo, an ancient tree seeded millions of years ago, has survived to impart such a profound influence on human physiology.

COGNITIVE FUNCTION

Modern day uses of Ginkgo are well established. In Europe it is used extensively to support cognitive function. Ginkgo and its constituents are the subjects of over 400 scientific publications, making it one of the most researched herbal products. Numerous clinical trials have documented Ginkgo's effects on cognitive function. Ginkgo has been shown to affect recall, recognition memory, reaction time, attention, concentration, psychomotor function, mood, information processing, and energy levels.

Many clinical trials have been conducted on concentration and memory, absentmindedness, confusion, lack of energy, decreased physical performance, and anxiety. In one of the earliest placebo-controlled double-blind trials, patients demonstrated improvements in short term memory, concentration power, attention span, and mental flexibility.

One of the first reviews of Ginkgo was published in the journal Lancet in 1992. The authors reviewed over 40 double-blind controlled trials of Ginkgo and cerebral function. After reviewing the trials, the authors concluded that Ginkgo is an effective support for cerebral function.

A 52-week randomized, double-blind placebo-controlled, multi-center trial was conducted on 309 people. Subjects received either 40 mg of Ginkgo extract (24% Gingko flavonoids) three times a day, or a placebo. Compared to the subjects taking the placebo, those taking Gingko showed improvement in cognitive function. The authors concluded that Ginkgo was safe and appears capable of stabilizing and improving both cognitive performance and social functioning. Recently, an analysis of this study was performed to determine the efficacy of 26 weeks of treatment. After a six-month period, Gingko was effective in two areas: cognitive performance and social behavior. There was a significant worsening in all areas of assessment in the placebo group. There were no differences between Ginkgo and placebo with regards to side effects.

Randomized, double blind placebo-controlled studies have also found Ginkgo to be effective in ordinary age-related memory loss. In two trials, healthy participants demonstrated an improvement in memory and improved speed of information processing.

MECHANISM OF ACTION

Many diverse actions contribute to the overall effectiveness of Gingko. Not all of these mechanisms have been elucidated. Actions that possibly contribute to its effectiveness include direct and indirect antioxidant activity, neurotransmitter/receptor modulation, platelet activating factor antagonism, and neuro-protective actions. The combined therapeutic effects are probably greater than that of an individual mechanism and are perhaps the result of the synergistic effects of multiple constituents of the total extract.

COMPLEMENTARY PHYTO-CAPS/LIQUID FORMULAS/LIQUID EXTRACTS

Anti-Oxidant Supreme Liquid Phyto-Caps™, Mental Alertness Liquid Phyto-Caps™, Hawthorn Supreme Liquid Phyto-Caps™

SAFETY EVALUATIONS / CONTRAINDICATIONS

Do not use during pregnancy or lactation.

KNOWN DRUG INTERACTIONS

Consult a physician if taking any pharmaceutical drugs. Contraindications exist with blood thinning agents. Do not use with cholesterol-reducing drugs, drugs that inhibit blood clotting and platelet aggregation including but not limited to Warfarin (Coumadin®), heparin, aspirin or any other medication that blocks platelets or otherwise increases bleeding.

REFERENCES

Glimn-Lacy J and Kaufman PB. Botany Illustrated. New York. Van Nostrand Reinhold Company; 1984: 72-73.

Huang KC. The Pharmacology of Chinese Herbs. Boca Raton.CRC Press;1993: 85-86.

Diamond BJ, et al. Ginkgo biloba extract: Mechanisms and clinical indications. Arch Phys Med Rehabil. 2000;81:668-678.

Vesper J and Hansgen KD. Efficacy of ginkgo biloba in 90 outpatients with cerebral insufficiency caused by old age. Results of a placebo-controlled double-blind trial. Phytomedicine. 1994; 1:9-16.

Kleijnen J and Knipschild P. Ginkgo biloba for cerebral insufficiency. Br. J. Clin. Pharmaco 1992; 34:352-358.

Le Bars PL, et al. A placeo-controlled, double blind, randomized trial of an extract of ginkgo biloba for dementia. JAMA. 1997; 278(16): 1327-1332.

Le Bars PL, et al. A 26-week analysis of a double-blind, placebo-controlled trial of the ginkgo biloba extract Egb 761 in dementia. Dement Geriatr Cogn Disord. 2000;11:230-237.

Rigney U, et al. The effects of acute doses of standardized ginkgo biloba extract on memory and psychomotor performance in volunteers. Phytotherapy Research. 1999: 13:408-415.

Mix JA and Crews WD. An examination of the efficacy of ginkgo biloba extract Egb 761 on the neuropsychologic functioning of cognitively intact older adults. J of Alternative and Complementary Medicine. 2000;6(3):219-229.

Gardès-Albert M, et al. Oxygen-centered free radicals and their interactions with EGb 761 or CP 202. Advances in Ginkgo biloba Extract Research, Vol 2. Paris. Elsevier; 1993:1-11.

Köse L and Do an P. Lipoperoxidation induced by hydrogen peroxide in human erythrocyte membranes. 1. Comparison of the antioxidant effect of ginkgo biloba extract (EGb 761 with those of water-soluble and lipid-soluble antioxidants. The Journal of International Medical Research 1995; 23: 9-18..

Lugasi A, et al. Additional information to the in vitro antioxidant activity of ginkgo biloba L. Phytotherapy Research. 1999; 13: 160-162.

Braquet P. Proofs of involvement of PAF-acether in various immune disorders using BN 52021 (ginkgolide B): a powerful PAF-acether antagonist isolated from ginkgo biloba L. Advances in Prostaglandin, Thromboxane, and Leukotriene Research 1986; 16: 179-198.

Logani S, et al. Actions of ginkgo biloba related to potential utility for the treatment of conditions involving cerebral hypoxia. Life Sciences. 2000; 67: 1389-1396.

Calapai G, et al. Neuro-protective effects of ginkgo biloba extract in brain ischemia are mediated by inhibition of nitric oxide synthesis. Life Sciences. 2000; 67:2673-2683.

Di Renzo G. Ginkgo biloba and the central nervous system. Fitoterapia. 2000; 71: S43-S47.

Miller L. Herbal Medicinals: Selected Clinical Considerations Focusing on Known or Potential Drug-Herb Interactions. Arch Intern Med. 1998; 158(9): 2200-2211.

GLYCEMIC HEALTH

Supports Healthy Blood Sugar Metabolism*

ALCOHOL-FREE CONCENTRATED EXTRACTS OF:

FORMULA	MG PER 2 CAPSULES
Cinnamon bark extract, (*Cinnamomum burmanii*)	150 mg
Gymnema leaf (*Gymnema sylvestre*)	50 mg
Turmeric rhizome (*Curcuma longa*)	50 mg
Cinnamon bark, Supercritical CO_2 Extract (*Cinnamomum burmanii*)	50 mg
Fenugreek (*Trigonella foenum-graecum*)	50 mg
Blueberry leaf (*Vaccinium* spp.)	30 mg
Bitter Melon (*Momordica charantia*)	25 mg
Jambul seed (*Syzygium cumini*)	25 mg
Indian Ginger (*Alpinia officinarum*)	20 mg

STANDARDIZED TO FULL SPECTRUM ACTIVITY PROFILE

BIOACTIVITY PER 2 CAPSULES	MG ACTIVITY
Chlorogenic Acids (from Blueberry leaf)	6 mg
Cinnamaldehydes (from Cinnamon bark)	33.75 mg
Total Phenols (from Cinnamon bark)	33.75 mg

DOSAGE

2 Liquid Phyto-Caps 2 times daily.

DURATION OF USE

3-4 months

BEST TAKEN

After meals, with a small amount of warm water.

DESCRIPTION OF FORMULA

The herbs found in Glycemic Health have been studied and show favorable results for their efficacy in promoting healthy blood sugar levels that are within a normal range and protecting cells from oxidative damage.*

Maintaining a healthy blood sugar level is critical to promoting optimal health. Healthy blood sugar is associated with healthy vision, heart/circulation, kidneys and nervous system.*

The herbs found in Glycemic Health offer potent antioxidant actions and healthy

*THIS STATEMENT HAS NOT BEEN EVALUATED BY THE FOOD AND DRUG ADMINISTRATION. THIS PRODUCT IS NOT INTENDED TO DIAGNOSE, TREAT, CURE OR PREVENT ANY DISEASE.

blood sugar within a normal range, balancing actions that together serve to support a healthy liver and pancreas and promote the healthy functioning of insulin and other glucose-regulating factors in the body.*

Cinnamon Bark is a culinary spice that maintains blood sugar balancing effects. Cinnamon contains the constituent, cinnamaldehyde, found in the volatile oil fraction of the plant. Cinnamaldehyde has potent antioxidant actions, protecting cells from oxidative damage. Cinnamon bark also contains polyphenolic polymers that support healthy blood glucose balance.*

Gymnema Leaf contains a blood-normalizing constituent called gymnemic acid. Gymnema supports healthy blood glucose, cholesterol and triglyceride levels within a normal range. The gymnemic acids found in this herb reduce the intestinal absorption of glucose, slowing its release into the blood stream, thereby maintaining healthy glucose and insulin levels. This herb can also stimulate the healthy secretion of insulin and aid in the growth of pancreatic B cells (the cells that secrete insulin).*

Turmeric rhizome offers potent antioxidant protection to maintain cellular health in organs associated with glucose regulation. Turmeric contains sesquiterpenes and diarylheptanoids including curcumin, that function together to neutralize reactive oxygen species and support healthy sugar metabolism. This herb also enhances the proper breakdown of dietary fats.*

Fenugreek seeds contains complex carbohydrates, fiber and protein. Rich in the amino acid, 4-hydroxyisoleucine, fenugreek seeds support healthy blood glucose levels by encouraging healthy insulin secretion by the pancreas. Fenugreek seeds work together with the Gymnema leaf in this formula to support healthy release of glucose into the blood stream, further supporting its glucose balancing actions. Fenugreek seeds also support healthy cholesterol and triglyceride levels, and offer antioxidant protection.*

Blueberry Leaf maintains normal blood glucose levels within a normal range by slowing down the absorption of glucose from food, reducing the amount of glucose produced by the liver and enhancing the metabolism of glucose. Important phenolic compounds found in blueberry leaf, such as chlorogenic acid and caffeic acids, work together to support healthy dietary glucose absorption, encourage the healthy metabolism of glucose and production of glucose in the liver. Chlorogenic acid acts directly on the enzyme glucose-6-phosphatase (G6P) in the liver, which plays a major role in maintaining healthy blood glucose balance, while caffeic acids and chlorogenic acid function to support the healthy release of dietary glucose into the blood. Blueberry leaf also helps to support the healthy metabolism of fat, an action that further supports the maintenance of normal blood glucose levels.*

Bitter Melon is a popular Southeast Asian ingredient used to encourage healthy blood sugar metabolism. This light green, pointed cucumber is unique in that it contains a polypeptide compound similar in structure to insulin, known as "p-insulin," or "plant-insulin." This compound is likely responsible for its unique actions in supporting glycemic health. Bitter melon also contains constituents (including flavonoids) that offer the added benefits of supporting healthy cholesterol levels within a normal range and maintaining immune system function.*

Jambul Seed promotes optimal antioxidant status in the pancreas and liver, two important blood glucose regulating organs that are susceptible to oxidative stress. Jambul seed also encourages healthy cholesterol and glucose levels within a normal range in the blood.*

Indian Ginger may enhance the overall actions and bioavailability of the herbs found in the Glycemic Health formula.*

COMPLEMENTARY PHYTO-CAPS/LIQUID FORMULAS/LIQUID EXTRACTS

Adrenal Health Liquid Phyto-Caps™, Cinnamon Bark Liquid Phyto-Caps™

SAFETY EVALUATION/CONTRAINDICATIONS

Before using this product, talk with your healthcare professional if you suffer from a medical condition. Please visit www.gaiaherbs.com to obtain information regarding potential contraindications and/or side effects that may be associated with herbs found in this formula.*

KNOWN DRUG INTERACTIONS

Before using this product, talk with your healthcare professional if you take any medications. Please visit www.gaiaherbs.com to obtain information regarding any possible drug interactions that may be associated with herbs found in this formula.*

REFERENCES

Anderson RA, Broadhurst CL, Polansky MM, et al. Isolation and Characterization of Polyphenol Type-A Polymers from Cinnamon with Insulin-like Biological Activity. J Agric Food Chem 2004;52:65-70.

Baskaran K, Kizar-Ahamath B, Shanmugasundaram MR, Shanmugasundaram ERB. Antidiabetic effect of leaf extract from Gymnema sylvestre in non-insulin-dependent diabetes mellitus patients. J Ethnopharmacol 1990;30:295-300.

Broadhurst CL, Polansky MM, Anderson RA. Insulin-like biological activity of culinary and medicinal plant aqueous extracts in vitro. J Agric Food Chem 2000 Mar;48(3):849-52.

Cignarella A, Nastasi M, Cavalli E, Puglisi L. Novel lipid-lowering properties of Vaccinium myrtillus L. leaves, a traditional antidiabetic treatment, in several models of rat dyslipidaemia: a comparison with ciprofibrate. Thromb Res 1996 Dec 1;84(5):311-22.

Johri RK, Zutshi U. An Ayurvedic formulation 'Trikatu' and its constituents. J Ethnopharmacol 1992 Sep;37(2):85-91.

Khan A, Safdar M, Ali Khan M, et al. Cinnamon improves glucose and lipids of people with type 2 diabetes. Diabetes Care 2003;26:3215-8.

Persaud SJ, Al-Majed H, Raman A, Jones PM. Gymnema sylvestre stimulates insulin release in vitro by increased membrane permeability. J Endocrinol 1999;163:207-12.

Ravi K, Ramachandran B, Subramanian S. Effect of Eugenia Jambolana seed kernel on antioxidant defense system in streptozotocin-induced diabetes in rats. Life Sci 2004 Oct 15;75(22):2717-31.

Ravi K, Ramachandran B, Subramanian S. Protective effect of Eugenia jambolana seed kernel on tissue antioxidants in streptozotocin-induced diabetic rats. Biol Pharm Bull 2004 Aug;27(8):1212-7.

Ravi K, Sivagnanam K, Subramanian S. Anti-diabetic activity of Eugenia jambolana seed kernels on streptozotocin-induced diabetic rats. J Med Food 2004 Summer;7(2):187-91.

Shanmugasundaram ER, et al. Use of Gymnema sylvestre leaf extract in the control of blood glucose in insulin-dependent diabetes mellitus. J Ethnopharmacol 1990;30:281-94.

Welsch CA, Lachance PA, Wasserman BP. Effects of native and oxidized phenolic compounds on sucrase activity in rat brush border membrane vesicles. J Nutr 1989 Nov;119(11):1737-40.

Yeh GY, Eisenberg DM, Kaptchuk TJ, Phillips RS. Systematic review of herbs and dietary supplements for glycemic control in diabetes. Diabetes Care 2003 Apr;26(4):1277-94.

GREEN TEA

Rich in
Naturally Occurring Antioxidants*

ALCOHOL-FREE CONCENTRATED EXTRACTS OF:

FORMULA	**MG PER 2 CAPSULES**
Green Tea (*Camellia sinensis*)	

WHOLE PLANT STANDARDIZATION PROCESS™ PROFILE

Total Polyphenols	300 mg
Total Catechins	240 mg

Calculated as:
- EGC (Epigallocatechin)
- EC (Epicatechin)
- EGCG (Epigallocatechingallate)
- EGC (Epicatechingallate)
- (and others)

DOSAGE

2 Liquid Phyto-Caps, 2 times daily

DURATION OF USE

4-6 months

BEST TAKEN

After meals, with warm water

*THIS STATEMENT HAS NOT BEEN EVALUATED BY THE FOOD AND DRUG ADMINISTRATION.
THIS PRODUCT IS NOT INTENDED TO DIAGNOSE, TREAT, CURE OR PREVENT ANY DISEASE.

HISTORY

The green tea shrub has been cultivated and consumed for thousands of years in China and Southeast Asia. More recently, there has been a renewed interest in green tea due to its high polyphenol content and powerful free radical scavenging activity.*

The main constituents found in green tea are the alkaloids, tannins and phenolic acids. Of particular interest to researchers today are the polyphenols known as catechins, and more specifically, epigallocatechin (EGC), epicatechin (EC), epigallocatechingallate (EGCG), and epicatechingallate (ECG). These catechins demonstrate the most promise in reacting with most free radicals. It is also interesting to note that the actual structure of these constituents help to prevent the production of free radicals and also bind to heavy metals that challenge health and cause cellular damage.*

A POTENT ANTIOXIDANT

Green tea provides assistance in maintaining a healthy balance between free radicals necessary for the healthy functioning of the body, and an excess of free radicals. While free radicals are part of normal human body function, too many free radicals cause cellular damage.*

We are exposed to free radicals daily, from our external environment (our food, air and water supply) to our own internal environment (a result of normal biological processes). Research now demonstrates that consuming antioxidants such as green tea is one of the most powerful methods we know of to help neutralize the actions of too many free radicals in our body.*

There is a well recognized connection between an excess of free radicals in the body (also known as oxidative stress) and healthy brain function.* Accordingly, green tea is demonstrating particular benefit for promoting healthy brain function by providing antioxidant support to fragile brain tissue.*

GREEN TEA AND BRAIN HEALTH

Brain cells (neurons) are extremely sensitive to free radical attacks, particularly as you age. This is in part because neurons have a low glutathione (antioxidant) content, brain metabolism consumes a great deal of oxygen, and neurons have a very limited ability to repair damage to their DNA caused by free radicals.*

In addition, metal ions (such as iron, copper, zinc, and aluminum) can generate free radicals that challenge brain tissue. Specifically, beta-amyloid aggregates, found in the neurons of people faced with brain health challenges, form free radicals in the presence of existing free radicals such as metal ions. This beta-amyloid affect is reduced or eliminated by herbs, foods and nutrient recognized for their free radical scavenging effect.*

Green tea contains antioxidant and metal-binding actions that help to maintain healthy brain tissue, even as we age and are exposed to an overabundance of free radicals.*

GREEN TEA AND THE INFLAMMATORY CASCADE

Green tea also has an inflammatory-cascade normalizing action that promotes the healthy metabolism and activity of arachadonic acid, prostaglandins, leukotrienes and platelets. When tissues are stressed, these compounds can be found at unhealthy levels and ratios, and their actions can sometimes contribute to the inflammatory cascade when not kept in check.*

The body normally responds to stress by activating what is known as the inflammatory cascade. Essentially, the immune system's cells send out signals telling the stressed area to protect and repair itself. Scientific research has demonstrated, however, that it is important to maintain this response at an appropriate level.*

Green tea promotes healthy communication between the immune system and strained cells, supporting the body's natural, shielding response to environmental stressors such as free radicals.*

COMPLEMENTARY PHYTO-CAPS/LIQUID FORMULAS/LIQUID EXTRACTS

Anti-Oxidant Supreme Liquid Phyto-Caps™

SAFETY EVALUATION/CONTRAINDICATIONS

Do not take during pregnancy or lactation. This green tea product contains naturally occurring caffeine and hence consuming large amounts of the product could theoretically cause insomnia and other symptoms associated with caffeine.*

KNOWN DRUG INTERACTIONS

There are no well-known drug interactions with the use of green tea. However, the high tannin content of green tea may theoretically affect the metabolism of some medications such as codeine, atropine, ephedrine and pseudoephedrine, among others. Before using this product, talk with your healthcare professional if you take any medications.*

REFERENCES

Brinker F. Herb Contraindications and Drug Interactions. 2nd ed. Sandy, OR: Eclectic Medical Publications, 1998.

Eastwood, M. A. 1999. Interaction of dietary antioxidants in vivo: How fruit and vegetables prevent disease? QJM 92: 527-30.

Gey, K. F. Prospects for the prevention of free radical disease, regarding cancer and cardiovascular disease. Br Med Bull 1993;49(3): 679-99.

Gey, K. F. et al. Poor plasma status of carotene and vitamin C is associated with higher mortality from ischemic heart disease and stroke: Basel Prospective Study. Clin Invest 1993;71: 3-6.

Hong J, Smith TJ, Ho CT, August DA, Yang CS. Effects of purified green and black tea polyphenols on cyclooxygenase- and lipoxygenase-dependent metabolism of arachidonic acid in human colon mucosa andcolon tumor tissues. Biochem Pharmacol. 2001;62(9):1175-83.

Meyer, J. S. et al. Actiological considerations and risk factors for multi-infarct dementia. J Neurol Neurosurg Psychiatry 1988;51: 1489-97.

Nick, G. Whole food protection from age-related cognitive disorders and neurodegenerative disorders. TLDP 2002;8:144-4.

Rimm, E.B. et al. Vegetable, fruit, and cereal fiber intake and risk of coronary heart disease among men. JAMA 1996;275: 447-51

Ronzio B. Polyphenols as anti-inflammatory agents. J Naturopathic Med 2000;9:44-50.

Siesjo, B. K. Pathophysiology and treatment of focal cerebral ischemia. Part I: Pathophysiology. J Neurosurg 1992;77(2): 169-84.

Yang CS, Chung JY, Yang GY, Li C, Meng X, Lee MJ. Mechanisms of inhibition of carcinogenesis by tea. Biofactors. 2000;13(1-4):73-9.

HAWTHORN SUPREME

Ultimate Support of Cardiovascular Function*

ALCOHOL-FREE CONCENTRATED EXTRACTS OF:

FORMULA	MG EXTRACT PER 2 CAPSULES
Hawthorn berry (*Crataegus* spp.)	240 mg
Hawthorn leaf & flower (*Crataegus* spp.)	100 mg

STANDARDIZED TO FULL SPECTRUM ACTIVITY PROFILE

Oligomeric procyanadins	40 mg

DOSAGE

1 liquid Phyto-Cap, 2 times daily

DURATION OF USE

4-6 months or longer, for best results

BEST TAKEN

Between meals, with warm water

FOOD FOR THOUGHT

Hawthorn trees grow readily in the northern temperate zones of North America, Europe and East Asia. Each of these zones appreciates a long traditional history of Hawthorn as both food and folk remedy. The earliest records declared the Hawthorn tree as a symbol of marriage, love and hope. Later, it gained a reputation for its properties. For the American Eclectics, Hawthorn was considered specific for maintaining heart function. The Chinese and Native Americans used Hawthorn to promote healthy circulation. For all cultures blessed with Hawthorn trees, the berries provided food. It is the berries, flowers, and leaves used primarily as a

*THIS STATEMENT HAS NOT BEEN EVALUATED BY THE FOOD AND DRUG ADMINISTRATION. THIS PRODUCT IS NOT INTENDED TO DIAGNOSE, TREAT, CURE OR PREVENT ANY DISEASE.

cardiac tonic. Reported uses also include digestive tonic. The berries, flowers, and leaves are used collectively and independently to support a healthy heart.*

Hawthorn is considered specifically nourishing to the cardiovascular system. Rich bioflavonoids are present in Hawthorn, and may help offset the lack of bioflavonoids in typical American foods. These bioflavonoids promote connective and cardiovascular tissue integrity. There are two groups of active flavonoids in Hawthorn. One group of flavonoids promotes normal rhythmic activity of the heart, while the other group reinforces healthy collagen tissue of the cardiovascular system.*

Today, Hawthorn is recognized in scientific literature for its influence on heart function. Besides the above-mentioned actions relating to bioflavonoid content, Hawthorn is shown to help maintain normal cholesterol levels, to have good antioxidant properties, and to generally economize heart action. The German Commission E includes Hawthorn leaf and flower for maintenance of cardiovascular function. Hawthorn is a classic tonic, in that it gently helps maintain healthy heart function.*

Hawthorn flowers and leaves possess similar properties and chemistry to the Hawthorn berry. While the berries are higher in certain constituents, such as the potent antioxidants known as oligoproanthocyanidins (OPC), the flower and leaf are higher in others, such as vitexin, quercitin and hyperoside. They have been combined here in Hawthorn Supreme to offer the full spectrum of Hawthorn's chemistry.*

COMPLEMENTARY PHYTO-CAPS/LIQUID FORMULAS/LIQUID EXTRACTS
Hawthorn Berry Solid Extract, Anti-Oxidant Supreme Liquid Phyto-Caps™, Ginkgo Leaf Liquid Phyto-Caps™

SAFETY EVALUATION/CONTRAINDICATIONS
This formula should be avoided in pregnancy and lactation. If you have any signs or symptoms of cardiac disease, including but not limited to shortness of breath, and/or pain around the heart that may spread to the abdomen, the neck, and the arms, and/or fluid accumulation in the legs, seek medical attention promptly. Use with caution and seek the advise of a qualified medical professional if you are currently being treated for a heart condition.*

KNOWN DRUG INTERACTIONS
This formula should be used with caution in combination with cardiovascular drugs (such as those used to treat angina, hypertension, heart failure, and arrhythmias), including but not limited to Digoxin or digitalis, as concomitant use may potentiate the effects of the drugs, and dosages may need to be adjusted accordingly. Further, central nervous system depressants and coronary vasodilators, including but not limited to caffeine, papaverine, and epinephrine, when used with Hawthorn, can have a potentiating effect. Before using this formula, talk with your healthcare professional if you take any medications.*

REFERENCES

Al Makdessi S, et al. Myocardial Protection by Pretreatment with Crataegus oxyacantha. Arzneim.-Forsch. 1996; 46(1): 25-27.

Ammon H, Handel M. Crataegus, Toxikologie und Pharmakologie Teil II: Pharmakodynamik Planta Med. 1991; 43(3): 209-39.

Djumlija. Crataegus oxycantha. Aust J Med Herbalism. 6(2): 37-42.

Hobbs C, Foster S. Hawthorn - A Literature Review. Herbalgram. 1990; 22:19-33.

Loew D. Phytotherapy in heart failure. Phytomedicine. 1997; 4(3): 267-71.

McGuffin M, et al., ed. American Herbal Products Association's Botanical Safety Handbook. Boca Raton, FL: CRC Press, 1997:37.

Mitchell W. Plant Medicine. Seattle, Wa. Self-published. 2000.

Murray M. The healing power of herbs - The enlightened persons guide to the wonders of medicinal plants. 2nd ed. Prima publishing. Rocklin, Ca. 1995.

Popping S, et al. Effect of a Hawthorn Extract on Contraction and Energy Turnover of Isolated Rat Cardiomyocytes. Arzneim.-Forsch. 1995; 45(1): 1157-61.

Schussler M, et al. Functional and Antiischaemic Effects of Monoacetyl-vitexinrhamnoside in Different In Vitro Models. Gen. Pharmac. 1995; 26(7): 1565-70.

Upton R, Ed. Hawthorn leaf with flower: quality control, analytical and therapeutic monograph. Santa Cruz, CA: Am Herbal Pharmacopoeia, 1999:1-29.

Witchl M. (Bisset NG, Ed.) Herbal Drugs and Phytopharmaceuticals. Medpharm, CRC Press: Boca Raton. 1994

HEP SUPPORT

For
Deep Liver Support*

ALCOHOL-FREE CONCENTRATED EXTRACTS OF:

FORMULA	MG EXTRACT PER 2 CAPSULES
Astragalus root (*Astragalus membranaceous*)	200 mg
Chinese Skullcap root (*Scutellaria baicalensis*)	100 mg
Chinese Bupleurum root (*Bupleurum chinense*)	60 mg
Reishi mushroom (*Ganoderma lucidum*)	30 mg
Maitake mushroom (*Grifola frondosa*)	20 mg
Licorice root (*Glycyrrhiza uralensis & G. glabra*)	20 mg

DOSAGE
1 Liquid Phyto-Cap, 2 times daily

DURATION OF USE
6-12 months or longer

BEST TAKEN
Between meals with warm water

*THIS STATEMENT HAS NOT BEEN EVALUATED BY THE FOOD AND DRUG ADMINISTRATION. THIS PRODUCT IS NOT INTENDED TO DIAGNOSE, TREAT, CURE OR PREVENT ANY DISEASE.

THE LIVER'S IMPORTANT ROLE

The liver is the most important organ for carrying out detoxification and metabolic functions. This means it helps eliminate toxins (either from the environment or made by the body) and transforms food into all the nutrients needed by the body. When the liver is disrupted, its various functions become more and more compromised. The immune system can become hyperactive. Unfortunately, the result is that the immune system can begin to damage healthy tissue throughout the body. A large portion of this damage is due to generation of free radicals by immune cells. Free radicals can stress healthy cells. Hep Support addresses these multiple problems. It helps maintain normal liver function while it helps normalize the immune system. The formula also provides antioxidant defenses against free radicals.

Astragalus has a long history of use in traditional Chinese medicine. This root supports normal function to the immune system and the liver.*

Chinese Skullcap root is a potent antioxidant. In traditional Chinese medicine it was recommended for all manner of "hot" conditions and as a support to proper immune function.*

Chinese Bupleurum root has primarily been researched as part of a traditional Chinese formula known as sho-saiko-to (which contains about 20% Bupleurum). Sho-saiko-to fosters normal liver function. Chinese Bupleurum appears to protect the liver, calm the immune system, and possibly directly support protein synthesis in the liver. This plant is highly regarded in traditional Chinese herbal medicine where it is considered helpful in a variety of circumstances, including as a support for the liver.*

Reishi mushroom helps regulate the immune system, eliminate free radicals, and protect normal liver function. Numerous studies have supported its uses in traditional Chinese medicine.*

Maitake mushroom is one of many mushrooms used in traditional Asian and European herbal systems that, like Reishi, helps maintain normal immune function.*

Licorice has been used in traditional Western herbalism as well as Traditional Chinese herbalism. In Traditional Chinese herbalism, licorice was widely used to support the liver, digestive, and respiratory systems and to make other herbs work together in a formula. Licorice root is one of the most widely researched herbs. In particular, it appears to support normal liver function. Licorice root inhibits the breakdown of the body's own cortisol, thus making the cortisol available for a longer period of time. This results in an indirect anti-inflammatory effect throughout the body. The presence of higher amounts of natural cortisol would also tend to normalize immune reactions. Studies suggest that the benefit of licorice is mediated by its effects on the immune system.*

COMPLEMENTARY PHYTO-CAPS/LIQUID FORMULAS/LIQUID EXTRACTS

Anti-Oxidant Supreme Liquid Phyto-Caps™, Liver Health Liquid Phyto-Caps™, Milk Thistle Seed Liquid Phyto-Caps™

SAFETY EVALUATION/CONTRAINDICATIONS

Do not use during pregnancy and lactation.

KNOWN DRUG INTERACTIONS

Consult a physician if you are taking any pharmaceutical drugs.

Use with caution when combining this formula with aspirin, warfarin (Coumadin®), heparin, or any other medication that blocks platelets or otherwise increases bleeding. Also use caution when combining this formula with digitalis or related heart medications.

There are reports that Bupleurum combined with interferon can very rarely lead to serious inflammation of the lungs. Do not combine Bupleurum with interferon without first consulting a physician knowledgeable in herbal medicine.

REFERENCES

Gibo Y, Nakamura Y, Takahashi N, et al. Clinical study of sho-saiko-to therapy for Japanese patients with chronic hepatitis C (CH-C). Prog Med 1994;14:217-9.

Oka H, Yamamoto S, Kuroki T, et al. Prospective study of chemoprevention of hepatocellular carcinoma with sho-saiko-to (TJ-9). Cancer 1995;76:743-9.

Reichert R. Phytotherapeutic alternatives for chronic active hepatitis. Q Rev Natural Med 1997;summer:103-8.

Werbach M, Murray M. Botanical Influences on Illness. Tarzana, CA: Third Line Press, 1994:176-83

Mizoguchi Y, Sakagami Y, Okura Y, et al. Effects of sho-saiko-to (TJ-9) in hepatitis patients and on the metabolism of arachidonic acid. In: Hoyosa E, Yamamura Y (eds) Recent Advances in the Pharmacology of Kampo (Japanese Herbal) Medicines. Amsterdam: Excerpta Medica, 1988:396-404.

Yamamoto M, Kumagai A, Yamamura Y. Structure and actions of saikosaponins isolated from Bupleurum falcatum L. I. Anti-inflammatory action of saikosaponins. Arzneim Forsch 1975;25:1021-3.

Shimizu I, Ma YR, Mizobuchi Y, et al. Effects of sho-saiko-to, a Japanese herbal medicine, on hepatic fibrosis in rats. Hepatology 1999;29:149-60.

Bensky D, Gamble A, Kaptchuk T. Chinese Herbal Medicine Materia Medica, Revised Edition. Seattle: Eastland Press, 1993: 49-50.

Van Rossum TGJ, Vulto AG, Hop WCJ, et al. Intravenous glycyrrhizin for the treatment of chronic hepatitis C: A double-blind, randomized, placebo-controlled phase I/II trial. J Gastroenterol Hepatol 1999;14:1093-9.

Suzuki H, Ohta Y, Takino T, et al. Effects of glycyrrhizin on biochemical tests in patients with chronic hepatitis. Double blind trial. Asian Med J 1983;26:423-38.

Arase Y, Ikeda K, Murashima N. The long term efficacy of glycyrrhizin in chronic hepatitis C patients. Cancer 1997;79:1494-500.

Tamura Y, Nishikawa T, Yamada K, et al. Effects of glycyrrhetinic acid and its derivatives on 4-sulpha- and 5-beta-reductase in rat liver. Arzneim Forsch 1979;29:647-9.

Yoshikawa M, Matsui Y, Kawamoto H, et al. Effects of glycyrrhizin on immune-mediated cytotoxicity. J Gastroenterol Hepatol 1997;12:243-8.

Felter HW. Eclectic Materia Medica, Pharmacology and Therapeutics. Sandy, OR: Eclectic Medical Publications, 1922:395.

Weiss RF. Herbal Medicine. Gothenberg, Sweden: Ab Arcanum and Beaconsfield: Beaconsfield Publishers Ltd, trans. Meuss AR, 1985:59-61.

Hoffmann D. The Complete Illustrated Herbal. New York: Barnes & Noble Books, 1996;:99.

Davis EA, Morris DJ. Medicinal uses of licorice through the millennia: The good and plenty of it. Mol Cell Endocrinol 1991;78:1-6.

Foster S, Yue CX. Herbal Emissaries: Bringing Chinese Herbs to the West. Rochester VT: Healing Arts Press, 1992:112-121.

Shiao MS, Lee KR, Lin LJ, Wang CT. Natural products and biological activities of the Chinese medicinal fungus Ganoderma lucidum. In: Ho CT, Osawa T, Huang MT, Rosen RT (eds) Food Phytochemicals for Cancer Prevention II: Teas, Spices and Herbs. Washington, DC: American Chemical Society, 1994: 342-54.

Lin JM, Lin CC, Chen MF, et al. Radical scavenger and antihepatotoxic activity of Ganoderma formosanum, Ganoderma lucidum and Ganoderma neo-japonicum. J Ethnopharmacol 1995;47:33-41.

Jones K. Reishi mushroom: Ancient medicine in modern times. Alt Compl Ther 1998;4(4):256-67.

Schar D. Grifola frondosa: A "new" immunostimulant? Br J Phytother 1997;4:168-75.

Zhang ZL, Wen QZ, Liu CX. Hepatoprotective effects of astragalus root. J Ethnopharmacol 1990;30:145-9.

Murray M, Pizzorno P. An Encyclopedia of Natural Medicine. Rocklin, CA: Prima Publishing, 1991:230.

van Loon IM. The golden root: Clinical applications of Scutellaria baicalensis Georgi flavonoids as modulators of the inflammatory response. Alt Med Rev 1997;2:472-80.

Huang CK. The Pharmacology of Chinese Herbs. 290-1.

Salmond S. Herbs and hepatitis C. Int J Alt Compl Med 1997;15:17-19.

Willard T, Jones K. Reishi Mushroom: herb of spiritual potency and medical wonder. Issaquah, WA: Sylvan Press, 1990.

Ishizaki T, Saski F, Ameshima S, et al. Pneumonitis during interferon and/or herbal drug therapy in patients with chronic active hepatitis. Eur Respir J 1996;9:2691-6.

HOLY BASIL

FULL SPECTRUM SUPERCRITICAL CO_2 EXTRACT

Maintains Healthy Cortisol Levels*
Promotes Feeling of Emotional Well-Being*
Promotes COX-2 Modulation*

ALCOHOL-FREE CONCENTRATED EXTRACTS OF:

FORMULA	MG EXTRACT PER 2 CAPSULES
Holy Basil Supercritical CO_2 Extract (*Ocimum sanctum*)	100 mg
Holy Basil, Hydro-ethanol Extract (*Ocimum sanctum*)	200 mg

STANDARDIZED TO FULL SPECTRUM ACTIVITY PROFILE

Total Eugenols (measured as Eugenol and Methyl Eugenol)	17 mg
Carophylene	4 mg
Total Triterpenoids (measured as Ursolic acid, Oleanoic acid)	13 mg
Rosmarinic acid	7.6 mg

DOSAGE
Liquid Phyto-Caps: 1 capsule, 2 times daily

DURATION OF USE
3 months

BEST TAKEN
Between meals, with warm water

HISTORY

Holy Basil or "Tulsi" has long been used in Ayurvedic medicine to support a healthy response to stress, maintain blood sugar levels within a normal range, promote longevity, nourish the mind and elevate the spirit. Revered by Ayurvedic practitioners as "the incomparable one," this herb's documented actions on the body date back thousands of years. Today, we know that Holy Basil contains a variety of constituents, including eugenol, camphor, caryophyllene, ursolic acid, luteolin and apigenin that function collectively to normalize stress-related neuroendocrine hormones and enhance immune function.*

Holy Basil exhibits impressive adaptogenic activity. Helping the body adapt to stresses of various kinds, this plant has a normalizing, broad-spectrum action that maintain homeostasis.*

*THIS STATEMENT HAS NOT BEEN EVALUATED BY THE FOOD AND DRUG ADMINISTRATION.
THIS PRODUCT IS NOT INTENDED TO DIAGNOSE, TREAT, CURE OR PREVENT ANY DISEASE.

A popular general tonic, Holy Basil maintains equilibrium among biochemicals associated with the stress system in the body. This system involves neuroendocrine and immune structures that produce a variety of chemicals, including cortisol, epinephrine, dopamine, and inflammatory mediators, responsible for maintaining balance of all body systems and promoting health and vitality.*

As a natural consequence of maintaining a healthy stress system in the body, Holy Basil enhances emotional well being by encouraging the release of hormones associated with a positive state of mind, and discouraging the release of hormones associated with too much stress. *

Holy Basil is also showing great promise in promoting healthy blood sugar levels in persons with normal levels. Maintaining a healthy blood sugar level is critical to promoting optimal health.*

Holy Basil also has an inflammatory-cascade normalizing action that promotes the healthy metabolism and activity of arachadonic acid, prostaglandins, leukotrienes and platelets. When tissues are stressed, it is important to keep these compounds within the healthy range.*

The body normally responds to stress by activating what is known as the inflammatory cascade. Essentially, the immune system's cells send out signals telling the stressed area to protect and repair itself. Scientific research has demonstrated, however, that it is important to maintain this response at an appropriate level.*

Holy Basil is a natural COX-2 enzyme modulator. By stopping the cascading effect caused by COX-2 enzyme, Holy Basil helps to maintain many of the body's functions in a healthy range. Holy Basil is also an anti-oxidant that helps to support the body's functions and maintain them in a normal range by neutralizing free radicals.*

Holy Basil promotes healthy communication between the immune system and strained cells, supporting the body's natural, shielding response to environmental stressors such as free radicals.*

This remarkable herb contains an assortment of chemical constituents that encourage a healthy stress system, immune system and hormonal balance. Used regularly, it functions to enhance the body's natural resistance and adaptation to stressful influences. Likewise, Holy Basil supports mental endurance and promotes overall metabolic efficiency and longevity.*

COMPLEMENTARY PHYTO-CAPS/LIQUID FORMULAS/LIQUID EXTRACTS

Adrenal Health Liquid Phyto-Caps™, Rhodiola Rosea Liquid Phyto-Caps™, Serenity Liquid Phyto-Caps™

SAFETY EVALUATION/CONTRAINDICATIONS

Before using this product, talk with your healthcare professional if you suffer from a medical condition. Please visit www.gaiaherbs.com to obtain information regarding potential contraindications and/or side effects that may be associated with the herbal extract found in this product.*

KNOWN DRUG INTERACTIONS

Before using this product, talk with your healthcare professional if you take any medications. Please visit www.gaiaherbs.com to obtain information regarding any possible drug interactions that may be associated with the herbal extract found in this product.*

REFERENCES

Agrawal P, Rai V, Singh RB. Randomized placebo-controlled, single blind trial of Holy Basil leaves in patients with noninsulin-dependent diabetes mellitus. Int J Clin Pharmacol Ther. 1996 Sep;34(9):406-9.

Chattopadhyay RR. Hypoglycemic effect of Ocimum sanctum leaf extract in normal and streptozotocin diabetic rats. Indian J Exp Biol. 1993 Nov;31(11):891-3.

Gholap S, Kar A. Hypoglycaemic effects of some plant extracts are possibly mediated through inhibition in corticosteroid concentration. Pharmazie. 2004 Nov;59(11):876-8.

Rai V, Iyer U, Mani UV. Effect of Tulasi (Ocimum sanctum) leaf powder supplementation on blood sugar levels, serum lipids and tissue lipids in diabetic rats. Plant Foods Hum Nutr. 1997;50(1):9-16.

Vats V, Yadav SP, Grover JK. Ethanolic extract of Ocimum sanctum leaves partially attenuates streptozotocin-induced alterations in glycogen content and carbohydrate metabolism in rats. J Ethnopharmacol. 2004 Jan;90(1):155-60.

INFLA-PROFEN

For Ultimate Support of Back & Joint Mobility*

ALCOHOL-FREE CONCENTRATED EXTRACTS OF:

FORMULA	MG EXTRACT PER 2 CAPSULES
Devil's Claw root (*Harpagophytum procumbens*)	200 mg
Feverfew tops (*Tanacetum parthenium*)	150 mg
Turmeric rhizome (*Curcuma longa*)	100 mg
Yucca root (*Yucca* spp.)	46 mg
Burdock root & seed (*Arctium lappa*)	32 mg
Celery seed (*Apium graveolens*)	16 mg
Jamaican Dogwood bark (*Piscidia erythrina*)	12 mg
Nettle leaf & seed (*Urtica dioica*)	10 mg
Ginger rhizome, Supercritical CO_2 Extract (*Zingiber* off.)	8 mg

STANDARDIZED TO FULL SPECTRUM ACTIVITY PROFILE

Parthenolide (from Feverfew)	1.4 mg

DOSAGE
2 Liquid Phyto-Caps, 2-3 times daily

DURATION OF USE
4-6 Months

BEST TAKEN
Between meals, with warm water

DESCRIPTION OF FORMULA
The Infla-Profen formula provides multiple herbs that enhance immune system function and help to support the normal functioning of cytokines and prostaglandins. These compounds are essential for maintaining normal function in nearly all parts of the body, including the joints and the musculoskeletal system, particularly when they are stressed by exercise. The body normally responds to stress by activating what is known as the inflammatory cascade. Essentially, the immune system's cells send out signals telling the stressed area to protect and repair itself. Scientific research has demonstrated, however, that it is important to maintain this response at an appropriate level. This formula promotes healthy communication between the immune system and strained cells, nourishing the body's natural, shielding response to environmental stressors. Likewise, Infla-Profen protects cells against damage from their own physiologic immune response.*

Devil's Claw tuber is a plant from southern Africa valued by the native peoples for joints and as a digestive tonic. Europeans brought the plant from Africa in the early 20th century. This herb contains iridoid glycoside constituents that work to maintain normal fluid levels in the interstitial spaces of tissues that encase the joints, encouraging overall joint health. Further, the compounds in Devil's Claw function to promote muscle tissue health.*

Feverfew leaf promotes the healthy metabolism and activity of prostaglandins, leukotrienes, platelets and serotonin. Further, feverfew contains melatonin, a hormone that may play a role in encouraging a healthy sleep cycle and promoting a healthy response to stressors that cause occasional temporary pain.*

Turmeric rhizome, like Ginger, is a potent modulator of healthy prostaglandin and thromboxane formation. It maintains and supports healthy joints and contains compounds that provide antioxidant protection against the damaging effects of toxins and other environmental stressors.*

Yucca root is a common desert plant in the southwestern United States. Saponins in Yucca root may help to maintain healthy joints, though the mechanisms of action are unknown. Some researchers speculate that Yucca root may encourage the healthy metabolism of toxins in the gastrointestinal tract.*

Burdock root & seed have long been used in traditional cultures to support skin health and immune function. Burdock root acts as an antioxidant and appears to normalize the messenger chemical known as platelet-activating factor (PAF).

Further, Burdock may encourage the healthy elimination of toxins from the body. There is insufficient reliable research to scientifically validate the actions of burdock root and seeds in humans.*

Celery seed supports various systems in the body, including the cardiovascular and musculoskeletal systems. It shows particular promise in supporting joint health and in promoting the normal relaxation of muscle tissue. Likewise these seeds may also encourage a healthy response to temporary nervous tension.*

Jamaican Dogwood bark may promote relaxation in muscle tissue. In addition, this bark may encourage restful sleep and a healthy nervous system. Insufficient human clinical trials have been done to support these theoretical effects of Jamaican Dogwood bark.*

Nettle leaf is a highly nutritious herb that helps to support and maintain the health of joints. Further, Nettle leaf encourages a healthy immune reaction when an inflammatory response is induced.*

Ginger rhizome is one of the most powerful botanical promoters of healthy prostaglandin and thromboxane activity, compounds associated with immune function. Further, this highly valued herb promotes healthy circulation, vital joints, and a proper response to environmental stress.*

COMPLEMENTARY PHYTO-CAPS/LIQUID FORMULAS/LIQUID EXTRACTS

Migra-Profen Liquid Phyto-Caps™, Anti-Oxidant Supreme Liquid Phyto-Caps™, Kava Kava Liquid Phyto-Caps™

SAFETY EVALUATION/CONTRAINDICATIONS

This formula should be avoided in pregnancy and lactation. Do not exceed the recommended dose. Use with caution if you are allergic to the Astercaceae/Compositae (includes daisies, marigolds, ragweeds and others) family. If you experience fast or irregular breathing, itching, skin rash or hives, seek medical attention promptly. Also, use with caution and seek the advice of a qualified healthcare professional if you have a heart disorder such as heart disease or congestive heart failure, diabetes, stomach disorder, a kidney disorder, or high/low blood pressure.

KNOWN DRUG INTERACTIONS

This formula should be used with caution in combination with drugs used for blood pressure, diabetes, and cardiac conditions and in drugs that inhibit blood clotting and platelet aggregation including but not limited to warfarin (Coumadin®) and the blood thinning drug, aspirin. Do not use this formula in conjunction with central nervous system depressant, antihypertensive and antidiabetic medications. Concomitant use with PUVA therapy can cause phototoxicity. Before using this formula, talk with your healthcare professional if you take any medications.

REFERENCES

Bingham R, Bellew BA, Bellew JG. Yucca plant saponin in the management of arthritis. J Appl Nutr 1975;27:45-50.

*THIS STATEMENT HAS NOT BEEN EVALUATED BY THE FOOD AND DRUG ADMINISTRATION.
THIS PRODUCT IS NOT INTENDED TO DIAGNOSE, TREAT, CURE OR PREVENT ANY DISEASE.

Blumenthal M, Busse WR, Goldberg A, et al. (eds). The Complete German Commission E Monographs: Therapeutic Guide to Herbal Medicines. Austin: American Botanical Council and Boston: Integrative Medicine Communications, 1998:120-1.

Bone ME, Wilkinson DJ, Young JR, et al. Ginger rhizome--a new antiemetic: The effect of Ginger rhizome on postoperative nausea and vomiting after major gynaecological surgery. Anaesthesia 1990;45:669-71.

Brinker F. Herb Contraindications and Drug Interactions. 2nd ed. Sandy, OR: Eclectic Medical Publications, 1998.

Chantre P, Cappelaere A, Leblan D, et al. Efficacy and tolerance of Harpagophytum procumbens versus diacerhein in the treatment of osteoarthritis. Phytomedicine 2000;7:177-83

Chopra A, Lavin P, Patwardhan B, Chitre D. Randomized double blind trial of an Ayurvedic plant derived formulation for treatment of rheumatoid arthritis. J Rheumatol 2000;27:1365-72.

Chrubasik S, Enderlein W, Bauer R, Grabner W. Evidence for the antirheumatic effectiveness of herba Urticae dioicae in acute arthritis: A pilot study. Phytomedicine 4:105-8.

Chrubasik S, Junck H, Breitschwerdt H, et al. Effectiveness of Harpagophytum extract WS 1531 in the treatment of exacerbation of low back pain: A randomized placebo-controlled double-blind study. Eur J Anaesthesiol 1999;16:118-29.

Della Loggia R, Zilli C, Del Negro P, et al. Isoflavones as spasmolytic principles of Piscidia erythrina. Prog Clin Biol Res 1988;280:365-8.

Deodhar SD, Sethi R, Srimal RC. Preliminary study on antirheumatic activity of curcumin (diferuloyl methane). Indian J Med Res 1980;71:632-4.

Ebadi M, Govitrapong P, Phansuwan-Pujito P, et al. Pineal opioid receptors and analgesic action of melatonin. J Pineal Res 1998;24(4):193-200.

Ellingwood F. American Materia Medica, Pharmacognosy and Therapeutics 11th ed. Sandy, OR: Eclectic Medical Publications, 1919:378.

Felter HW. Eclectic Materia Medica, Pharmacology and Therapeutics. Sandy, OR: Eclectic Medical Publications, 1922:548-9.

Handa SS, Chawla AS, Sharma AK. Plants with anti-inflammatory activity. Fitoterapia 1992;63:3-31.

Heptinstall S, White A, Williamson L, et al. Extracts of feverfew inhibit granule secretion in blood platelets and polymorphonuclear leucocytes. Lancet 1985;i:1071-4.

Hobbs C. Feverfew: Tanacetum parthenium. HerbalGram 1989;20:26-35, 47.

Hoffmann D. The Complete Illustrated Herbal. New York: Barnes & Noble Books, 1996:150.

Iwakami S, Wu J, Ebizuka Y, Sankawa U. Platelet activating factor (PAF) antagonists contained in medicinal plants: Lignans and sesquiterpenes. Chem Pharm Bull (Tokyo) 1992;40:1196-8.

Kawakishi S, Morimitsu Y, Osawa T. Chemistry of ginger components and inhibitory factors of the arachidonic acid cascade. In: Ho CT, Osawa T, Huang MT, Rosen RT (eds) Food Phytochemicals for Cancer Prevention vol 2: Tea, Spices and Herbs. Washington, DC: American Chemical Society, 1994:244-50.

Kirchhoff HW. Urtica juice as a diuretic. Z Phytother 1983;4:621-6.

Kiuchi F, Iwakami S, Shibuya M, et al. Inhibition of prostaglandin and leukotriene biosynthesis by gingerols and diarylheptanoids. Chem Pharm Bull 1992;40:387-91.

Klingelhoefer S, Obertreis B, Quast S, Behnke B. Antirheumatic effect of IDS 23, a stinging nettle leaf extract, on in vitro expression of T helper cytokines. J Rheumatol 1999;26:2517-22.

Leung AY, Foster S. Encyclopedia of Common Natural Ingredients Used in Food, Drugs and Cosmetics 2nd ed. New York: John Wiley & Sons Inc, 1996:141-3.

Lin CC, Lu JM, Yang JJ, et al. Anti-inflammatory and radical scavenge effects of Arctium lappa. Am J Chin Med 1996;24:127-37.

Mills S, Bone K. Principles and Practice of Phytotherapy: Modern Herbal Medicine. Edinburgh: Churchill Livingstone, 2000:345-9.

Moore M. Medicinal Plants of the Desert and Canyon West. Santa Fe: Museum of New Mexico Press, 1989:134-5.

Moussard C, Alber D, Toubin MM, et al. A drug used in traditional medicine, Harpagophytum procumbens: No evidence for NSAID-like effect on whole blood eicosanoid production in human. Prostagland Leukotr Essential Fatty Acids 1992;46:283-

Murch SJ, Simmons CB, Saxena PK. Melatonin in feverfew and other medicinal plants. Lancet 1997;350:1598-9.

Nadkarni AK, Nadkarni KM. Indian Materia Medica vol 2. Bombay: Popular Prakashan. 1976:414-18.

Obertreis B, Giller K, et al. Antiphlogistic effects of Urtica dioica folia extract in comparison to caffeic malic acid. Arzneim Forsch 1996;46:52-6.

Obertreis B, Ruttkowski T, Teucher T, et al. Ex-vivo in-vitro inhibition of lipopolysaccharide stimulated tumor necrosis factor-_ and interleukin-1_ secretion in human whole blood by extractum Urticae dioicae foliorum. Arzneim Forsch 1996;46:389-94.

Pattrick M, Heptinstall S, Doherty M. Feverfew in rheumatoid arthritis: a double blind, placebo controlled study. Ann Rheum Dis 1989;48:547-9.

Ronzio B. Polyphenols as anti-inflammatory agents. J Naturopathic Med 2000;9:44-50.

Shah BH, Nawaz Z, Pertani SA, et al. Inhibitory effect of curcumin, a food spice from turmeric, on platelet-activating factor- and arachidonic acid-mediated platelet aggregation through inhibition of thromboxane formation and Ca2+ signaling. Biochem Pharmacol 1999;58:1167-72.

Srivastava CK, Mustafa T. Ginger (Zingiber officinale) in rheumatism and musculoskeletal disroders. Medical Hypoth 1992;39:342-48.

Srivastava KC. Isolation and effects of some ginger components on platelet aggregation and eicosanoid biosynthesis. Prostaglandins Leukotrienes Med 1986;25:187-98.

Srivastava R, Dikshit M, Srimal RC, Dhawan BN. Anti-thrombotic effect of curcumin. Thromb Res 1985;404:413-7.

Srivastava R, Puri V, Srimal RC, Dhawan BN. Effect of curcumin on platelet aggregation and vascular prostacyclin synthesis. Arzneim Forsch 1986;36:715-7.

Vogler BK, Pittler MH, Ernst E. Feverfew as a preventive treatment for migraine: A systematic review. Cephalalgia 1998;18:704-8.

Weiss RF. Herbal Medicine. Gothenberg, Sweden: Ab Arcanum and Beaconsfield: Beaconsfield Publishers Ltd, trans. Meuss AR, 1985.

Yarnell E. Stinging nettle: A modern view of an ancient healing plant. Altern Complem Ther 1998;4:180-6.

JOINT HEALTH

Supports Joint Health and Mobility*

ALCOHOL-FREE CONCENTRATED EXTRACTS OF:

FORMULA	MG EXTRACT PER 2 CAPSULES
Devil's Claw root (*Harpgophytum procumbens*)	80 mg
Green Tea (*amellia sinensis*)	0 mg
Turmeric rhizome (*Curcuma longa*)	80 mg
MSM (Methylsulfonylmethane)	80 mg
Boswellia resin (*Boswellia serrata*)	40 mg
Brown Seaweeds (*Padina pavonica*)	40 mg
Camu Camu freeze dried (*Myriciaria dubia*)	40 mg
Chaga Mushroom (*Inonotus obliquus*)	40 mg
Hawthorn berry (*Crataegus* spp.)	40 mg
Ginger, Supercritical CO_2 Extract (*Zingiber officinalis*)	4 mg
Hops, Supercritical CO_2 Extract (*Humulus lupulus*)	4 mg
Rosemary, Supercritical CO_2 Extract (*Rosmarinus officinalis*)	4 mg

STANDARDIZED TO FULL SPECTRUM ACTIVITY PROFILE

Boswellic Acid	26 mg

DOSAGE

Liquid Phyto Caps: 2 capsules, 2-3 times daily

DURATION OF USE

3 months

BEST TAKEN

After meals, with warm water

DESCRIPTION OF FORMULA

Joint Health maintains optimal levels of the protective synovial fluid between the joints and maintains the health of cartilage. Joint Health also enhances immune system function and helps to support the normal functioning of cytokines and prostaglandins. These compounds are essential for maintaining normal function in nearly all parts of the body, including the joints and the musculoskeletal system.*

The body normally and naturally responds to stress by activating what is known as the inflammatory cascade. Nuclear factor-kB (NF-kB) has generated considerable attention as a promoter of the inflammatory cascade and COX 2

*THIS STATEMENT HAS NOT BEEN EVALUATED BY THE FOOD AND DRUG ADMINISTRATION. THIS PRODUCT IS NOT INTENDED TO DIAGNOSE, TREAT, CURE OR PREVENT ANY DISEASE.

enzyme activity, which causes inflammation in the joints. NF-kB is a family of factors in the body that regulate immune and inflammatory responses. Inhibition of this family reduces production of the pro-inflammatory prostaglandins. However, the NF-kB system is essential to immune function so it is important to target only its cascade manifestations.*

Joint Health supports the appropriate expression of COX 2 enzyme activity by neutralizing free radicals that stimulate NF-kB to initiate the inflammatory response. Other agents have selectively inhibited COX 2 enzyme activity throughout the body, which may cause health challenges like compromised heart function, while Joint Health works to modulate COX 2 activity without compromising heart function.*

Joint Health promotes healthy communication between the immune system and strained cells, nourishing the body's natural shielding response to environmental stressors and protecting joint tissue against challenge from the body's own physiologic responses. These responses include the body's natural inflammation response and excess fluid in the joints.*

Devil's Claw is a plant from southern Africa valued for its benefit in maintaining healthy joints. This herb contains iridoid glycoside constituents that maintain normal fluid levels in the interstitial spaces of tissues that encase the joints, encouraging overall joint health. Further, the compounds in Devil's Claw function to promote muscle tissue health.*

Green tea promotes healthy communication between the immune system and strained cells, supporting the body's natural shielding response to environmental stressors such as free radicals. It has an inflammatory-cascade normalizing action that promotes the healthy metabolism and activity of arachadonic acid, prostaglandins, leukotrienes and platelets. When joint tissue is stressed, these compounds, if not maintained at healthy levels, can contribute to the body's natural inflammatory cascade.*

Turmeric rhizome is a potent modulator of healthy prostaglandin and thromboxane formation. It maintains and supports healthy joints and contains compounds that provide antioxidant protection against the damaging effects of toxins and other environmental stressors. Together with ginger and rosemary, this herb works to suppress the NF-kB family of factors that can initiate the body's natural inflammatory cascade.*

MSM is a naturally occurring sulfur compound found within cartilaginous tissues, offering the body an efficient means of maintaining and rebuilding the joint matrix structure.*

Boswellia is an Ayurvedic herb that supports a healthy inflammation response and encourages optimal joint function.*

Brown Algael Seaweeds contain substances that stimulate the synthesis of glycosaminoglycans such as hyaluronic acid and chondroitin, recognized for their unique ability to encourage healthy joint tissue. Brown Algael Seaweeds also offer an active, highly absorbable form of calcium that protects joints from the damaging effects of bone resorption, associated with loss of calcium, collagen and other bone matrix components.*

Camu Camu offers a potent vitamin C complex that contains bioflavonoids, anthocyanins and other important co-factors to support healthy immune function and neutralize free radicals associated with inflammatory response and joint health.*

Chaga mushroom supports healthy immune function in a similar fashion to other popular health supporting mushrooms such as shiitake and Maitake. What sets this particular mushroom apart is its affinity for birch trees in northern Scandinavia, Russia and Canada. It derives its nutrients directly from living birch trees, rather than from the ground, and consequently is particularly high in betulinic acid (also referred to as betulin). This phytochemical, isolated from birch trees, demonstrates significant immune-supporting actions and has an affinity for tissues that have a low pH. Typically, unhealthy joint tissue will maintain a lower pH, attracting this potent phytochemical to that area; supporting healthy immune function where it is needed most.*

Hawthorn Berry maintains and supports healthy joints and contains compounds that provide antioxidant protection against the damaging effects of environmental toxins and other stressors. Hawthorne berries promote healthy fluid levels in the body, reducing excessive levels in the joints that can compromise function.*

Ginger rhizome is a powerful botanical promoter of healthy prostaglandin and thromboxane activity; compounds associated with inflammation and immune function. Further, this highly valued herb promotes healthy circulation, vital joints, and a proper response to environmental stress. Together with turmeric and rosemary, this herb works to suppress the NF-kB family of factors that can initiate the body's natural inflammatory cascade.*

Hops remove water from the body, by effectively increasing urinary outflow and maintaining healthy fluid levels in the joints. Hops, also inhibits COX 2 activity associated with joint health.*

Rosemary leaf is a natural antioxidant that helps reduce free-radical damage that compromises the health of joints. Together with ginger and turmeric, this herb works to address the NF-kB family of factors that can initiate the body's natural inflammatory cascade.*

COMPLEMENTARY PHYTO-CAPS/LIQUID FORMULAS/LIQUID EXTRACTS

Infla-Profen Liquid Phyto-Caps™, Turmeric Supreme Liquid Phyto-Caps™, Holy Basil Liquid Phyto-Caps™

SAFETY EVALUATION/CONTRAINDICATIONS

Before using this product, talk with your healthcare professional if you suffer from a medical condition. Please visit www.gaiaherbs.com to obtain information regarding potential contraindications and/or side effects that may be associated with herbs found in this formula.*

KNOWN DRUG INTERACTIONS

Before using this product, talk with your healthcare professional if you take any medications. Please visit www.gaiaherbs.com to obtain information regarding any possible drug interactions that may be associated with herbs found in this formula.*

REFERENCES

Adcocks C, Collin P, Buttle DJ. Catechins from green tea (Camellia sinensis) inhibit bovine and human cartilage proteoglycan and type II collagen degradation in vitro. J Nutr. 2002 Mar;132(3):341-6.

Aggarwal BB, Shishodia S. Suppression of the Nuclear Factor-{kappa}B Activation Pathway by Spice-Derived Phytochemicals: Reasoning for Seasoning. Ann N Y Acad Sci. 2004 Dec;1030:434-41.

Bone ME, Wilkinson DJ, Young JR, et al. Ginger rhizome—a new antiemetic: The effect of Ginger rhizome on postoperative nausea and vomiting after major gynaecological surgery. Anaesthesia 1990;45:669-71.

Chantre P, Cappelaere A, Leblan D, et al. Efficacy and tolerance of Harpagophytum procumbens versus diacerhein in the treatment of osteoarthritis. Phytomedicine 2000;7:177-83.

Chopra A, Lavin P, Patwardhan B, Chitre D. Randomized double blind trial of an Ayurvedic plant derived formulation for treatment of rheumatoid arthritis. J Rheumatol 2000;27:1365-72.

Chrubasik S, Junck H, Breitschwerdt H, et al. Effectiveness of Harpagophytum extract WS 1531 in the treatment of exacerbation of low back pain: A randomized placebo-controlled double-blind study. Eur J Anaesthesiol 1999;16:118-29.

Fujita T. [Active absorbable algal calcium (AAACa) changes calcium paradigm.] [Article in Japanese] Clin Calcium 2005 Jan;15(1):87-93.

Fujita T. Active Absorbable Algal Calcium (AAA Ca): new Japanese technology for osteoporosis and calcium paradox disease. Assoc Physicians India 2004 Jul;52:564-7.

Kawakishi S, Morimitsu Y, Osawa T. Chemistry of ginger components and inhibitory factors of the arachidonic acid cascade. In: Ho CT, Osawa T, Huang MT, Rosen RT (eds) Food Phytochemicals for Cancer Prevention vol 2: Tea, Spices and Herbs. Washington, DC: American Chemical Society, 1994:244-50.

Kimmatkar N, et al. Efficacy and tolerability of Boswellia serrata extract in treatment of osteoarthritis of knee—a randomized double blind placebo controlled trial. Phytomedicine 2003 Jan;10(1):3-7.

Kiuchi F, Iwakami S, Shibuya M, et al. Inhibition of prostaglandin and leukotriene biosynthesis by gingerols and diarylheptanoids. Chem Pharm Bull 1992;40:387-91.

Lemay M, et al. In vitro and ex vivo cyclooxygenase inhibition by a hops extract. Asia Pac J Clin Nutr. 2004;13(Suppl):S110.

Lo AH, et al. Carnosol, an antioxidant in rosemary, suppresses inducible nitric oxide synthase through down-regulating nuclear factor-kappaB in mouse macrophages. Carcinogenesis. 2002 Jun;23(6):983-91.

Methylsulfonylmethane(MSM). Monograph. Altern Med Rev. 2003 Nov;8(4):438-41.

Tripathi YB, et al. Anti-inflammatory properties of BHUx, a polyherbal formulation to prevent atherosclerosis. Inflammopharmacology 2004;12(2):131-52.

KAVA KAVA

(Piper methysticum)

Ultimate Support for Relaxation*

ALCOHOL-FREE CONCENTRATED EXTRACTS OF:

KAVA KAVA ROOT	MG EXTRACT PER 3 CAPS
(*Piper methysicum*)	409 mg

STANDARDIZED TO FULL SPECTRUM ACTIVITY PROFILE

Total Kavalactones (from Kava Kava)	225 mg

DOSAGE

1 liquid Phyto-Cap, three times daily, use only as directed

DURATION OF USE

Continuous use of Kava should be limited to 4 weeks.

BEST TAKEN

Between meals, with warm water

HISTORY

Kava is a slow growing, perennial shrub. A member of the pepper family (Piperaceae), it is native to the tropical Pacific Islands region. Islanders who use it as a ritual beverage during ceremonies have long revered it. It is traditionally used as a social beverage for chiefs and noblemen for its calming, relaxing effect. The root is also used traditionally for stress-related conditions. Kava is cultivated commercially, where it is totally dependent on human intervention for propagation.

HIGHLY REGARDED FOR ANXIETY

Kava is highly regarded in Europe as an effective treatment for anxiety. Numerous clinical studies have verified its efficacy. A randomized placebo-controlled trial evaluated Kava's effectiveness in 101 patients with anxiety of non-psychotic origin. Subjects were followed for 6 months. Symptoms were evaluated using the Hamilton Anxiety Scale (HAM-A). Significant improvements were seen at 8 weeks (reduction of HAM-A score from 30-17) and continued for another 16 weeks. At the end of the trial the HAM-A score was reduced to 9.*

Similar, but quicker results were seen in a placebo-controlled double blind study of 40 women with menopause-related symptoms of anxiety. However, unlike the previous study there was a significant decrease (measured by HAM-A) in symptoms after just 1 week of treatment. Improvement continued throughout the full study period.

Several studies have been conducted comparing Kava with other agents. A double-blind study of 174 patients with anxiety compared Kava with other agents. Patients were followed for 6 weeks. Similar improvements in HAM-A scores were seen in all treatment groups. Statistically there was no difference in the outcome of the therapies. Kava was well tolerated with none of the side effects associated with the other agents.

A recent meta-analysis reviewed several clinical trials to determine the efficacy of Kava for the treatment of anxiety. The reviewers concluded that Kava was superior to placebo as a symptomatic for anxiety. The authors agreed that Kava is an herbal option for the treatment of anxiety.

MECHANISM OF ACTION

The exact mechanism of Kava on the central nervous system is unknown. One possible mode of action is that Kava may interact with Gama-Aminobutyric acid (GABA) receptors. Early in vivo and in vitro research found that Kavalactones demonstrated only weak GABA receptor binding actions. However, a more recent study found that Kava pyrones mediate effects in GABA-A receptors, particularly in the hippocampus and amygdala. Other possible mechanisms include inhibition of noradrenaline uptake and activation of mesolimbic dopaminergic neurons. It is likely that there is more than one pathway responsible for Kava's activity on the central nervous system.

COMPLEMENTARY PHYTO-CAPS/LIQUID FORMULAS/LIQUID EXTRACTS

Phyto-Proz Supreme Liquid Phyto-Caps™, St. John's Wort Liquid Phyto-Caps™, Valerian Root Liquid Phyto-Caps™, Serenity with Kava Kava Liquid Phyto-Caps™, Infla-Profen Liquid Phyto-Caps™

SAFETY EVALUATION/CONTRAINDICATIONS

Do not use during pregnancy and lactation.

Caution: US FDA advises that a potential risk of rare, but severe, liver injury may be associated with kava-containing dietary supplements. Ask a healthcare professional before use if you have or have had liver problems, frequently use alcoholic beverages, or are taking any medication. Stop use and see a doctor if you develop symptoms that may signal liver problems, including jaundice (yellowing of the skin or whites of the eyes) and brown urine. Other nonspecific symptoms can include nausea, vomiting, light-colored stools, unexplained tiredness, weakness, stomach or abdominal pain, and loss of appetite. Not for use by persons under 18 years of age, or by pregnant or breastfeeding women. Not for use with alcoholic beverages. Excessive use, or use with products that cause drowsiness, may impair your ability to operate a vehicle or heavy equipment.

KNOWN DRUG INTERACTIONS

Consult a physician if you are taking any prescription drugs.

REFERENCES

Piscopo G. Kava Kava. Gift to the islands. Alt Med Rev. 1997; 2(5): 355-364. Voltz HP and Kieser M. Kava Kava extract WS 1490 versus placebo in anxiety disorders- a randomized placebo-controlled 25 week outpatient trial. PHAM-Acopsychiat. 1997; 30:1-5.

Warnecke G. [Psychosomatic dysfunctions in the female climacteric. Clinical effectiveness and tolerance of Kava extract WS 1490]. Fortschr Med. 1991; 109 (4): 119-122. [in German]

Woelk H, et al. The treatment of patients with anxiety. A double blind study: Kava extract WS 1490 vs benzodiazepine. Zitschrift for Allgemenie Medizine. 1993; 69: 271-277. [in German]

Pittler MH, et al. Efficacy of Kava extract for treating Anxiety: Systematic review and meta-analysis. J Clin Psychopharmacology. 2000; 20: 84-89.

Davis LP, et al. kavapyrones and resin: studies on GABAA, GABAB, and benzodiazepine binding sites in rodent brain. Pharmacol Toxicol. 1992; 71 (2): 120-126.

Jussofie A, et al.kavapyrone enriched extract from piper methysticum as modulator of GABA biding site in different regions of rat brain. Psychopharmacology. 1994; 116: 469-474.

Seitz U, et al. [3H]-monoamine uptake inhibition properties of Kava pyrones. Planta Medica. 1997; 63(6): 548-549.

Baum SS, et al. Effect of Kava extract and individual kavapyrones on neurotransmitter levels in the nucleus accumbens of rats. Prog Neuropsychopharmacol Biol Psychiatry. 1998; 22 (7): 1105-1120.

Blumenthal M, et al. The Complete German Commission E Monographs: Therapeutic Guide to Herbal Medicines. Austin. American Botanical Council; 1998: 156-157

Schulz V, et al. Rational Phytotherapy. New York; Springer-Verlag; 1998: 65-73.

LACTATE SUPPORT

Supports Healthy Lactation
During the Breastfeeding Months*

ALCOHOL-FREE CONCENTRATED EXTRACTS OF:

FORMULA	MG PER 2 CAPSULES
Fenugreek seed (*Trigonella foenum-graecum*)	150 mg
Fennel seed (*Foeniculum vulgare*)	100 mg
Red Raspberry leaf (*Rubus idaeus*)	50 mg
Blessed Thistle (*Cnicus benidictus*)	50 mg
Marshmallow root (*Althaea officinalis*)	14 mg

DOSAGE
1 Liquid Phyto-Cap 3 times daily.

DURATION OF USE
3 weeks and then as needed

BEST TAKEN
Between meals, with a small amount of warm water.

*THIS STATEMENT HAS NOT BEEN EVALUATED BY THE FOOD AND DRUG ADMINISTRATION.
THIS PRODUCT IS NOT INTENDED TO DIAGNOSE, TREAT, CURE OR PREVENT ANY DISEASE.

DESCRIPTION OF FORMULA

Lactate Support is a unique formula specifically designed for women who are breastfeeding and wish to maintain a healthy lactation response. The majority of herbs in this formula are classified as galactagogues, meaning they promote the secretion and flow of milk, improving a lactating woman's milk supply. Not surprisingly, these herbs have been used for centuries by breastfeeding women around the world. Accompanying herbs in this formula also maintain a strengthening and nutritive role for lactating mothers. Lactate Support distinguishes itself as a superior formula for lactating mothers, with all of the herbs in the formula being organically grown or ecologically wildcrafted.*

Fenugreek seed contains complex carbohydrates, protein, steroid saponins, flavonoids, and sterols that function collectively to encourage healthy lactation during the breastfeeding months. The fenugreek seed has been an important ally to breastfeeding women throughout the world. In fact, its use for stimulating milk flow in lactating women has been documented in Egypt, Iraq, Sudan, Argentina, North America and India. In India, women eat halva, a paste made from fenugreek seeds, in the weeks following the birth of their child to encourage the healthy flow of milk.*

Fennel seed, like fenugreek seed, has enjoyed centuries of use as a galactagogue. While its exact mechanism of action is not yet known, we do know that it offers the nursing mother essential nutrients. It contains calcium, magnesium, beta carotene, iron and vitamin C, all of which are important to remaining vital and strong during the breastfeeding months.*

Red Raspberry leaf functions as a galacatagogue, encouraging the healthy flow of milk, and plays a nutritive role for lactating women, by enriching the breast milk with bioflavonoids, polypeptides, vitamin C, calcium and iron. Red Raspberry leaf also serves to strengthen and invigorate the nursing mother, helping to restore her system to a place of health and balance after childbirth.*

Blessed thistle is also classified by herbalists as a galactagogue, and is revered for its ability to encourage healthy digestive function and a healthy appetite-important for maintaining strength and vitality in lactating women.*

Marshmallow root contains mucilage and other compounds that serve to support healthy breast milk and healthy gastrointestinal function.*

COMPLEMENTARY PHYTO-CAPS/LIQUID FORMULAS/LIQUID EXTRACTS

Fenugreek Seed Liquid Extract, Fenugreek Liquid Phyto-Caps™

SAFETY EVALUATION/CONTRAINDICATIONS

A lack of milk flow in women after childbirth may indicate a serious health condition that must be treated by a qualified healthcare professional. Do not use this product during pregnancy. Some ingredients found in this formula are contraindicated in patients with insulin-dependent diabetes. In rare instances, one

*THIS STATEMENT HAS NOT BEEN EVALUATED BY THE FOOD AND DRUG ADMINISTRATION. THIS PRODUCT IS NOT INTENDED TO DIAGNOSE, TREAT, CURE OR PREVENT ANY DISEASE.

herb in this formula has caused allergic reactions affecting the skin and respiratory system. Do not use if you are allergic to the Astercaceae/Compositae (includes daisies, marigolds, ragweeds and others) family. If you experience fast or irregular breathing, itching, skin rash or hives, seek medical attention promptly.*

KNOWN DRUG INTERACTIONS

This product may affect the rate of absorption of other drugs taken at the same time. Some of the herbs in this formula have not been studied extensively to determine their interactions with other medications. Before using this product, talk with your healthcare professional if you take any medications.*

REFERENCES

Blumenthal M, ed. The Complete German Commission E Monographs: Therapeutic Guide to Herbal Medicines. Trans. S. Klein. Boston, MA: American Botanical Council, 1998.

Brinker F. Herb Contraindications and Drug Interactions. 2nd ed. Sandy, OR: Eclectic Medical Publications, 1998.

Gladstar R. Herbal Healing for Women. New York, NY: Simon & Schuster, 1993.

http://currantsandspice.fateback.com/lactation.html Accessed 03/03/04

Riordan J, Auerbach K. Human Lactation and Breastfeeding. 2nd edition. Boston, MA: Jones & Bartlett, 1998.

Weed S. Wise Woman Herbal for the Childbearing Year. New York, NY: Ash Tree; 1986.

Zhu M, Wong PY, Li RC. Effect of oral administration of fennel (Foeniculum vulgare) on ciprofloxacin absorption and disposition in the rat. J Pharm Pharmacol 1999;51(12):1391-6.

LIQUI-LIEVE

Promotes Natural Excretion of Wastes*

ALCOHOL-FREE CONCENTRATED EXTRACTS OF:

FORMULA	MG EXTRACT PER 2 CAPSULES
Dandelion leaf and root (*Taraxacum officinalis*)	200 mg
Parsley, leaf and root (*Petroselinum crispum*)	108 mg
Juniper berry (*Juniperus communis*)	134 mg
Fenugreek seed (*Trigonella foenum-graecum*)	96 mg
Cascara Sagrada aged bark (*Rhamnus purshiana*)	72 mg
Fennel seed (*Foeniculum vulgare*)	16 mg
Bladderwrack fronds (*Fucus vesculosis*)	16 mg
Cilantro leaf (*Coriandrum sativum*)	14 mg

DOSAGE

Liquid Phyto-Caps: 2 capsules, 3 times daily

DURATION OF USE

4-6 months

BEST TAKEN

Between meals, with warm water

HEALING PRINCIPLES OF VITALITY

Medicine today has its roots in herbal healing. Hippocrates, Aristotle and Galen are examples of herbalists who began the development of science in general. Pharmacy, pharmacognosy, and chemistry have roots with the men (and women) who collected healing information about the plants that grew around them. Herbal medicine has long been the medicine of the world, and was almost exclusively so until the advancement of modern science allowed for chemical isolation.

Historically, herbal healing is based on principles. One of the basic tenets is that of cleansing. All systems of healing, from Chinese to Native American, have some cleansing methods that play a significant role in the overall healing approach. The belief is that the vital essence of health is assisted when blocks to excretion are removed. (Now we recognize toxins as causing free radical damage to cells).

The Eclectic and Physio-medicalist practitioners of the late 19th and early 20th century refined the process of promoting the removal of wastes, generating the term "alterative" to define the process. For many years the term alterative has been defined as "blood cleansing" but this is somewhat misleading. While it is true that blood does carry the metabolites of various catabolic reactions, the organs of waste removal themselves are generally targeted by the plants.

*THIS STATEMENT HAS NOT BEEN EVALUATED BY THE FOOD AND DRUG ADMINISTRATION. THIS PRODUCT IS NOT INTENDED TO DIAGNOSE, TREAT, CURE OR PREVENT ANY DISEASE.

Botanicals may support liver, lymphatic, kidney, gall bladder, digestive, skin and/or lung function to achieve what we refer to as alterative activity. Indeed, it is specifically the support of the normal function of organs of elimination that results in efficient removal of waste from the blood.

Liqui-Lieve is based on these ancient principles of healing. It is designed to support the organs of elimination. Additionally, many of these herbs provide many nutrients that help to build healthy tissue and provide the building blocks of various eliminatory pathways. While these actions are generally quite gentle, they may have profound effects on health and vitality. A build up of toxins can result in sluggishness both physically and mentally. Helping the body perform these processes can go a long way toward promoting health. Liqui-Lieve is designed to gently promote the normal excretion of waste from tissue and organs. As such, this formula can support general vitality in a significant way.

Dandelion leaf is both revered and despised. It is certain, however, that lawn-owners would reconsider the weed if they only understood its value. Dandelion leaves provide a complex of tasty nutrients, enjoyed all over the world when they are young. Interestingly, the root of dandelion is renowned for its support to liver function, while the leaves target kidney function. Another aspect of Dandelion's normalizing properties is the relatively high level of potassium it contains. Kidney activity tends to deplete potassium, so Dandelion is able to support the function of the kidney while providing valuable nutrients to further support its function. The 1950's-1970's generated a great deal of European interest in research on Dandelion, especially its constituent inulin. Much of this supported the traditional uses indicating promise for further study of this humble plant.*

Parsley leaf also finds a place in both traditional healing and the kitchen. Traditional use of seed and leaf centers mainly on digestive support and promoting liver, lung and kidney function. It therefore results in an overall boost to elimination. Parsley has a significant essential oil content believed to be at least part of the active chemical profile. However, the essential oils can be irritating in large doses, so reason is required when consuming this food. There is little scientific research on Parsley, yet some preliminary studies indicate antioxidant activity.*

Juniper berries are renowned for their effect on kidney health. Interestingly, though, they are included in the German Commission E Monographs for their use as an antispasmodic for the digestive system. Like Parsley, Juniper berries have significant essential oil content which can be irritating in large doses.*

Fenugreek seed is an ingredient of curry powder. The seed contains a demulcent activity that soothes digestion and benefits the lungs. Like other plants, this food is nutrient rich. Additionally, Fenugreek seeds contain a great deal of fiber. The fiber aids in digestive function. Rich steroidal components allow the seed to affect the structure and function of many systems in the body. Plant steroids are made from cholesterol like endogenous steroids. They tend to have a normalizing effect

*THIS STATEMENT HAS NOT BEEN EVALUATED BY THE FOOD AND DRUG ADMINISTRATION.
THIS PRODUCT IS NOT INTENDED TO DIAGNOSE, TREAT, CURE OR PREVENT ANY DISEASE.

on structure and function. A good deal of research interest currently exists in Fenugreek. Investigations into its effect on the glucose system indicate potential for its use in normalizing blood sugar levels. While these studies are preliminary, there is plenty of good evidence on Fenugreek's role in maintaining vital health.*

Cascara Sagrada bark is a traditional Native American remedy that has become a favorite around the world. The bark must age one year or be exposed to heat and aeration to destroy free anthrones, which will cause severe vomiting. Once the anthrones are destroyed, the plant is used to promote normal bowel movements. Its reputation and an understanding of the mechanism of action have earned Cascara Sagrada a place in the German Commission E as an approved herb. It is understood that beta-glycosides are converted into anthrones in the colon by bacterial enzymes. Anthrones are the metabolites that affect bowel function. Long term use is not advised.*

Fennel seed joins the crowd of spices in this blend. It has a taste reminiscent of Licorice. It is also rich in essential oil. It enjoys a long history of use as a flavoring for everything from candy to pickles. Traditional healing use focused on its support to healthy digestion. Research on Fennel is still limited.*

Bladderwrack fronds are eaten as food especially in the Orient. This seaweed is rich in nutrients, notably absorbable iodine and mucilage. The mucilage supports healthy function in the digestive system and lungs. Bladderwrack has a reputation of supporting thyroid function, which may be associated with its iodine content. The thyroid functions to regulate body metabolism, which will have an indirect effect on every elimination system.*

Cilantro leaf falls into the category of nutrient and oil rich seeds. It possesses digestive properties similar to those of Fenugreek and Fennel seeds.*

COMPLEMENTARY PHYTO-CAPS/LIQUID FORMULAS/LIQUID EXTRACTS

Cascara Sagrada, Dandelion Root & Leaf

SAFETY EVALUATION/CONTRAINDICATIONS

Do not use during pregnancy or lactation. Contraindicated in inflammatory kidney conditions, due to essential oil content of Parsley and Juniper Berry.

"Do not use this product if you have abdominal pain or diarrhea. Discontinue use in the event of diarrhea or watery stools. Do not exceed recommended dose. Not for long-term use."

KNOWN DRUG INTERACTIONS

Please see a physician if you are taking any pharmaceutical drugs.

REFERENCES

American Herbal Products Association. Rediscovering The "Roots" of Medicine [supplement]. Herbs for Your Health. 1992; Jan/Feb, S5-S8.

Clark E. Monograph on Taraxacum officinale in A Handbook of Plant Form. Transl. Hobbs, Christopher. Portland: Eclectic Institute, 1985 (orig. 1904).

Willard T. The Wild Rose Scientific Herbal. 1991; 106-109. Wild Rose College, Canada.

Grases F, et. al. Urolithiasis and phytotherapy. Int Urol Nephrol 1994; 26(5): 507-11.

Newall C, et al. Herbal Medicines: A Guide for Health-care Practitioners. London: Pharmaceutical Press, 1996.

Trautwein EA, et. al. Dietary inulin lowers plasma cholesterol and triacylglycerol and alters biliary bile acid profile in hamsters. J Nutr. 1998 Nov; 128(11): 1937-43.

Rowland IR, et. al. Effect of Bifidobacterium longum and inulin on gut bacterial metabolism and carcinogen-induced aberrant crypt foci in rats. Carcinognesis. 1998 Feb; 19(2): 281-5.

Kleesen B, et. al. Effects of inulin and lactose on fecal microflora, microbial activity, and bowel habit in elderly constipated persons. Am J Clin Nutr. 1997 May; 65(5): 1397-402.

Nielson SE, et al. Effect of parsley (Petroselinum crispum) intake on urinary apigenin excretion, blood antioxidant enzymes and biomarkers for oxidative stress in human subjects. Br J Nutr. 1999 Jun; 81(6): 425-6.

Adzamli IK, Kim HO, and Sykes AG. Neutral complexes as oxidants for the reduced form of parsley (Petroselinum crispum) [2FE—2S] ferredoxin. Evidence for partal blocking by redox-inactive Cr (III) complexes. Biochem J. 1982, Jun; 43(2): 201-4.

Fupta A, et al. Effect of Trigonella foenum-graecum (feunugreek) seeds on glycaemic control and insulin resistance in type 2 diabetes mellitus: a double blind placebo controlled study. J Assoc Physicians India. 2001 Nov; 49: 1057-61.

Vats V, et al. Evaluation of anti-hyperglycemic and hypoglycemic effect of Trigonella foneum-graecum Linn, Ocimum sanctum Linn and Pterocarpus marsupium Linn in normal and alloxanized diabetic rats. J Ethnopharmacol. 2002 Jan; 79(1): 95-100.

Pederson M. Nutritional Herbology. IN: Whitman, 1995.

Mills S. Out of the Earth: The Essential Book of Herbal Medicine. England: Viking Group, 1991.

LIVER HEALTH

For Ultimate Support of Healthy Liver Function*

ALCOHOL-FREE CONCENTRATED EXTRACTS OF:

FORMULA	MG EXTRACT PER 2 CAPSULES
Milk Thistle seed (*Silybum marianum*)	100 mg
Turmeric rhizome (*Curcuma longa*)	100 mg
Schizandra berry (*Schizandra chinensis*)	100 mg
MSM (Methylsulfonylmethane)	100 mg
Chinese Skullcap root (*Scutellaria baicalensis*)	56 mg
Licorice root (*Glycyrrhiza* spp.)	20 mg

STANDARDIZED TO FULL SPECTRUM ACTIVITY PROFILE

Silymarins (from Milk Thistle)	80 mg

DOSAGE
Liquid Phyto-Caps: 1 capsule, 2 times daily

DURATION OF USE
4-6 months

BEST TAKEN
Between meals with a small amount of warm water

FORMULA FOR LIVER SUPPORT

This powerful liver-protective formula helps to prevent the free-radical damage to liver tissue that is generated during stressful engagement with so-called toxins. When a substance is metabolized in the liver, free-radicals are generated; this is a simple fact of Nature. There is an evolving understanding in modern Naturopathy that it is the free-radical response to a toxin that does the damage, rather than the toxin itself. What this formula endeavors to achieve, is a reduction in the damage that might occur as a consequence to the generation of free-radical molecules. By direct antioxidant action, as well as by enhancing the function of the liver, this formula exerts a powerful influence. The building of healthy tissue is also relevant for a number of herbs in this formula.

Milk Thistle seed has a long history of traditional use; primarily as a support to liver health. In modern times, we understand its ability to protect liver tissue from the free-radical stress generated during liver metabolism.

Simply stated, Milk Thistle seed has the following effects on the liver:

*THIS STATEMENT HAS NOT BEEN EVALUATED BY THE FOOD AND DRUG ADMINISTRATION.
THIS PRODUCT IS NOT INTENDED TO DIAGNOSE, TREAT, CURE OR PREVENT ANY DISEASE.

A. It is a powerful antioxidant
B. It increases the liver's natural antioxidant system (that is, the "mixed function oxidation system" including cytochrome P-450)
C. It protects against damage from toxins, in part, by strengthening cellular membrane stability
D. It increases glutathione concentrations, supporting healthy liver function

It is the combination of Milk Thistle's diverse actions that lend powerful support for the liver.

It is interesting to note that the benefits of a number of 'spice cabinet' herbs used from ancient to modern times (such as Black Pepper, Ginger, Cayenne, Garlic, Turmeric, etc.) are being brought more fully to light by modern science. One of these kitchen herbs, Turmeric rhizome, is traditionally recognized to support digestive and liver function. A cousin of Ginger, Turmeric is a powerful antioxidant. It also demonstrates liver-protective and normalizing effects. Like Milk Thistle, Turmeric aids liver function primarily by reducing the damage caused by free-radicals. Reducing this stress encourages normal function of this metabolic organ.*

Schizandra berry is a valued kidney and male tonic of the Traditional Chinese system of healing. Within this system it is often referred to as a 'king' or 'harmonizing' remedy, alluding to the broad-reaching influence of this small 'five flavored' berry. It is also deserving of great respect as an adaptogen (increasing non-specific resistance to stress). In fact, the power of its adaptogenic influence has been compared to the highly regarded Eleuthero. The depth of modern research compiled over the years on its use attests to Schizandra's validity. It has been shown, specifically, to promote liver detoxification and to support healthy function of the liver. In China, compounds derived from Schizandra are being used for liver support with greater effect than the silymarins from the Milk Thistle. In a similar manner as Milk Thistle, Schizandra increases in the liver's antioxidant systems while promoting the health of liver tissue. Schizandra has also been shown to increase liver cyclic AMP, which improves hormonal function at the cellular level. This in turn results in an increase in overall function. It simply cannot be overstated how valuable the Schizandra berry is to this formula.*

MSM is a naturally occurring sulfur compound found within cartilaginous tissues, offering the body an efficient means of maintaining and rebuilding the joint matrix structure.*

Chinese Skullcap has a long list of traditional applications to its credit, including use as a detoxifying and soothing herb. It is valued here as a powerful and soothing antioxidant. Similar to the other ingredients of this formula, Chinese Skullcap provides further support for the reduction of free-radical stress that is well-known to be generated at times of enhanced detoxification or challenges from external 'toxins'.*

Licorice root claims more than 3,000 years of use. Its early use to promote respiratory health is now being 'rediscovered' by modern scientific research. Licorice research indicates support for digestive health, among many reported effects. Like Schizandra, it increases cyclic AMP. Perhaps most relevant to this formula, however, is the ability of Licorice to protect against the damage caused by free-radicals to liver cells. Research has also shown that compounds from Licorice may protect against the body's self-inflicted liver impairment. In addition, Licorice is able to enhance the ability of the liver to handle toxins.*

COMPLEMENTARY PHYTO-CAPS/LIQUID FORMULAS/LIQUID EXTRACTS

Sweetish Bitters Elixir, Hep-Support Liquid Phyto-Caps™, Milk Thistle Seed Liquid Phyto-Caps™

SAFETY EVALUATION/CONTRAINDICATIONS

Do not use this product during pregnancy or lactation.

KNOWN DRUG INTERACTIONS

Consult a physician if you are taking any pharmaceutical drugs.

REFERENCES

Pizzorno J, Murray M. Textbook of Natural medicine. New York. Churchill Livingstone; 1999.

Legalon. Madaus Education Monograph. Madaus. Germany. 1/2/10.94

Detoxification Profile. GSDL Education Monograph. Great Smokies Diagnostic Lab (GSDL). Asheville, NC. 1998.

Snow JM. Curcuma longa L. (Zingiberaceae). The Protocol Journal of Botanical Medicine. 1995; Autumn: 43-46.

Srimal RC. Turmeric: A brief review of medicinal properties. Fitoterapia; 1997; 68(6):483-493.

Selvam R. The antioxidant activity of turmeric (Curcuma longa). Journal of Ethnopharmacology. 1995; 47:59-67.

Gengtao L. Hepato-pharmacology of Fructus Schizandrae. Advances in Chinese Medicinal Materials Research. 1985.

Ko KM, et al. Effect of a lignan-enriched Fructus Schizandrae extract on hepatic glutathione status in rats: Protection against carbon tetrachloride toxicity. Planta Medica. 1995; 61: 134-137.

Kent C. Licorice – More than just candy. Journal of the Australian Traditional Medicine Society. 1994; Autumn: 9-14.

Davis E, Morris DJ. Medicinal uses of Licorice through the millennia: The good and plenty of it. Molecular and Cellular Endocrinology. 1991; 78:1-6.

Snow JM. Glycyrhizza glabra L. (Leguminaceae). The Protocol Journal of Botanical Medicine. 1996; Winter: 9-14

Newmark TM, Schulick P. Beyond Aspirin. Prescott, Az. HOHM Press. 2000.

MAITAKE DEFENSE

Supports Healthy Immune System Function*

ALCOHOL-FREE CONCENTRATED EXTRACTS OF:

FORMULA	MG EXTRACT PER 2 CAPSULES
Cordyceps Mushroom (*Cordyceps sinensis*)	100 mg
Reishi Mushroom (*Ganoderma lucidum*)	50 mg
Chaga Mushroom (*Inonotus obliquus*)	50 mg
Maitake PD Fraction (*Grifola frondosa*)	10 mg
STANDARDIZED TO FULL SPECTRUM ACTIVITY PROFILE	
Total Polysaccharides (including Beta-Glucans)	20 mg

DOSAGE

Liquid Phyto-Caps: Take 1 capsule, 2 times.

DURATION OF USE

3 months

BEST TAKEN

Between meals, with warm water

PRODUCT DESCRIPTION

Currently, there are several species of mushrooms, once utilized as traditional folk medicines, under critical study by medical researchers. Maitake, Reishi, Chaga, and Cordyceps are prominent among those being researched for their potential immune-enhancement properties. Maitake Defense combines the most widely researched and potent medicinal mushrooms. Our synergistic blend of highly concentrated extracts of Maitake, Reishi, Cordyceps, and Chaga mushrooms represents genuine potency and bioactivity.*

Indigenous to northeastern Japan, Maitake mushrooms typically grow at the foot of Oak trees in clusters that resemble fluttering butterflies. This resemblance led the Japanese to refer to this type of mushroom as Maitake, which means "dancing mushroom." Maitake's primary use within traditional Chinese and Japanese medicine centers around its ability to enhance the immune system. In particular, this mushroom includes a beta-glucan polysaccharide known as grifolan. Grifolan is credited for rousing macrophages, natural killer cells, interleukin-1 and -2, and T-cells within the immune system.*

For more than 2,000 years, Chinese and Japanese medicine have venerated Reishi as nature's best mushroom. This ancient mushroom helps regulate the

*THIS STATEMENT HAS NOT BEEN EVALUATED BY THE FOOD AND DRUG ADMINISTRATION. THIS PRODUCT IS NOT INTENDED TO DIAGNOSE, TREAT, CURE OR PREVENT ANY DISEASE.

immune system, eliminate free radicals, and protect normal liver function. Several of its constituents, such as its water-soluble polysaccharides, polysaccharide-peptide complex, and polyphenols, lend Reishi its powerful antioxidant properties.*

Chaga mushroom supports healthy immune function in a similar fashion to other popular mushrooms such as Shiitake and Maitake. What sets this particular mushroom apart is its affinity for birch trees in northern Scandinavia, Russia, and Canada. It derives its nutrients directly from living birch trees, rather than from the ground. As a result, it is particularly high in betulinic acid. This phytochemical, isolated from birch trees, demonstrates significant immune-supporting actions and has an affinity for tissues that have a lower pH. Typically, unhealthy joint tissue will maintain a lower pH, attracting this potent phytochemical to that area. As such, it supports proper immune function where it is needed most.*

Hailing from the plateaus of China, Tibet, and Nepal, Cordyceps is another mushroom highly valued for its ability to support immune function. Research indicates Cordyceps provides a wide range of defense. This mushroom works by stimulating natural killer cells, enhancing intereferon-gamma and interleukin-1 levels, while boosting T-helper cells and lymphocytes, and fueling blood's mononuclear cells.*

By combining the most studied mushrooms into one formula, Maitake Defense Liquid Phyto-Caps™ represents a broad, full-spectrum, immune supporting formula intended to enhance the vitality of our cellular resistance. Utilizing the most specific extraction techniques, the formula delivers highly concentrated extracts of Maitake, Reishi, Cordyceps, and Chaga mushrooms representing the best in genuine potency and bioactivity the herbal industry has to offer.*

*Note: The intention of this information is to represent the traditional use of the individual botanicals found in these formulas and to inform the reader of any evolving scientific inquiry relevant to the formula's ingredients.

COMPLEMENTARY HERBS/FORMULAS

Astagalus Supreme Liquid Phyto-Caps™, Anti-Oxidant Supreme Liquid Phyto-Caps™, Whole Body Defense Liquid Phyto-Caps™

SAFETY EVALUATION/CONTRAINDICATIONS

Before using this product, talk with your healthcare professional if you suffer from a medical condition. Please visit www.gaiaherbs.com to obtain information regarding potential contraindications and/or side effects that may be associated with herbs found in this formula.*

KNOWN DRUG INTERACTIONS

Before using this product, talk with your healthcare professional if you take any medications. Please visit www.gaiaherbs.com to obtain information regarding any possible drug interactions that may be associated with herbs found in this formula.*

REFERENCES

Nanba H. Activity of Maitake. Ann N Y Acad Sci 1995;768:243-5.

Yoon SY, Eo SK, Kim YS, et al. AB activity of Ganoderma lucidum extract alone and in combination. Arch Pharm Res 1994;17:438-42.

Park YK, Lee HB, et al. Chaga mushroom extract inhibits oxidative DNA damage in human lymphocytes as assessed by comet assay. Biofactors 2004;21(1-4):109-12.

Zhu JS, Halpern GM, Jones K. The scientific rediscovery of an ancient Chinese herbal medicine: Cordyceps sinensis: part I. J Altern Complement Med 1998;4:289-303.

MALE LIBIDO

For Ultimate Enhancement of Male Stamina and Performance*

ALCOHOL-FREE CONCENTRATED EXTRACTS OF:

FORMULA	MG EXTRACT PER 3 CAPSULES
Maca tuber (*Lepidium meyenii*)	120 mg
Saw Palmetto (*Serenoa repens*) Supercritical CO_2 Extract	84 mg
Horny Goat weed (*Epimedium grandiflorum*)	54 mg
Tribulus fruit (*Tribulus terrestris*)	45 mg
Yohimbe bark (*Corynanthe yohimbe*)	30 mg
Sarsaparilla root (*Smilax* off. *v. ornata*)	24 mg
Muira puama bark (*Ptychopetalum olacoides*)	15 mg
Fo-Ti (*Polygonum multiflorum*)	15 mg
Wild Oats Milky seed (*Avena sativa*)	15 mg

DOSAGE
Liquid Phyto-Caps: 1 capsule, 3 times daily

DURATION OF USE
2-3 months

BEST TAKEN
Between meals, with warm water

A COMPREHENSIVE APPROACH

This formula supports sexual health for men. For most of us who live in modern society – we are stressed beyond the natural bounds of our physiology. Stress levels affect sexual performance. Whether it's the stress of the job, or the stress of a bad diet, the effects may very well be the same. This compound takes a tonic approach. We have brought together powerful nervous system tonics that are reported to enhance sexual performance and/or desire. We have not used stimulants here. To drive an already exhausted physiology with stimulants is counterproductive. While maintaining balance in the hormonal system and liver is addressed here, maintaining nervous system health is the primary focus of this formula.

Maca is reported being used by native Peruvians for some 5,000 years. In fact, it is believed due to the plant's effect that the Inca's traditionally restricted Maca's use to the court of royalty. Its reputation is primarily as a performance enhancer and as an aphrodisiac. Early clinical reports suggest its effects are perhaps due to its normalizing influence over the endocrine system – specifically, the Hypothalamus-Pituitary-Adrenal (HPA) axis. Following the first U.S. study of this Andean Mountain herb, researchers have corroborated Maca's aphrodisiac effects in animals.*

Saw Palmetto is well known for its ability to support the prostate. Traditionally, it was said to exert its influence over all the reproductive organs, helping to sustain sexual activity after 'exhaustive excesses'. Wherever compromised performance is accompanied by stress, Saw Palmetto is said to be useful; particularly when taken with a nervous system tonic, such as Wild Oats (see below).*

Epimedium is better known by its common name, Horny Goat Weed. As such a name might imply, this plant is considered an aphrodisiac. Traditionally it is also used as a tonic. In the Chinese system of Medicine, Epimedium is known to increase sexual desire and activity.*

Tribulus is reported to be a folkloric medicine used to support the cardiovascular system and healthy vision. It has also been used traditionally as an aphrodisiac. A small number of *in-vitro* studies have leant support to this traditional use as an aphrodisiac, suggesting that protodiosin (an isolated constituent of Tribulus) can promote healthy sexual activity (in animals).*

Yohimbe is a highly praised traditional aphrodisiac. Scientific research focusing on the alkaloid yohimbine has implied support to normal sexual function. In addition to these popularized benefits, Yohimbe has been included here for its support to the central nervous system.*

Sarsaparilla is an alterative (blood purifier) that is known for its normalizing activity. Liver supportive properties are also noted. Sarsaparilla is included in this performance formula for its overall influence on healthy metabolism.*

Muira Puama is commonly known as Potency Wood. This herb is said to strengthen the digestion and tonify the nervous system – particularly where stress is evident. This rainforest botanical has a reputation as an aphrodisiac. One preliminary clinical trial has suggested its benefits with normal sexual function. Both psychological and physical aspects of sexual function were supported in this particular trial.*

Fo-Ti is traditionally considered to be of much value for maintaining the health of

*THIS STATEMENT HAS NOT BEEN EVALUATED BY THE FOOD AND DRUG ADMINISTRATION.
THIS PRODUCT IS NOT INTENDED TO DIAGNOSE, TREAT, CURE OR PREVENT ANY DISEASE.

the liver and kidneys. It has been included here as a nervous tonic. Traditional Chinese Medicine (TCM) regards Fo-Ti as one of the five major tonic herbs. Due to the fact that many hormones are metabolized in the liver, modern research focusing on the liver effects of this plant suggest it is a highly valuable addition to this performance formula.*

Wild Oats are present here for their influence on stress. They are often used to promote digestive health where there is also temporary physical weakness and fatigue. Wild Oats may also be used as nourishment. This plant combines well with Saw Palmetto where stress temporarily compromises sexual performance.*

COMPLEMENTARY PHYTO-CAPS/LIQUID FORMULAS/LIQUID EXTRACTS

Adrenal Health Liquid Phyto-Caps™, Energy & Vitality Liquid Phyto-Caps™, Ginseng/Schizandra Supreme

SAFETY EVALUATION/CONTRAINDICATIONS

Do not use this product during pregnancy, lactation or hypertension.

KNOWN DRUG INTERACTIONS

Consult a physician if you are taking any pharmaceutical drugs.

REFERENCES

Walker M. Medical Journalist Report of Innovative Biologics. Townsend Letter for Doctors. 1998; Nov: 18-22.

Zheng BL, et al. Effect of a lipidic extract from lepidium meyenii on sexual behavior in mice and rats. Urology. 2000;55(4):598-602.

Agricultural Research Service. Dr. Duke's Phytochemical and Ethnobotanical Databases: Ethnobotanical uses Tribulus terrestris. Online. Internet. [8/23/00]. Available WWW: http://www.ars-grin.gov/cgi-bin/duke/ethnobot.pl

Arcasoy HB, et al. Effect of Tribulus terrestris L. saponin mixture on some smooth muscle preparations: a preliminary study. Boll Chim Farm 1998;137(11):473-5.

Adaikan PG, et al. Proerectile pharmacological effects of Tribulus terrestris extract on the rabbit corpus cavernosum. Ann Acad Med Singapore 2000;29(1):22-6.

Adimoelja A. Phytochemicals and the breakthrough of traditional herbs in the management of sexual dysfunctions. Int J Androl. 2000;23 Suppl 2:82-4.

Agricultural Research Service. Dr. Duke's Phytochemical and Ethnobotanical Databases: Ethnobotanical uses Epimedium grandiflorum. Online. Internet. [8/30/00]. Available WWW: http://www.ars-grin.gov/cgi-bin/duke/ethnobot.pl

Blumenthal M, et al. Ed. The Complete German Commission E Monographs.Austin, TX: American Botanical Council; 1998. Pg. 201.

Easterling J. Traditional uses of rainforest botanicals. Self Published?

Werbach M, Murray M. Botanical Influences on Illness: A sourcebook of clinical research. CA: Third Line Press, 1994. Pg. 200.

Agricultural Research Service. Dr. Duke's Phytochemical and Ethnobotanical Databases: Ethnobotanical uses Polygonum multiflorum. Online. Internet. [8/30/00]. Available WWW: http://www.ars-grin.gov/cgi-bin/duke/ethnobot.pl

Duke J, Ayensu ES. Medicinal Plants of China. Michigan: Reference Publications, 1985. Pg. 508.

Blumenthal M, et al. Ed. The Complete German Commission E Monographs.Austin, TX: American Botanical Council; 1998. Pg. 356.

Agricultural Research Service. Dr. Duke's Phytochemical and Ethnobotanical Databases:

Ethnobotanical uses Corynanthe yohimbe. Online. Internet. [8/30/00]. Available WWW: http://www.ars-grin.gov/cgi-bin/duke/ethnobot.pl

Jacobsen FM. Fluoxetine-induced sexual dysfunction and an open trial of yohimbine. J Clin Psychiatry. 1992;53:119-122.

Susset JG, et al. Effect of Yohimbine hydrochloride on erectile impotence: A double-blind study. J Urol. 1989;141:1360-1363.

MENTAL ALERTNESS

Ultimate Support to Improve Memory*

ALCOHOL-FREE CONCENTRATED EXTRACTS OF:

FORMULA	MG EXTRACT PER 2 CAPSULES
Eleuthero root (*Eleutherococcus senticosus*)	80 mg
Ginkgo leaf (*Ginkgo biloba*)	40 mg
Gotu Kola herb (*Centella asiatica*)	40 mg
Fo-Ti (*Polygonum multiflorum*)	26 mg
Wild Oats milky seed (*Avena sativa*)	22 mg
Peppermint herb (*Mentha piperita*)	20 mg
Vinpocetine (from *Voacanga africana* seed)	10 mg
Rosemary leaf, Supercritical CO_2 Extract (*Rosmarinus* off.)	8 mg

STANDARDIZED TO FULL SPECTRUM ACTIVITY PROFILE

Ginkgo flavonoid glycosides (from Ginkgo)	4.8 mg
Triterpenoids (from Gotu Kola)	1.0 mg
Eleutherosides B & E (from Eleuthero root)	0.64 mg

DOSAGE

Liquid Phyto-Caps: 2 capsules, 2 times daily

DURATION OF USE

3-4 months

BEST TAKEN

Between meals, with warm water

DESCRIPTION OF FORMULA

Mental Alertness enhances mental function, memory and circulation, and aids the body in developing its inherent ability to adapt to temporary stress. The herbs in this formula work together to encourage overall health and stamina, and improve one's natural ability to endure both physical and emotional stress. Several

*THIS STATEMENT HAS NOT BEEN EVALUATED BY THE FOOD AND DRUG ADMINISTRATION. THIS PRODUCT IS NOT INTENDED TO DIAGNOSE, TREAT, CURE OR PREVENT ANY DISEASE.

ingredients in Mental Alertness also provide antioxidant protection from free radical damage to brain cells and tissue.*

Gotu Kola leaf & root contain key constituents that maintain healthy neurotransmitter function, promoting mental alertness and a sound memory. Gotu kola also improves the body's inherent ability to acclimate to temporary stress. As well, this herb supports a healthy circulation by encouraging the elimination of excess fluid.*

Eleuthero, or Siberian Ginseng, has been in use in China for over 4,000 years. A popular general tonic, this root serves to promote health and vitality. It contains an assortment of chemical constituents that encourage a healthy brain, immune system and hormonal balance. Used regularly, it functions to enhance the body's natural resistance and adaptation to stressful influences. Likewise, Eleuthero supports mental endurance and promotes overall metabolic efficiency.*

Ginkgo leaf derives the majority of its support from modern science, rather than from established traditional use. Ginkgo leaf helps to enhance blood flow and oxygen to the brain, encourage mental clarity, and provide antioxidant protection. Together, these actions work to support healthy cognitive function.*

Chinese Fo-Ti root supports healthy neurotransmitter function. Accordingly, this root serves as a valuable general tonic for the nervous system and encourages healthy brain chemistry. In addition, Chinese Fo-Ti root may enhance the body's immune system and overall capacity to tolerate occasional environmental stressors. These actions have not been studied in human clinical trials as of yet.*

Wild Oats milky seed contains numerous compounds that promote a vital nervous system and ease temporary nervous stress, weakness, and exhaustion.*

Peppermint has traditionally been used to promote digestive health and maintain healthy smooth muscle tissue. Peppermint also improves the taste of the formula.*

Vinpocetine supports healthy oxygenated blood flow to the brain. Accordingly, this phytochemical promotes mental clarity, focus and concentration.*

Rosemary leaf is a natural antioxidant and a soothing plant. It has been proposed that antioxidants, such as Rosemary, may be useful to help reduce the free-radical damage that occurs with aging. Rosemary has been used for centuries as a tonic and mild stimulant, to support digestion, and to promote nervous system health. Known as the 'herb of remembrance', Rosemary has a long history of supporting a sound memory.*

COMPLEMENTARY PHYTO-CAPS/LIQUID FORMULAS/LIQUID EXTRACTS

Anti-Oxidant Supreme Liquid Phyto-Caps™, Ginkgo Leaf Liquid Phyto-Caps™

SAFETY EVALUATION/CONTRAINDICATIONS

This formula should be avoided in pregnancy and lactation. It may occasionally cause gastrointestinal upset if taken away from food and may increase one's sensitivity to sunlight. Discontinue use during an acute infection or fever. Women with hormone sensitive conditions such as breast, uterine or ovarian cancer, endometriosis, and uterine fibroids should consult a qualified healthcare professional before using this formula due to its potential hormonal effects. Adverse reactions such as headaches, sleep disturbances, heart palpitations, dizziness, and allergic skin reactions can occur. Also, use with caution and seek the advice of a qualified healthcare professional if you have a blood clotting disorder, hyperlipidemia (high triglyceride and/or cholesterol levels), a psychiatric condition, a seizure disorder, a hiatal hernia, heartburn, heart disease, congestive heart failure, diabetes, gallstones, a kidney disorder, or high/low blood pressure.

KNOWN DRUG INTERACTIONS

This formula should be used with caution in combination with cholesterol-reducing drugs, and drugs that inhibit blood clotting and platelet aggregation including but not limited to warfarin (Coumadin®). Additionally, Eleuthero might interact with hormone therapies such as estradiol (Alora®, Estrace®), estrogen (Premarin®, Prempro®, Cenestin®), Demulen, Loestrin, Lo/Ovral, Alesse, Triphasil, Ortho Tri-Cyclen, and many others. Some of the herbs in this formula have not been studied extensively to determine their interactions with other medications. Before using this formula, talk with your healthcare professional if you take any medications.

REFERENCES

Akopov SE, Gabrielian ES. Effects of aspirin, dipyridamole, nifedipine and cavinton which act on platelet aggregation induced by different aggregating agents alone and in combination. Eur J Clin Pharmacol 1992;42(3):257-9.

Blumenthal M, et al. ed. The Complete German Commission E Monographs: Therapeutic Guide to Herbal Medicines. Trans. S. Klein. Boston, MA: American Botanical Council, 1998.

Bohn B, et. al. Flow-cytometric Studies with Eleutherococcus senticosus Extract as an Immunomodulatory Agent. Arzneim.-Forsch. 1987; 37: 1193-1196.

Bolanos-Jimenez, et. al. Stress-induced 5-HT 1A receptor desensitization: protective effects of Ginkgo biloba extract (Egb 761). Fundam Clin Pharmacol. 1995; 9, 169-74

Brekhman II and Dardymov IV. New Substances of Plant Origin Which Increase Nonspecific Resistance. Ann Rev Pharmacol. 1969; 9: 419-430.

Duke J. CRC Handbook of Medicinal Herbs. Boca Raton. CRC Press. 1985.

Duke J. The Green pharmacy. Emmaus, Pa. Rodale Press. 1997.

Dumont, et. al. Protection of Polyunsaturated Fatty Acids Against Iron-Dependent Lipid Peroxidation by a Ginkgo biloba Extract (EGb 761). Meth Find Exp Clin Pharmacol. 1995; 17(2), 83-88.

Fulder SJ. Ginseng and the hypothalamic-pituitary control of stress. Am J Chin Med. 1981 sum; 9(2): 112-8.

Gebner, et. al. Study of the Long-term Action of a Ginkgo biloba Extract on Vigilance and Mental Performance as Determined by Means of Quantitative Pharmaco-EEG and Psychometric Measurements. Arzneim.-Forsch. 1985; 35 (II), 1459-1465.

Gruenwald J, et al. PDR for Herbal Medicines. 1st ed. Montvale, NJ: Medical Economics Company, Inc., 1998.

Hutchens AR. A handbook of Native American herbs. Shambhalla publications. 1992.

Kamen B. Siberian Ginseng: latest research on the fabled oriental tonic herb. CT: Keats, 1988.

Kose and Dogan. Lipoperoxidation Induced by Hydrogen Peroxide in Human Erythrocyte Membranes. Comparison of the Antioxidant Effect of Ginkgo biloba Extract (EGb 761) with those of Water-soluble and Lipid-soluble Antioxidants. J of Int Med Res. 1995; 23: 9-18.

Krieglstein, et. al. Neuroprotective effects of Ginkgo biloba constituents. Euro J of Pharma Sci. 1995; 3, 39-48.

Kulkarni Sk, Verma A. Evidence for Nootropic Effect of BR-16A (Mentat R), A Herbal Psychotropic Preparation, in Mice. Indian J Physiol Pharmacol. 1992; 36(1): 29-34.

Leung AY, Foster S. Encyclopedia of Common Natural Ingredients Used in Food, Drugs and Cosmetics. 2nd ed. New York, NY: John Wiley & Sons, 1996.

McGuffin M, et al., ed. American Herbal Products Association's Botanical Safety Handbook. Boca Raton, FL: CRC Press, 1997.

McRae S. Elevated serum digoxin levels in a patient taking digoxin and Siberian ginseng. CMAJ 1996;155:293-5.

Miyazaki M. The effect of a cerebral vasodilator, vinpocetine, on cerebral vascular resistance evaluated by the Doppler ultrasonic technique in patients with cerebrovascular diseases. Angiology 1995;46(1):53-8.

Murray M. The healing power of herbs - The enlightened persons guide to the wonders of medicinal plants. 2nd ed. Prima publishing. Rocklin, Ca. 1995.

Nalini, et. al. Effect of Centella asiatica fresh leaf aqueous extract on learning and memory and biogenic amine turnover in albino rats. Fitoterapia. 1992; LXIII(3): 2332-7.

Newall CA, Anderson LA, Philpson JD. Herbal Medicine: A Guide for Healthcare Professionals. London, UK: The Pharmaceutical Press, 1996.

Petkov, et. al. Memory Effects of Standardized Extracts of Panax ginseng (G115), Ginkgo biloba (GK 501) and their Combination Gincosan R (PHL-00701). Planta Med. 1993; 59, 106-113.

Priest AW, Priest LR. Herbal medication. A clinical dispensary handbook. 1982.

Snow JM. Ginkgo biloba L. (Ginkgoaceae). The Protocol Journal Of Botanical Medicine. 1996; 2(1): 9-15.

Subhan Z, Hindmarch I. Psychopharmacological effects of vinpocetine in normal healthy volunteers. Eur J Clin Pharmacol 1985;28(5):567-71.

Szakall S, Boros I, Balkay L, et al. Cerebral effects of a single dose of intravenous vinpocetine in chronic stroke patients: a PET study. J Neuroimaging 1998;8(4):197-204.

The Review of Natural Products by Facts and Comparisons. St. Louis, MO: Wolters Kluwer Co., 1999.

Vogler BK, Pittler MH, Ernst E. The efficacy of ginseng. A systemic review of randomized clinical trials. Eur J Clin Pharmacol 1999;55:567-75.

Wagner H, et. al. Immunostimulant action of polysaccharides (heteroglycans) from higher plants. Arzneim.-Forsch. 1985; 35(7): 1069-75.

Werbach M and Murray M. Botanical Influences on Illness: A sourcebook of clinical research. CA: Third Line, 1994.

Wesnes, et. al. A Double-blind Placebo-controlled Trial of Tanakan in the Treatment of Idiopathic Cognitive Impairment in the Elderly. Human Psychopharmacology. 1987; Vol 2, 159-169.

Witchl M. Herb drugs and phytopharmaceuticals. CRC Press.1994

METABOLIC SUPPORT

Helps Support
Optimum Cellular Energy*

ALCOHOL-FREE CONCENTRATED EXTRACTS OF:

FORMULA	MG PER 2 CAPSULES
Coleus root (*Coleus forskohlii*)	114 mg
Chinese Skullcap (*Scutellaria baicalensis*)	88 mg
Bupleurum root (*Bupleurum chinense*)	70 mg
Feverfew (*Tanacetum parthenium*)	60 mg
Jujube Date seed (*Zizyphus jujuba*)	32 mg
Licorice root (*Glycyrrhiza glabra & G. uralensis*)	20 mg
Ginger rhizome, Supercritical CO_2 Extract (*Zingiber* off.)	8 mg

DOSAGE
Liquid Phyto-Caps: 2 capsules, twice daily

DURATION OF USE
3-4 months

BEST TAKEN
Between meals, with warm water

HORMONES, CYCLIC AMP AND CELLULAR FUNCTION

Hormones are considered to be first messengers to cells, in that they bring a message to the cell that triggers a cascade of activity. This hormonal message activates adenylate cyclase, an enzyme, that is converted into a second messenger within the cell. There are several second messengers, but the most abundant one is the cyclic nucleotide adenosine monophosphate (cyclic AMP or cAMP).

This pathway causes a cascade of activity in virtually every system of the body. Thus, cAMP's influence is much broader than just endocrine function. The primary pharmacodynamic focus of this formula is to increase intra-cellular levels of cAMP. Cyclic AMP is involved in the regulatory function of every cell: so its role is found in thyroid, reproductive, and immune function, in lipolysis (breakdown and utilization of fats), muscle cell contraction and relaxation, cell secretion and permeability, just to name a few of its areas of impact. Obviously, maintaining appropriate levels of cAMP can have far reaching impact on maintaining general well-being. The breadth of use of this formula cannot be overstated.

Coleus Forskohlii is one of the world's most researched plants. The majority of research has focused on forskolin, which is believed to be the plant's most active

*THIS STATEMENT HAS NOT BEEN EVALUATED BY THE FOOD AND DRUG ADMINISTRATION.
THIS PRODUCT IS NOT INTENDED TO DIAGNOSE, TREAT, CURE OR PREVENT ANY DISEASE.

constituent. It is known to activate the enzyme adenylate cylclase that forms cyclic AMP within cells. Forskolin is shown to exert a 6- to 400-fold increase in levels of cAMP. The plant is native to India, where a long history of use includes supporting cardiovascular, respiratory, kidney, and nervous system function. It is said to increase the memory of cells.*

In addition to cyclic AMP stimulating activity, Chinese Skullcap root possesses antioxidant activity. This is another plant native to China with a long history of use.

Bupleurum root has also been shown to increase cAMP. This plant is native to China where it is very popular as a 'liver herb'. A fair amount of preliminary research on the group of constituents known as saikosaponins lends support to its role in maintaining liver health, as well as indicating a potential role in supporting immune function.*

Feverfew herb is known to stimulate the formation of cyclic AMP. Additionally, it helps maintain a normal inflammatory response to stress, as indicated by a regulatory effect on prostaglandin, leukotriene, and thromboxane production. As its name suggests, Feverfew was traditionally used to maintain normal body processes, including temperature regulation.*

Jujube dates are reported to support liver, nervous system and respiratory health. Jujube adds an invigorating and nutritive aspect along with cAMP stimulation.

Licorice root is included in this formula as an excellent harmonizing component with soothing and antispasmodic properties. It is well known to support respiratory health and soothe the mucosal lining of the respiratory tract.*

Ginger rhizome is known in the Ayurvedic tradition as vishwabhesaj, meaning the universal medicine. It is known for its pronounced effect upon gastrointestinal function. Ginger is also known to increase cyclic AMP. The value that this botanical brings to this formula is simply too vast to sum up here.*

Note: The intention of this information is to represent the traditional use of the individual botanicals found in these formulas and to inform the reader of any evolving scientific inquiry relevant to the formula's ingredients.

SAFETY EVALUATION/CONTRAINDICATIONS

Do not use during pregnancy or lactation.

DRUG INTERACTIONS

Consult a physician if you are using any pharmaceutical drugs.

COMPLEMENTARY PHYTO-CAPS/LIQUID FORMULAS/LIQUID EXTRACTS

Turmeric/Catechu Supreme, Hep Support Liquid Phyto-Caps™

REFERENCES

Pizzorno J, Murray M. Textbook of Natural Medicine. New York: Churchill Livingstone; 1999.

NAPRALERT Search results. Program for Collaborative Research in the Pharmaceutical Sciences College of Pharmacy, University of Illinois at Chicago. October 1994.

*THIS STATEMENT HAS NOT BEEN EVALUATED BY THE FOOD AND DRUG ADMINISTRATION.
THIS PRODUCT IS NOT INTENDED TO DIAGNOSE, TREAT, CURE OR PREVENT ANY DISEASE.

Bone K. Bupleurum: A natural steroid effect. Canadian Journal of Herbalism. 1996; Early Winter: 22-41.

Anonymous. Feverfew. The Lawrence Review of Natural products. 1994;September: 1-3.

Heptinstall S. Parthenolide content and bioactivity of Feverfew (Tanacetum parthenium (L.) Schultz-Bip.). Estimation of commercial and authenticated Feverfew Products. J. Pharm. Pharmacol. 1992; 44:391-395.

Newmark T, Schulick P. Beyond aspirin. Prescott. Hohm Press; 2000.

Brown D. Common Drugs and Their Potential Interactions with Herbs or Nutrients. HNR. 1999; 6(3): 209-22.

Brown D. Common Drugs and Their Potential Interactions with Herbs or Nutrients. HNR. 1999; 6(2): 124-141.

Snow JM. Coleus forskohlii Wild. (Lamiaceae). PJBM. 1995 Autumn; 1(2): 39-42.

Arner P, et al. Importance of the cyclic AMP concentration for the rate of lipolysis in human adipose tissue. Clin Sci.1980; 59(3): 199-201.

Verma AK, et al. Croton oil and benzo(a)pyrene induced changes in cyclic adenosine 3'5'-monophosphate and cyclic guanosine 3'5' monophosphate phosphodiesterase activities in mouse epidermis. Canc Res.1976; 36:81-7.

Agarwal KC, et al. Forskolin: A potent antimetastatic agent. Int J Cancer.1983; 32(6): 801-804.

Marone G, et al. Inhibition of IgE mediated release of histamine and peptide leukotriene from human basophils and mast cells by forskolin. Biochem Pharmacol.1987; 36(1): 13

MIGRA-PROFEN

Ultimate Support During Stress and Tension*

ALCOHOL-FREE CONCENTRATED EXTRACTS OF:

FORMULA	MG EXTRACT PER 2 CAPSULES
Feverfew leaf (*Tanacetum parthenium*)	240 mg
Chinese Skullcap root (*Scutellaria baicalensis*)	110 mg
Kava Kava rhizome (*Piper methysticum*)	70 mg
Valerian root (*Valeriana officinalis*)	30 mg
Jamaican Dogwood bark (*Piscidia erythrina*)	20 mg
Rosemary leaf, Supercritical Extract (*Rosmarinus* off.)	8 mg
Ginger rhizome, Supercritical CO_2 Extract (*Zingiber* off.)	8 mg

STANDARDIZED TO FULL SPECTRUM ACTIVITY PROFILE

Kavalactones (from Kava Kava)	38.5 mg
Parthenolide (from Feverfew)	1.4 mg

DOSAGE

Liquid Phyto-Caps: 2 capsules at the onset of pain and repeat 2-3 times at 15 minute intervals (4-6 capsules)

DURATION OF USE

Use as directed above or as needed

BEST TAKEN

Between meals, with warm water

STRESS AND TENSION: THEIR EFFECTS ON HEALTH

The renowned physician Hans Selye is credited as the first to elucidate the profound effect stress can have on human physiology. Dr. Selye clarified that people experience stress differently. Ultimately, how an individual responds to an event determines the extent that event will have on health. The stress response is known as the general adaptation syndrome. This process describes a series of physical reactions to stressful events. During the alarm phase, stress related hormones are released. These allow the body to counteract any physical threat by producing a number of changes in the body such as increased heart rate and reduction of digestive activity. While this phase is short-lived, the resistance phase is designed to allow long term handling of the crisis at hand. During this phase different stress hormones are released, resulting in increased energy and circulatory changes to allow for the longer term coping. While this action is

*THIS STATEMENT HAS NOT BEEN EVALUATED BY THE FOOD AND DRUG ADMINISTRATION. THIS PRODUCT IS NOT INTENDED TO DIAGNOSE, TREAT, CURE OR PREVENT ANY DISEASE.

necessary, many of us seem to find little relief from the release of stress related hormones. Ultimately, we tend to reach the exhaustion phase, where we experience low levels of the stress hormones. This leads to a general weakening of various organ systems. This deep exhaustion due to chronic stress is far too familiar in these modern times.

Fortunately, the plant world provides remarkable support for the stress and tension of modern life. Research has demonstrated that many plants display binding activity with synaptic function in the nervous system. This may help explain the long traditional use of a number of plants for strengthening nervous system function and providing a calmative effect. Some of these plants possess other actions that further support their use in stress. Stress can affect the immune system and the digestive system. It can create an abundance of damaging free radical molecules that affect all types of cells. Inflammation may be involved in the immune response or the free radical response to stress. Antioxidants can help to counteract the free radical damage. Some plants strengthen the immune response while others strengthen digestion. The overall goal of support during stress and tension is achieved by the combination of these actions.

Feverfew leaf has a long history of use in supporting joint health and addressing temporary stress that manifests as headache. Extensive study has shown that Feverfew acts on immune cells to normalize their signals to other cells. This includes blocking release of precursors to prostaglandin production, inhibiting production of inflammation-promoting prostaglandins, and interfering with serotonin's pro-inflammatory effects. Feverfew also seems to prevent platelets from releasing chemical messengers that provoke inflammation. These actions may be particularly important for maintaining the normal structure and function of blood vessels in the brain, as well as for supporting a normalized immune response to stress.*

Chinese Skullcap root was and is extensively used in Traditional Chinese Medicine. Its application covers a broad range of uses, including as a support to liver function. It has drawn extensive research interest. Chinese Skullcap possesses powerful anti-oxidant activity. The anti-oxidant activity is thought to be responsible for its liver supportive properties. Numerous mechanisms of Chinese Skullcap appears to help normalize the immune inflammatory response. These immuno-modulating properties result from activity affecting prostaglandin and neutrophil responses.*

Kava Kava root is native to the tropical Pacific region. Islanders who use it as a ritual beverage during ceremonies have long revered it. It is traditionally used as a social beverage for chiefs and noblemen for its calming, relaxing effect. Kava is highly regarded in Europe as an effective treatment for anxiety. Numerous clinical studies have supported Kava's use. A recent meta-analysis reviewed several clinical trials to determine the efficacy of Kava for the treatment of anxiety. The

*THIS STATEMENT HAS NOT BEEN EVALUATED BY THE FOOD AND DRUG ADMINISTRATION.
THIS PRODUCT IS NOT INTENDED TO DIAGNOSE, TREAT, CURE OR PREVENT ANY DISEASE.

reviewers concluded that Kava was superior to placebo as a symptomatic treatment for anxiety. Anxiety is clearly a common condition related to stress and tension, making Kava a welcome addition to this formula.*

Valerian root's use as a calmative plant dates back to the 18th century. Today, Valerian is listed as an approved herb in the German Commission E Monographs for restlessness and for promoting sound sleep. There are numerous mechanisms of action behind Valerian's calming action. Various constituents in the Valerian root demonstrate supportive activity to the nervous system. In particular, aqueous extract of the whole root and/or the constituent valerenic acid appear to inhibit metabolism of the neurotransmitter GABA. High levels of GABA are associated with mood fluctuations. Several clinical trials have shown good results in improving various aspects of sleep quality. In addition to these benefits, Valerian brings powerful anti-spasmodic activity to this formula.*

Jamaican Dogwood grows in the Caribbean, Mexico and Texas. The bark is known to support healthy sleep when stress and tension play a role. It is also known to support female reproductive health, particularly where its powerful antispasmodic activities can ease pain associated with a normal menstrual cycle.*

Rosemary is an antioxidant and soothing plant with a history of use for stress that manifests as headache. It is also used as an anti-spasmodic for muscle spasm and for the digestive system. Although some conflicting reports exist - a number of compounds found in Rosemary appear to support the immune system by normalizing the inflammatory response associated with immunity. Rosemary does all this under the guise of tasty spice; it is a favorite of cooks around the world.*

Ginger rhizome is another favorite herb in the kitchen, with a long traditional use as a food and spice. Its folk use included support to the digestion and anti-spasmodic application. It is a warming herb that supports cardiovascular function as well. Research suggests that Ginger has an effect on the immune inflammatory response, by normalizing prostaglandin and leukotriene production.*

COMPLEMENTARY PHYTO-CAPS/LIQUID FORMULAS/LIQUID EXTRACTS

Infla-Profen Liquid Phyto-Caps™

SAFETY EVALUATION/CONTRAINDICATIONS

Do not use during pregnancy and lactation.

Caution: US FDA advises that a potential risk of rare, but severe, liver injury may be associated with kava-containing dietary supplements. Ask a healthcare professional before use if you have or have had liver problems, frequently use alcoholic beverages, or are taking any medication. Stop use and see a doctor if you develop symptoms that may signal liver problems, including jaundice (yellowing of the skin or whites of the eyes) and brown urine. Other nonspecific symptoms can include nausea, vomiting, light-colored stools, unexplained tiredness, weakness, stomach or abdominal pain, and loss of appetite. Not for use by persons under 18 years of age, or by pregnant or breastfeeding women. Not for use with alcoholic beverages. Excessive use, or use with products that cause drowsiness, may impair your ability to operate a vehicle or heavy equipment.

KNOWN DRUG INTERACTIONS

Consult a physician if you are taking any pharmaceutical drugs. Migra-Profen should be used with caution when combining with aspirin, non-steroidal anti-inflammatory drugs (NSAIDs) such as ibuprofen, warfarin (Coumadin®), heparin, or any other drug that affects blood clotting.

REFERENCES

Pizzorno J, Murray M. Textbook of Natural Medicine. New York: Churchill Livingstone; 1999.

Anonymous. Feverfew. The Lawrence Review of Natural products. 1994; September: 1-Sumner H, et al. Inhibition of 5-lipoxygenase and cyclo-oxygenase in leukocytes by feverfew. Involvement of sesquiterpene lactones and other components. Biochem Pharmacol. 1992; 43(11): 2313-20.

Patel NM, et al. Paclitaxel sensitivity of breast cancer cells with constitutively active NF-kappa B is enhanced by I kappa B-alpha super-repressor and parthenolide. Oncogene 2000; 19(36): 4159-4169.

Lin SC. Protective and therapeutic effects of Banzhi lian on hepatotoxin-induced liver injuries. Am J Chin Med. 1994; 22: 29-42.

Shieh D, et all. Antioxidant and Free Radical Scavenging Effects of Baicalein, Baicalin and Wogonin. Anticancer Res. 2000; 20: 2861-2866.

Snow JM. Curcuma longa L. (Zingiberaceae). The Protocol Journal of Botanical Medicine. 1995; Autumn: 43-46.

Srimal RC. Turmeric: A brief review of medicinal properties. Fitoterapia; 1997; 68(6): 483-493.

Selvam R. The antioxidant activity of turmeric (Curcuma longa). Journal of Ethnopharmacology. 1995; 47: 59-67.

Newmark TM, Schulick P. Beyond Aspirin. Prescott, Az. HOHM Press. 2000.

Kelm MA, et al. Antioxidant and cyclooxygenase inhibitory phenolic compounds from Ocimum sanctum Linn. Phytomedicine. 2000; 7(1): 7-13.

Zhang F, et al. Curcumin inhibits Cyclooxygenase-2 transcription in bile acid and phorbol ester treated human gastrointestinal epithelial cells. Carcinogenesis. 1999; 20(3): 445-451.

Kapoor LD. Handbook of Ayurvedic Medicinal Plants. Florida. CRC Press; 1990.

Astwood JD, et al. Stability of food allergens to digestion in vitro. Nat Biotechnol. 1996; 14(10): 1269-73.

Majamaa H, et al. Evaluation of the gut mucosal barrier: evidence for increased antigen transfer in children with atopic eczema. J Allergy Clin Immunol. 1996; 97(4): 985-90.

Schulick P. Ginger, common spice or wonder drug. Herbal Free Press, Vermont. USA.

Morazzoni P, Bombardelli E. Valeriana officinalis: traditional use and recent evaluation of activity. Fitoterapia. 1995; 66(2): 99-112.

Brown D. Valerian: Clinical Overview. Townsend Letter for Doctors. 1995; May: 150-151.

Della Loggia R, et al. Isoflavones as spasmolytic principles of Piscidia erythrina. Progress in clinical and biological research. 1988; 280: 366-368.

Voltz HP and Kieser M. Kava Kava extract WS 1490 versus placebo in anxiety disorders- a randomized placebo-controlled 25 week outpatient trial. Phamacopsychiat. 1997; 30:1-5.

Warnecke G. [Psychosomatic dysfunctions in the female climacteric. Clinical effectiveness and tolerance of kava extract WS 1490]. Fortschr Med. 1991; 109 (4): 119-122. [in German]

Woelk H, et al. The treatment of patients with anxiety. A double blind study: kava extract WS 1490 vs benzodiazepine. Zitschrift for Allgemenie Medizine. 1993; 69: 271-277. [in German]

Pittler MH, et al. Efficacy of kava extract for treating Anxiety: Systematic review and meta-analysis. J Clin Psychopharmacology. 2000; 20: 84-89.

Kiuchi, et al. Inhibitors of prostaglandin biosynthesis from ginger. Chem Pharm Bull. 1982; 30(2): 754-7.

Kiuchi , et al. Inhibition of Prostaglandin and Leukotriene Biosynthesis by Gingerols and Diarylheptanoids. Chem Pharm Bull. 1992; 40(2): 387-91.

Santos MS, et. al. The Amount of GABA Present in Aqueous Extracts of Valerian is Sufficient to Account for [3H] GABA Relaease in Synaptosomes. Planta Med. 1994; 60: 475-6.

Lindahl O and Lindwall L. Brief Communication: Double Blind Study of a Valerian Preparation. Pharmacol Biochem Behavior. 1989; 32: 1065-66.

Balderer G and Borbely AA. Effect of valerian on human sleep. Psychopharmacol. 1985; 87: 406-9.

Leathwood PD, et. al. Aqueous Extract of Valerian Root (Valeriana officinalis L.) Improves Sleep Quality in Man. Phamacol Biochem Behavior. 1982; 17: 65-71.

Mustaf T and Srivatava KC. Ginger (Zingiber officnale) in Migraine Headache. J of Ethnopharm. 1990; 29: 267-273.

MILK THISTLE SEED

(Silybum marianum)

Ultimate Support for Healthy Liver Function*

ALCOHOL-FREE CONCENTRATED EXTRACT OF:

MILK THISTLE SEED	MG EXTRACT PER 3 CAPS
(*Silybum marianum*)	450 mg

STANDARDIZED TO FULL SPECTRUM ACTIVITY PROFILE

Silymarins (from Milk Thistle)	360 mg

DOSAGE
3 Liquid Phyto-Caps

DURATION OF USE
4-6 Months

BEST TAKEN
With warm water, after the evening meal

HISTORY

Milk Thistle is a herbaceous annual or biennial plant with a dense-prickly flower head and reddish-purple tubular flowers. It is native to the Mediterranean region and has been naturalized in Central Europe, North and South America, and Southern Australia. Milk Thistle has an extensive history of use as an edible plant. In the 1st century AD, Pliny the Elder reported its use for supporting liver health. Theophrastus (4th century BC) and Dioscorides (1st century AD) also wrote of its value. The English herbalist, Nicholas Culpeper (1650) claimed it was effective for supporting the normal functioning of the liver. At the turn of the 20th century, Eclectic physicians also used Milk Thistle to support healthy liver function. Much of the modern day research has been conducted in Germany where it is a monographed herb in The German Commission E Monographs.*

Numerous scientific studies have explored Milk Thistle and a group of its constituents called silymarins. Many of these clinical studies have demonstrated that this herb supports healthy liver function and provides powerful antioxidant protection, particularly from free radicals and other toxins that normally enter into the liver. A primary constituent of silymarin called silibinin also helps to support healthy liver function, encouraging healthy cholesterol synthesis by the liver.*

In addition to its well-recognized role in promoting liver health, key constituents in Milk Thistle also help to maintain normal kidney function and promote optimal immune function. Limited research suggests that this herb may also support healthy prostate function, and encourage a vital gastrointestinal tract by protecting it from free radical damage. More research is warranted to support the use of this herb for supporting its role beyond enhancing healthy liver function.*

COMPLEMENTARY PHYTO-CAPS/LIQUID FORMULAS/LIQUID EXTRACTS

Liver Health Liquid Phyto-Caps™, Hep Support Liquid Phyto-Caps™

SAFETY EVALUATION/CONTRAINDICATIONS

Milk thistle may occasionally cause a mild, transient laxative effect, which will generally pass within 3 days of use. On rare occasion, this herb can cause mild gastrointestinal distress with symptoms including nausea, diarrhea, flatulence, and bloating. Use with caution if you are allergic to the daisy or chrysanthemum family. If you experience fast or irregular breathing, itching, skin rash or hives, seek medical attention promptly.

KNOWN DRUG INTERACTIONS

Before using this herb, talk with your healthcare professional if you take any medications.

REFERENCES

Blumenthal M, et al. The Complete German Commission E Monographs: Therapeutic Guide to Herbal Medicines. Austin. American Botanical Council; 1998: 169-170.

Bosisio E, et al. Effect of the flavanolignans of silymarin marianum L. on lipid peroxidation in rat liver microsomes and freshly isolated hepatocytes. Pharmacol Res. 1992: 25(2): 147-154.

Chrungoo VJ, et al. Silymarin mediated differential modulation of toxicity induced by carbon tetrachloride , paracetamol, and D-galactosamine in freshly isolated rat hepatocytes. Indian J Exp Biol. 1997; 35(6): 611-617.

Dehmlow C, et al. Inhibition of kupffer cell functions as an explanation for the hepatoprotective properties of silibinin. Hepatology. 1996; 23(4): 749-54.

Dehmlow C, et al. Scavenging of reactive oxygen species and inhibition of arachidonic acid metabolism by silibinin in human cells. Life Sci. 1996; 58(18): 1591-1600.

Fantozzi R, et al. FMLP-activated neutrophils evoke histamine release from mast cells. Agents Actions. 1986; 18(1-2): 155-158.

Favari L, et al. Comparative effects of colchicine and silymarin on CCl4- chronic liver damage in rats. Arch Med Res. 1997; 28(1): 11-17.

Ferenci P, et al. Randomized controlled trial of silymarin treatment in patients with cirrhosis of the liver. J of Hepatology. 1989; 9: 105-113.

Hikino H, et al. Natural products for liver disease. In: Wagner H, et al. Economic and Medicinal Plant Research, vol. 2. New York. Academic Press;1988: 39-72.

Kropacova K, et al. Protective and therapeutic effect of silymarin on the development of latent liver damage. Radiats Biol Radioecol. 1998; 38(3): 411-415.

Luper S. A review of plants used in the treatment of liver disease: Part 1. Altern Med Rev. 1998; 3(6): 410-421.

Magliulo E, et al. [Results of a double blind study on the effect of silymarin in the treatment of acute viral hepatitis, carried out at two medical centers]. Med Klin.1978;73(28-29): 1060-1065. [article in German]

Morazzoni P and Bombardelli E. Silybum marianum (carduus marianus). Fitoterapia. 1995; 66: 3-42.

Muzes G, et al. [Effect of silimarin (legalon) therapy on the antioxidant defense mechanism and lipid peroxidation in alcoholic liver disease]. Orv Hetil. 1990; 131(16):863-866. [article in Hungarian]

Nick, G. Clinical Purification: A Complete Treatment and Reference Manual. Brookfield; LTP Publishing; 2001: 117-125.

Parish RC and Doering PL. Treatment of amanita mushroom poisoning: a review. Vet Hum Toxicol. 1986; 28(4): 318-322.

Pietrangelo A, et al. Antioxidant activity of silybin in vivo during long-term iron overload in rats. Gastroenterology. 1995; 109(6): 1941-1949.

Salmi HA and Sarna S. Effect of silymarin on chemical, functional, and morphological alterations of the liver: A double-blind controlled study. Scan J Gastroenterol. 1982:17(4): 517-521.

Schulz V, et al. Rational Phytotherapy. New York; Springer-Verlag; 1998: 214-220.

Shear NH, et al. Acetaminophen- induced toxicity to human epidermoid cell line A431 and heptoblastoma cell line Hep G2, in vitro, is diminished by silymarin. Skin Pharmacol. 1995; 8(6): 279-291.

Sonnenbichler J, Scalera F, Sonnenbichler I, Weyhenmeyer R. Stimulatory effects of silibinin and silicristin from the milk thistle Silybum marianum on kidney cells. J Pharmacol Exp Ther 1999;290:1375-83.

Zhu W, Zhang JS, Young CY. Silymarin inhibits function of the androgen receptor by reducing nuclear localization of the receptor in the human prostate cancer cell line LNCaP. Carcinogenesis 2001;22:1399-403.

NETTLE LEAF

(Urtica dioica)

Supports Healthy Function of the Upper Respiratory System*

ALCOHOL-FREE CONCENTRATED EXTRACTS OF:

NETTLE LEAF	**MG EXTRACT PER 2 CAPS**
(*Urtica dioica*)	100 mg

STANDARDIZED TO FULL SPECTRUM ACTIVITY PROFILE

Caffeic acid derevatives (from Nettle)	2.0 mg

DOSAGE
1 Liquid Phyto-Cap, 2 times daily

DURATION OF USE
4-6 Months

BEST TAKEN
Between meals, with warm water

HISTORY

Nettle is a herbaceous perennial, infamous for the stinging hairs on its leaf and stem. The genus name is from the Latin "uro" (to burn) in reference to the painful rash caused by its biting hairs. The herb grows in fields, moist thickets and along roadsides and can be found throughout North America and Europe. Nettle has been used since ancient times. The Greek physicians Dioscorides and Galen used Nettle leaf in the 1st and 2nd centuries AD to support respiratory, urinary and reproductive health. By the late 19th and early 20th centuries, Eclectic physicians used this highly nutritious herb as an astringent and digestive aid and to support healthy skin. Nettle had further practical use as a fiber source and to this day is a favorite spring shoot that is cooked into soup, steamed, or pan sautéed.*

NETTLE IN MODERN TIMES

Nettle leaf is included among the reviewed and monographed herbs by the respected German Commission. It boasts a great number of nutrients, including significant amounts of chlorophyll, protein, ascorbic acid, calcium, magnesium, Vitamin K1, potassium and zinc. Such nutrients work together to promote the health of skin, bones and joints and encourage a healthy immune and respiratory system. As well, Nettle leaf contains flavonoids such as quercitin, kaempferol, and rutin that help to maintain healthy levels of histamine in the body. Histamine release is associated with response to environmental insult. Nettle leaf helps to maintain your body's defense system and increase histamine efficiency. Further, Nettle leaf extract promotes the healthy modulation of prostaglandins, leukotrienes, and cytokines key components associated with normal immune function. The immune system's natural response to environmental stresses is associated with the production of these compounds. These responses are healthy within a normal range. However, these compounds can be found to be altered when tissues are subjected to stress. Collectively the nutrients and phytochemicals in Nettle leaf support the body's normal and healthy response to poor nutrition, indoor and outdoor air pollution, and environmental insults.*

COMPLEMENTARY PHYTO-CAPS/LIQUID FORMULAS/LIQUID EXTRACTS

Aller-Leaf Liquid Phyto-Caps™, Turmeric/Catechu Supreme, Eyebright/Bayberry Supreme, Olive Leaf Liquid Phyto-Caps™, and Green Tea Liquid Phyto-Caps™.

SAFETY EVALUATION/CONTRAINDICATIONS

This formula should be avoided in pregnancy and lactation, unless otherwise indicated for use by a qualified healthcare professional. Use with caution and seek the advice of a qualified healthcare professional if you are taking anticoagulant therapy, as this herb may interact with such medications.

KNOWN DRUG INTERACTIONS

Nettle leaf should be used with caution in combination with drugs that inhibit blood clotting and platelet aggregation including but not limited to warfarin (Coumadin®) due to its vitamin K content. Additionally, Nettle Leaf may interact with antihypertention and antidiabetic medications. There is also a possibility that this herb might potentiate the effects of central nervous system depressants. Nettle leaf may potentiate the effects of Diclofenac. Before using this herb, talk with your healthcare professional if you take any medications.

REFERENCES

Blumenthal M, et al. Herbal Medicine: Expanded Commission E Monograph. Austin. American Botanical Council; 2000: 367.

Bombardelli E and Morazzoni P. Urtica dioica L. Fitoterapia. 1997; LXVIII: 387-402.

Chrubasik S, et al. Evidence for antirheumatic effectiveness of Herba Urticae dioicae in acute arthritis: A pilot study. Phytomedicine. 1997; 4(2), 105-108.

Duke J and Beckstrom-Sternberg S. "Dr. Duke's Phytochemical and Ethnobotanical Databases." 31 July 2000. Online. Internet. [31 July 2000]. Available WWW: http://www.ars-grin.gov/cgi-bin/duke/farmacy2.pl

Felter HW and Lloyd JU. King's American Dispensatory. Portland, Oregon. Eclectic Medical Publications; 1983: 2032-2034. (originally published in 1898).

Hyam R and Pankhurst R. Plants and Their Names: A Concise Dictionary. Oxford. Oxford University Press; 1995: 513

Klingelhoefer S, et al. Antirheumatic effect of IDS 23, a stinging nettle leaf extract, on in vitro expression of T helper cytokines. J. Rheumatol. 1999; 26(12): 2517-2522.

Mittman P. Randomized, double-blind study of freeze dried urtica dioica in the treatment of allergic rhinitis. Planta Medica. 1990;56:44-47.

Natural Medicines Comprehensive Database. Monograph : Stinging Nettle. Online. Internet. [15 May 2002]. http://www.naturaldatabase.com.

Obertreis B, et al. Antiphlogistic Effects of Urtica dioica folia extract in comparison to Caffeic Malic Acid.] Arzneimittelforschung. 1996; 46(1): 52-56. [in German]

Obertreis B, et al. Ex-vivo in vitro inhibition of Lipopolysaccharide Stimulated Tumor Necrosis Factor-alpha and interleukin-1 beta Secretion in Human Whole Blood by Extractum Urticae dioicae foliorum. Arzneimittelforschung. 1996; 46(4): 389-394.

Riehemann K, et al. Plant extracts from stinging nettle (urtica dioica), an antirheumatic remedy, inhibit the proinflammatory transcription factor NF-kappaB. FEBS Lett. 1999; 442(1): 89-94.

Riva R. Naturopathic specific condition review: allergies (immediate type hypersensitivity). Protocol J of Botanical Med. 1995; 1(2): 60-62.

Roitt I. Essential Immunology, 8th Edition. Oxford. Blackwell Scientific Publications; 1994.

Thornhill SM and Kelly AM. Natural treatment of perennial allergic rhinitis. Altern Med Rev. 2000; 5(5): 448-454.

OIL OF OREGANO

(Origanum vulgare)

Supercritical CO_2 Extract of Oregano

Support for Normal Yeast Balance

ALCOHOL-FREE CONCENTRATED EXTRACT OF:

OREGANO LEAF	MG EXTRACT PER 2 CAPS
Oregano leaf, (wild Mediterranean)	
Supercritical CO_2 Extract (*Origanum vulgare*)	460 mg

STANDARDIZED TO FULL SPECTRUM ACTIVITY PROFILE

Carvacrol	64 mg

DOSAGE

Liquid Phyto-Caps: 1 capsule, two times daily

DURATION OF USE

4 weeks

BEST TAKEN

Between meals, with warm water

HISTORY

There are many different species of plants called Oregano. Origanum vulgare is a hardy, aromatic, bushy perennial with rose-purple, sometimes pink to white flowers. It is a European native, where it is commonly called "Wild Marjoram." Oregano has been highly prized for thousands of years for its culinary, cosmetic, and folk uses. Ancient Greeks held the plant in such esteem that they believed that Aphrodite created it to be a symbol of happiness. The ancient Egyptians also held the plant in high regard and used it as an emollient and preservative.

THE HEALTH-GIVING ACTIONS OF OREGANO

Oregano contains key constituents that function synergistically to support the body's natural environmental immune response. Specifically, the volatile oils found in Oregano, including carvacrol and thymol, help to support a healthy microbial environment in the intestines and throughout the body. Further, Oregano leaf acts as an antioxidant and contains the flavonoid Rosmarinic acid that appears to normalize the chemical cyclooxygenase 2 (Cox-2). Cox-2 is associated with the body's response to environmental insult. As well, Oregano leaf may encourage the healthy elimination of toxins from the body and support the healthy production of bile. There is insufficient reliable research to scientifically validate these theoretical actions in humans.*

COMPLEMENTARY PHYTO-CAPS/LIQUID FORMULAS/LIQUID EXTRACTS

Black Walnut/Coptis Supreme, Wormwood/Black Walnut Supreme, Pau D'arco Supreme.

SAFETY EVALUATION/CONTRAINDICATIONS

Do not take pure essential oil of Oregano internally. Note that oil of Oregano contains essential oils, but is not a pure essential oil. This product should be avoided in pregnancy and lactation. Excessively high doses may cause intestinal upset, diarrhea, frontal headache, tinnitus, anorexia, nervousness and loss of taste. Do not exceed the recommended dose. Use with caution if you are allergic to the Lamiaceae (includes basil, sage, mint, hyssop, lavender and others) family. This herb may cause a systemic allergic reaction. If you experience fast or irregular breathing, itching, skin rash or hives, seek medical attention promptly.

KNOWN DRUG INTERACTIONS

There are no known drug interactions with Oregano. However, this herb may not have been studied sufficiently to determine its interactions with other medications. Before using Oregano, talk with your healthcare professional if you take any medications.

REFERENCES

Benito M, et al. Labiatae allergy: systemic reactions due to ingestion of oregano and thyme. Ann Allergy Asthma Immunol. May1996;76(5):416-8.

Birdsall TC. Gastrointestinal candidiasis: Fact or fiction? Alt Med Rev. 1997: 2(5):346-354.

Bremness L. The Complete Book of Herbs: A Practical Guide to Growing and Using Herbs. New York. Penguin Group; 1988:104-105

Dorman HJD and Deans SG. Antimicrobial agents from plants: antibacterial activity of plant volatile oils. J of Applied Microbiology. 2000; 88: 308-316.

Force M, et al. Inhibition of enteric parasites by emulsified oil of oregano in vivo. Phytotherapy Research. 2000; 14:213-214.

Gerard J. The Herbal or General History of Plants. New York. Dover Publications; 1975: 666-667. [The complete 1633 edition as revised and enlarged by Thomas Johnson]

Hammer KA, et al. Antimicrobial activity of essential oils and other plant extracts. J Appl Microbiol. 1999; 86(6):985-990.

Kelm MA, Nair MG, Strasburg GM. Antioxidant and Cyclooxygenase Inhibitory Phenolic Compounds from Ocimum sanctum Linn. Phytomedicine. Mar2000;7(1):7-13.

Lagouri V and Dimitrios B. Nutrient antioxidants in oregano. International J of Food Science and Nutrition. 1996; 47:493-497.

Milos M, et al. Chemical composition and antioxidant effect of glycosidically bound volatile compounds from oregano (Origanum vulgare L. ssp. Hirtum) Food Chemistry. 2000; 71:79-83.

Montes-Belmont R and Carvajal M. Control of Aspergillus flavus in maize with plant essential oils and their components. J Food Prot. 1998; 61(5): 616-619.

Tantaoui-Elaraki A and Beraoud L. Inhibition of growth and aflatoxin production in Aspergillus parasiticus by essential oils of selected plant materials. J Environ Pathol Toxicol Oncol. 1994;13(1): 67-72.

OLIVE LEAF

(Olea europaea)

Support for Healthy Immune Function*

ALCOHOL-FREE CONCENTRATED EXTRACT OF:

OLIVE LEAF	MG EXTRACT PER 2 CAPS
(*Olea europea*)	500 mg

STANDARDIZED TO FULL SPECTRUM ACTIVITY PROFILE

Oleuropeins	50 mg

DOSAGE
1 Liquid Phyto-Cap, 2 times daily

DURATION OF USE
4-6 Months

BEST TAKEN
Between meals, with warm water

HISTORY: A SYMBOL OF PEACE

Olive is an evergreen tree that grows to 8-12 meters in height. It is native to the Mediterranean region, where it has been cultivated for over 3,000 years. Olive leaf has long been used as a folk remedy. The Romans called the plant Olea from oleum, meaning oil, after the valuable oil extracted from its fruits. To both the Greeks and the Romans the olive was a symbol of peace. The ancient Egyptians used the oil to mummify their kings. The English herbalist, John Gerard (1633) reported that Olive leaves and buds were useful in supporting the body's proper function. In the 1898 edition of King's American Dispensatory, it was reported that a strong decoction of Olive leaves could play a role in maintaining body temperature.*

OLIVE AND THE IMMUNE SYSTEM

Several scientific investigations have examined the constituents of Olive leaves. One constituent that has received considerable attention is called oleuropein. First isolated in 1908, oleuropein enhances immune system function and offers antioxidant protection.*

OLIVE AND THE HEART

Fittingly, Olive Leaf's antioxidant properties may have a beneficial effect on cholesterol metabolism by protecting cholesterol from the damaging effects of free radicals. In addition to encouraging healthy cholesterol balance, this leaf may

*THIS STATEMENT HAS NOT BEEN EVALUATED BY THE FOOD AND DRUG ADMINISTRATION. THIS PRODUCT IS NOT INTENDED TO DIAGNOSE, TREAT, CURE OR PREVENT ANY DISEASE.

also play a role in maintaining normal blood pressure within a healthy range, assisting in maintaining healthy blood, and encouraging the normal flow of blood through the heart vessels. Collectively, the actions of this leaf serve to help to maintain healthy heart function.*

Olive leaf may also show promise in maintaining healthy blood sugar levels when taken in conjuction with a balanced diet, and in promoting a normal balance of healthy bacteria in the gastrointestinal tract. These are theoretical applications of Olive leaf's potential and more research is warranted to validate its use for these purposes.*

COMPLEMENTARY PHYTO-CAPS/LIQUID FORMULAS/LIQUID EXTRACTS

Echinacea Supreme Liquid Phyto-Caps™, Echinacea/Goldenseal Supreme Liquid Phyto-Caps™, Hep Support Liquid Phyto-Caps™, Astragalus Supreme Liquid Phyto-Caps™, Respiratory Defense Liquid Phyto-Caps™, Hawthorne Supreme Liquid Phyto-Caps™

SAFETY EVALUATION/CONTRAINDICATIONS

This product should be avoided in pregnancy and lactation. Use with caution if you are allergic to Olive tree pollen as it may cause a seasonal respiratory allergic reaction. This herb may cause mild gastrointestinal irritation, particularly if taken on an empty stomach.

KNOWN DRUG INTERACTIONS

Olive leaf may potentiate the effects of blood pressure lowering medications and theoretically may interact with antidiabetic medications due to its potential to affect glucose levels. Further, this herb may interact with drugs that inhibit blood clotting and platelet aggregation, including but not limited to warfarin (Coumadin®), heparin, clopidogrel (Plavix®), pentoxifylline (Trental®), and aspirin, due to its potential effects in encouraging healthy blood formation and blood flow. Before using this formula, talk with your healthcare professional if you take any medications.

REFERENCES

Aziz NH, et al. Comparative antibacterial and antifungal effects of some phenolic compounds. Microbios. 1998; 93(374):43-54.

Benavente-Garcia O, et al. Antioxidant activity of phenolics extracted from Olea europaea leaves. Food Chemistry. 2000; 68:457-462.

Bisignano G, et al. On the in-vitro antimicrobial activity of oleuropein and hydroxytyrosol. J Pharm Pharmacol. 1999; 51(8): 971-974.

Budavari S, et al. (editors). The Merck Index. A Encyclopedia of Chemicals, Drugs, and Biologicals. 12th Edition. Whitehouse Station, NJ. Merck and Company; pg.1171 (6967).

Coni E, et al. Protective effect of oleuropein, an olive oil biophenol, on low density lipoprotein oxidizability in rabbits. Lipids. 2000; 35(1): 45-54.

Felter HW and Lloyd JU. King's American Dispensatory. Portland, Oregon. Eclectic Medical Publications; 1983: pg 1376. (originally published in 1898).

Gerard J. The Herbal or General History of Plants. New York. Dover Publications; 1975: 1392-1393. [The complete 1633 edition as revised and enlarged by Thomas Johnson]

Martinez A, et al. Identification of a 36-kDa olive-pollen allergen by in vitro and in vivo studies. Allergy. Jun1999;54(6):584-92.

PDR for Herbal Medicines, 2nd edition. Montvale, NJ: Medical Economics Company; 2000:557.

Petroni A, et al. Inhibition of platelet aggregation and eicosanoid production by phenolic components of olive oil.Thromb Res. Apr1995;78(2):151-60.

Stuart M. (editor) The Encyclopedia of Herbs and Herbalism. New York. Orbis Publishing; 1979: 229-230.

Tranter HS, et al. The effect of the olive phenolic compound, oleuropein, on the growth and enterotoxin B production by staphylococcus aureus. J Appl Bacteriol. 1993; 74(3): 253-259.

Visioli F and Galli C. Oleuropein protects low density lipoprotein from oxidation. Life Sci. 1994; 55(24): 1965-1971.

Visioli F, et al. Oleuropein, the bitter principle of olives, enhances nitric oxide production by mouse macrophages. Life Sci.1998; 62(6): 541-546.

PARA-SHIELD

Supports Healthy Intestinal Environment*

ALCOHOL-FREE CONCENTRATED EXTRACTS OF:

FORMULA	MG PER 2 CAPSULES
Black Walnut green hulls (*Juglans nigra*)	160 mg
Wormwood absinthium (*Artemesia absinthium*)	80 mg
Wormwood annnua (*Artemesia annua*)	80 mg
Pomegranate seed (*Punica granatum*)	80 mg
Gentian root (*Gentiana lutea*)	80 mg
Chinese Coptis root & rhisome (*Coptis chinensis*)	40 mg
Ginger rhizome (*Zingiber officinalis*)	16 mg
Clove oil (*Syzygium aromaticum*)	.16 mg

DOSAGE
2 Liquid Phyto-Caps 2 times daily.

DURATION OF USE
2-4 weeks

BEST TAKEN
After meals, with a small amount of warm water.

DESCRIPTION OF FORMULA

Para-Shield contains key constituents that function synergistically to support the body's natural defense against and resistance to damaging stressors in our internal environment, while promoting healthy intestinal organism balance.*

Scientific studies have explored the herbs found in Para-Shield, and their specific effect on creating an internal environment that supports the growth of healthy microorganisms. Collectively the herbs in Para-Shield work by encouraging the natural and normal release of select chemicals that the body uses to support intestinal health, while optimizing digestive functions to remove them from the body.*

Black Walnut Green Hulls promote natural and healthy intestinal microorganisms. Providing a broad-spectrum of support for healthy microorganism balance, black walnut green hulls maintain the health of lymphatic fluid and blood, and organs including the liver, heart, brain and intestinal tract.*

Wormwood absinthium contains compounds that support the body's natural resistance to microscopic challenges from the environment. Specifically, it contains essential oil, absinthin, anabsinthin, resins, and organic acids that help to support a healthy microbial environment in the intestines and throughout the body.*

Wormwood annua has been revered throughout China for thousands of years for its ability to support the natural removal of unwelcome organisms housed in the body. Wormwood annua is an important source of artemisinin and its derivatives. Artemisinin reacts with iron which is released by hemoglobin, creating free radicals which in turn, support a healthy microbial environment by targeting certain proteins. They also support the healthy function of white blood cells, particularly those that promote and protect blood.*

Pommegrante Seed contains a significant quantity of punicic acid which is a fatty acid that is structurally similar to conjugated linolenic acid and is recognized for its actions in supporting healthy cellular metabolism and offering potent immune protection. It is also rich in polyphenols and other fatty acids, including palmitic acid, stearic acid, oleic acid, and linoleic acid. These compounds maintain and support healthy immune function and provide antioxidant protection against the damaging effects of toxins and other stressors released by opportunistic organisms in the body.*

Gentian root is a digestive bitter that supports gastrointestinal health and liver function.*

Chinese Coptis is an important source of the plant alkaloid, berberine, recognized for it beneficial actions of maintaining broad-spectrum microbial balance throughout the intestinal tract.*

Ginger rhizome is a powerful botanical promoter of healthy prostaglandin and thromboxane activity; compounds associated with immune function. Further, this highly valued herb promotes healthy circulation and digestion, and a proper response to environmental stress.*

Clove Oil complements the herbs in this formula by promoting immune and gastrointestinal health.*

COMPLEMENTARY PHYTO-CAPS/LIQUID FORMULAS/LIQUID EXTRACTS

Rejuve powder, Sweetish Bitters Elixir

SAFETY EVALUATION/CONTRAINDICATIONS

Before using this product, talk with your healthcare professional if you suffer from a medical condition. Please visit www.gaiaherbs.com to obtain information regarding potential contraindications and/or side effects that may be associated with herbs found in this formula.*

KNOWN DRUG INTERACTIONS

Before using this product, talk with your healthcare professional if you take any medications. Please visit www.gaiaherbs.com to obtain information regarding any possible drug interactions that may be associated with herbs found in this formula.*

REFERENCES

Anon. Berberine. Altern Med Rev. 2000 Apr;5(2):175-7.

Braga LC, et al. Pomegranate extract inhibits Staphylococcus aureus growth and subsequent enterotoxin production. J Ethnopharmacol. 2005 Jan 4;96(1-2):335-9.

Eckstein-Ludwig U, et al. Artemisinins target the SERCA of Plasmodium falciparum. Nature. 2003 Aug 21;424(6951):957-61.

Ficker C et al. Bioassay-guided isolation and identification of antifungal compounds from ginger. Phytother Res 2003 Sep;17(8):897-902.

Kumari MV.Modulatory influences of clove (Caryophyllus aromaticus, L) on hepaticde toxification systems and bone marrow genotoxicity in male Swiss albino mice. Cancer Lett. 1991 Oct;60(1):67-73.

Leung AY, Foster S. Encyclopedia of Common Natural Ingredients Used in Food, Drugs, and Cosmetics, 2d ed. New York: John Wiley & Sons, 1996, 1–3.

Liang CP, Wang M, Simon JE, Ho CT. Antioxidant activity of plant extracts on the inhibition of citral off-odor formation. Mol Nutr Food Res. 2004 Sep;48(4):308-17.

Lindberg CM, Melathopoulos AP, Winston ML. Laboratory evaluation of miticides to control Varroa jacobsoni (Acari: Varroidae), a honey bee (Hymenoptera: Apidae) parasite. Econ Entomol. 2000 Apr;93(2):189-98.

Wang RF, et al. Bioactive compounds from the seeds of Punica granatum (pomegranate). J Nat Prod. 2004 Dec;67(12):2096-8.

Yabu Y, et al. Antitrypanosomal effects of traditional Chinese herbal medicines on bloodstream forms of Trypanosoma brucei rhodesiense in vitro. Southeast Asian J Trop Med Public Health. 1998 Sep;29(3):599-604.

PHYTO-ESTROGEN

Support for the Peri-Menopause and Menopausal Years*

ALCOHOL-FREE CONCENTRATED EXTRACTS OF:

FORMULA	MG EXTRACT PER 3 CAPSULES
Alfalfa leaf (*Medicago sativa*)	300 mg
Vitex berry (*Vitex agnus-castus*)	90 mg
Black Cohosh rhizome (*Actaea racemosa*)	27 mg
Red Clover blossoms (*Trifolium pratense*)	21 mg
Wild Oats milky seed (*Avena sativa*)	21 mg
Blue Vervain herb (*Verbena hastata*)	18 mg
Dandelion leaf & root (*Taraxacum* off.)	12 mg
St. John's Wort flower bud (*Hypericum perforatum*)	12 mg
Sage leaf (*Salvia* off.)	12 mg

DOSAGE

Liquid Phyto-Caps: 1 capsule, three times daily

DURATION OF USE

4-6 months

BEST TAKEN

Between meals, with warm water

TRANSITIONAL YEARS

This formula assists the transition into and out of menopause. Common conditions associated with the menopausal years include menstrual irregularities, vaginal dryness, fatigue, depression, decreased libido, and sleep disturbances. By stabilizing hormonal function, the transition into this sacred and powerful time in a woman's life is made more smoothly. This formula works primarily to support the balance of estrogen and progesterone.

There are two mechanisms involved with supporting estrogen availability to women. First, some of the plants supply estrogen-like compounds - called isoflavones. These compounds are reported to be hundreds of times weaker in their effect than the body's estrogens. Environmental estrogens are even stronger. These weak estrogen-mimicking compounds found in plants help normalize estrogen levels in the body. If estrogen levels are low, the weak estrogens act as a small but valuable supply to the woman. If her estrogen levels are high, the weaker estrogens competitively bind to estrogen receptor sites, reducing the ability of stronger estrogens to bind with those same sites. The overall result is a gentle normalization of estrogen levels. The second way this formula addresses estrogen levels is by supporting adrenal function. As a woman ages and her ovaries produce less estrogen, the adrenal gland's production of estrogen becomes more important. General nervous system support can assist the adrenal gland's role in this production.

Alfalfa leaf brings several influential benefits to this formula. It is highly nutritive, notably containing relatively high levels of Vitamin K1. Vitamin K1 is reported to aid in the maturing of the body's calcium managing proteins. Alfalfa also contains significant quantities of isoflavones, the estrogen-like plant compounds discussed above. The combination of these factors makes this plant a welcome addition to this menopause formula.*

Note: Current concerns with Alfalfa inducing a reversible Systemic Lupus Erythematosus (SLE)-like syndrome are based on toxicology studies of canavanine – an alkaloid which is only found in Alfalfa's seeds and sprouts. As canavanine is not found in the mature tops of the plant, this concern is not clinically relevant when using the leaf or blade, as is the case here.*

Chaste tree (Vitex berry) has traditionally been used to support normal menstruation. Perhaps its most relevant influence relating to this formula is its ability to influence the pituitary gland, resulting in a normalization of estrogen and progesterone balance. By enhancing corpus luteal development, through a dopaminergic activity on the anterior pituitary gland, Chaste tree results in a net increase of progesterone. Low levels of progesterone are commonly noted during puberty and menopause. This effect on pituitary function may explain clinical reports that the Chaste tree berry helps to relieve the hot flashes and other conditions commonly associated with menopause.*

Black Cohosh has been used by Cherokee women to support healthy menstruation. Modern science has shed some light on its application to the menstrual cycle with the discovery that Black Cohosh is able to reduce levels of Luteinizing Hormone (LH) without effecting levels of the Follicle Stimulating Hormone (FSH). As LH is generally responsible for the release of progesterone and FSH is generally responsible for the release of estrogen, it may be that Black Cohosh produces an overall estrogen-like effect. Regardless of the exact process, clinical research has confirmed its value in treating conditions where there is an underlying imbalance between estrogen and progesterone.*

Red Clover is traditionally recognized as a so-called blood cleanser (alterative). By definition, such an alterative effect promotes correct metabolic function. Red Clover is similar to Alfalfa in the fact that it contains isoflavones that are known to produce estrogen-like effects. At least one clinical trial indicates that Red Clover is able to support cardiovascular health in menopause.*

Wild Oats have long been used as a nerve tonic for individuals with nervous exhaustion. Wild Oats has been included here because women transitioning

*THIS STATEMENT HAS NOT BEEN EVALUATED BY THE FOOD AND DRUG ADMINISTRATION.
THIS PRODUCT IS NOT INTENDED TO DIAGNOSE, TREAT, CURE OR PREVENT ANY DISEASE.

around menopause often require support for nervous system health. The highly respected German Commission E includes Wild Oats for anxiety, stress and weakness. It also is discussed as a tonic and a restorative.*

Blue Vervain is another example of a plant remedy that is traditionally used to support normal menstruation. Species related to Verbena hastata are reported to have influence over the nervous system. Blue Vervain is both calming and building to the nervous system. Such influence over the nervous system has lead to its use with stress.*

Dandelion leaf & root promotes healthy liver function, enabling improved metabolism of estrogens.*

St. John's Wort has a clear history of use for nervous system health as well as with menstrual function. It is a useful addition to this menopause formula for its effect on emotional well being and its support to liver function. In one clinical study with 111 pre- and post-menopausal women, psychological health improved significantly with St. John's Wort. Sexual function also improved.*

Sage grows wild in its native Mediterranean lands, but is cultivated worldwide as a favorite culinary herb. Folk use of the plant centers around digestive function and body temperature regulation. The ability to normalize body temperature speaks to its inclusion here and its long use for hot flashes associated with menopause.*

COMPLEMENTARY PHYTO-CAPS/LIQUID FORMULAS/LIQUID EXTRACTS

Black Cohosh Root, Astragalus Supreme Liquid Phyto-Caps™, Vitex/Alfalfa Supreme

SAFETY EVALUATION/CONTRAINDICATIONS

Do not use this product during pregnancy or lactation. Women with hormone sensitive conditions such as breast, uterine or ovarian cancer, endometriosis, and uterine fibroids should consult a qualified healthcare professional before using this formula due to its potential estrogenic effects.

KNOWN DRUG INTERACTIONS

Consult a physician if you are taking any pharmaceutical drugs.

REFERENCES

Snow JM. Vitex agnus-castus L. (Verbenaceae). The Protocol Journal of Botanical Medicine. 1996; Spring: 20-23.

Brown D. Vitex agnus-castus Clinical Monograph. The Quarterly Review of Natural Medicine. 1994; Summer: 111-121.

Anonymous. Chaste Tree. The Lawrence Review of Natural products. 1994; December.

Pizzorno J, Murray M. Textbook of Natural Medicine. New York: Churchill Livingstone; 1999. Pg. 1021.

Mitchell W. Plant Medicine. Seattle, Wa: Self-published; 2000. Pg. 14-15.

Reilly P. Clinical application Medicago sativa extracts. Journal of Naturopathic Medicine. 1 (1):

Brinker F. Macrotys. The Eclectic Medical Journals. 1996; 2(1): 2-4.

Snow JM. Cimicifuga racemosa. The Protocol Journal of Botanical Medicine. 1996; 1(4): 17-19.

Hudson T. A Woman's Guide to Herbal Care. Herbal Research Publications. Brevard, NC, 1998.

Nestel P, et al. Isoflavones from Red Clover improve systemic arterial compliance but not plasma lipids in menopausal women. The Journal of Clinical Endocrinology & Metabolism. 1999; 84(3): 895-898.

*THIS STATEMENT HAS NOT BEEN EVALUATED BY THE FOOD AND DRUG ADMINISTRATION. THIS PRODUCT IS NOT INTENDED TO DIAGNOSE, TREAT, CURE OR PREVENT ANY DISEASE.

Snow JM. Hypericum perforatum L. (Hyperiaceae). The Protocol Journal of Botanical Medicine. 1996; 2(1): 16-21.

Gruenwald J. Standardized St. John's Wort Extract Clinical Monograph. The Quarterly Review of Natural Medicine. 1997; Winter: 289-298.

Murray M. The healing power of herbs - The enlightened persons guide to the wonders of medicinal plants. 2nd ed. Prima publishing. Rocklin, Ca. 1995.

Grube B, et al. St. John's Wort extract: efficacy for menopausal symptoms of psychological origin. Adv Ther. 1999; 16(4)177-186.

Blumenthal M, et al. Ed. The Complete German Commission E Monographs.Austin, TX: American Botanical Council; 1998.

Witchl M. (Bisset NG, Ed.) Herbal Drugs and Phytopharmaceuticals. Medpharm, CRC Press: Boca Raton. 1994.

PHYTO-PRŌZ SUPREME

Ultimate Support for Emotional Well Being*

ALCOHOL-FREE CONCENTRATED EXTRACTS OF:

FORMULA	MG EXTRACT PER 3 CAPSULES
St. John's Wort flower bud (*Hypericum perforatum*)	105 mg
Kava Kava rhizome (*Piper methysticum*)	103 mg
Schizandra berry (*Schizandra chinensis*)	90 mg
Eleuthero root (*Eleutherococcus senticosus*)	45 mg
Ginkgo leaf (*Ginkgo biloba*)	30 mg
Passionflower vine (*Passiflora incarnata*)	27 mg
Wild Oats milky seed (*Avena sativa*)	21 mg
Gotu Kola herb (*Centella asiatica*)	18 mg
Prickly Ash bark (*Xanthoxylum clava-herculis*)	9 mg
Nettle seed (*Urtica dioica*)	6 mg
Rosemary supercritical extract (*Rosmarinus officinalis*)	3 mg

STANDARDIZED TO FULL SPECTRUM ACTIVITY PROFILE

Hypericins (from St. John's Wort)	0.525 mg
Kavalactones (from Kava Kava)	57.0 mg

DOSAGE
Liquid Phyto-Caps: 1 capsule, 3 times daily

DURATION OF USE
4-6 months

BEST TAKEN
Between meals, with warm water

*THIS STATEMENT HAS NOT BEEN EVALUATED BY THE FOOD AND DRUG ADMINISTRATION.
THIS PRODUCT IS NOT INTENDED TO DIAGNOSE, TREAT, CURE OR PREVENT ANY DISEASE.

A HEALTHY NERVOUS SYSTEM

This compound synergistically enhances emotional well being through a number of different strategies. The plants enjoy long historical use for supporting nervous system health. While some specifically build and support nervous system function, others address anxiety. Some act to support the function of the adrenal gland and its production of stress hormones. Adaptogens improve the body's ability to handle stress. Traditional use of these plants supports the formula's overall objective.

Modern research lends preliminary support to the formula as well. The strategic objective of Phyto-Proz includes the normalization of neurotransmitters in the central nervous system. This involves normalization of seratonin availability.

St. John's Wort is said to be "for the nervous system, what arnica is for the musculature." In other words, it has a profound soothing effect in the nervous system. St. John's Wort also is known traditionally for its positive affect upon digestion and liver function, although such use is seldom mentioned anymore. This plant is best known for its benefit with supporting emotional health. A number of well-controlled clinical trials have supported such use. St John's Wort is shown to effectively inhibit seratonin reuptake, making the neurotransmitter more available. This 'happy' neurotransmitter is vitally important to emotional well being. The Commission E has approved St. John's Wort for stabilizing moods, anxiety and/or nervous unrest.*

Kava Kava is often used today with nervous anxiety. Traditional use throughout its native land of the South Pacific islands centered around elevating the mind and relaxing the body. Kava has been the subject of numerous clinical trials for the treatment of nervous anxiety. The respected German Commission E has approved Kava for nervous anxiety, stress, and restlessness. Research into its mechanism of action have been inconclusive, though it does appear to have some kind of effect on neurotransmitters of the central nervous system.*

Schizandra berry is a powerful adaptogen and antioxidant. As an adaptogen Schizandra berry facilitates the body's ability to manage stress properly. As an anti-oxidant, Schizandra prevents oxidative damage to the brain and nerve cells. It also supports liver function.*

Eleuthero together with Schizandra are reportedly the finest combination of adaptogenic plants. This important herb improves the body's response to stress, normalizes endocrine responses, enhances liver function and builds nervous system health.*

Modern day uses of Ginkgo are well established. In Europe it is used extensively to support cognitive function. Ginkgo and its constituents are the subjects of over 400 scientific publications, making it one of the most researched herbal products. Numerous clinical trials have documented Ginkgo's effects on cognitive function. Ginkgo has been shown to affect recall, recognition memory, reaction time, attention, concentration, psychomotor function, mood, information processing, and energy levels.*

Passionflower is a favorite traditional herb, well suited as a relaxant. It specifically provides support when stress wears down the nerve force. Alkaloids from the Passionflower appear to affect the enzyme mono-amine oxidase, which could further contribute to the normalization of neurotransmitters associated with emotional well-being. Additionally, benzodiazapene binding with its constituent apigenin may be responsible for anti-anxiety effects. These studies are preliminary and not conclusive.*

Wild Oats are nutritive to all tissues within the body. This herb, as so many others in this formula, improves the nerve force and vitality especially when the body/mind have become exhausted.

Gotu Kola is traditionally known to reduce mental chatter, calming the mind while promoting increased clarity.*

Prickly Ash is the circulatory stimulant within the formula. It is particularly suited here to promote blood supply to the periphery.*

Nettle seed is a powerhouse of nutrition for the brain. It is said to supply brain nutrients such as choline and acetyl-choline and acts to build mental energy and wakefulness.*

Rosemary leaf has been demonstrated in studies to be a powerful antioxidant. Traditional reports of the benefits of rosemary include supporting cognitive abilities and poor memory ("weakness of the brain"), immune function, digestive health and circulation.*

COMPLEMENTARY PHYTO-CAPS/LIQUID FORMULAS/LIQUID EXTRACTS

Adrenal Health Liquid Phyto-Caps™, St. John's Wort Liquid Phyto-Caps™, Anti-Oxidant Supreme Liquid Phyto-Caps™

SAFETY EVALUATION/CONTRAINDICATIONS

Do not use this product during pregnancy or lactation.

Caution: US FDA advises that a potential risk of rare, but severe, liver injury may be associated with kava-containing dietary supplements. Ask a healthcare professional before use if you have or have had liver problems, frequently use alcoholic beverages, or are taking any medication. Stop use and see a doctor if you develop symptoms that may signal liver problems, including jaundice (yellowing of the skin or whites of the eyes) and brown urine. Other nonspecific symptoms can include nausea, vomiting, light-colored stools, unexplained tiredness, weakness, stomach or abdominal pain, and loss of appetite. Not for use by persons under 18 years of age, or by pregnant or breastfeeding women. Not for use with alcoholic beverages. Excessive use, or use with products that cause drowsiness, may impair your ability to operate a vehicle or heavy equipment.

KNOWN DRUG INTERACTIONS

Consult a physician if you are taking any pharmaceutical drugs.

REFERENCES

Blumenthal M, et al. Ed. The Complete German Commission E Monographs.Austin, TX: American Botanical Council; 1998. Pg. 156.

Anonymous. Natural anxiolytics – Kava and L.72 antianxiety formula. The American Journal of Natural Medicine. 1994; 1(2): 10-14.

Pittler MH, Ernst E. Efficacy of kava extract for treating anxiety: systematic review and meta-analysis. J Clin Psychopharmacol. 2000;20(1):84-9

Fugh-Berman A, Cott JM. Dietary supplements and natural products as psychotherapeutic agents. Psychosom Med. 1999;61(5):712-28

Volz HP, Kieser M. Kava-kava extract WS 1490 versus placebo in anxiety disorders - a randomized placebo-controlled 25-week outpatient trial. Pharmacopsychiatry. 1997;30(1):1-5.

Milspaugh C. American Medicinal Plants. New York. Dover Publications.1974.

Clymer RS. Natures Healing Agents. Philadelphia. Dorrance and Company. 1963.

Snow JM. Hypericum perforatum L. (Hyperiaceae). The Protocol Journal Of Botanical Medicine. 1996; 2(1):16-21.

Hobbs C. St. John's Wort: Hypericum perforatum L. – A Review. Herbalgram. 1998/9; 18/19:24-33.

Woelk H. Comparison of St John's wort and imipramine for treating depression: randomised controlled trial. BMJ. 2000;321(7260):536-9.

Brenner R, Azbel V, Madhusoodanan S, Pawlowska M Comparison of an extract of hypericum (LI 160) and sertraline in the treatment of depression: a double-blind, randomized pilot study. Clin Ther 2000;22(4):411-9

Natural Medicines Comprehensive Database. "Passionflower Monograph." Online. Internet. [12/21/01]. Available WWW:http://www.naturaldatabase.com/monograph. asp?ph_img= mono2. gif&mono_id=871&hilite=12/22/2001

PROSTATE HEALTH

Supports Healthy Prostate Function*

ALCOHOL-FREE CONCENTRATED EXTRACTS OF:

FORMULA	MG EXTRACT PER 2 CAPSULES
Saw Palmetto berry, Supercritical CO_2 Extract (*Serenoa repens*)	320 mg
Nettle root (*Urtica dioica*)	80 mg
Pygeum bark (*Pygeum africanum*)	80 mg
Green Tea (*Camellia sinensis*)	80 mg
Pumpkin seed oil (*Curcubita pepo*)	80 mg
Tomato Skin Extract	20 mg
Lycopene Extract	15 mg
Rosemary leaf, Supercritical CO_2 Extract (*Rosmarinus officinalis*)	10 mg

STANDARDIZED TO FULL SPECTRUM ACTIVITY PROFILE

85% Fatty acids (from Saw Palmetto)	272 mg
Myricitin (from Tomato skins)	16 mg

DOSAGE

Liquid Phyto-Caps: 1 capsule, 2 times daily

DURATION OF USE

3 months

BEST TAKEN

Between meals, with warm water

DESCRIPTION OF FORMULA

Prostate Health provides an effective combination of well-researched herbal extracts and nutritive components in scientifically supported dosages and forms that are designed to function synergistically to maximize healthy prostate function.*

The prostate is a walnut–sized gland that sits at the base of the bladder, astride the urethra. Forming part of the reproductive system, the prostate gland secretes fluid that helps to make up semen, and functions to energize and alkalize sperm. Medical scientists know little more about this gland's function. What scientists do know is that an unhealthy prostate can cause discomforting feelings associated with a decline in healthy urinary function and sexual performance.

*THIS STATEMENT HAS NOT BEEN EVALUATED BY THE FOOD AND DRUG ADMINISTRATION. THIS PRODUCT IS NOT INTENDED TO DIAGNOSE, TREAT, CURE OR PREVENT ANY DISEASE.

The herbs and nutrients found in Prostate Health contain scientifically substantiated compounds recognized for their ability to support the health and function of the prostate gland.*

Saw palmetto is a native plant of North America. It is a member of the fan palm family and has characteristic sharp edges that can literally "saw" through clothing, hence its common name, saw- palm-etto. The plant produces a one seeded berry, dark brown to black in color, that is harvested and used in the preparation of phytomedicines. Traditionally used to support the healthy functioning of the prostate and maintain normal sexual drive in men, saw palmetto was appropriately referred to as "old man's friend." Research is now focused on the lipophilic physiologically active extracts of these berries, including beta-sitosterol, tri, di, and monoglycerides, and free fatty acids.*

These constituents maintain healthy urinary and prostate function by encouraging healthy testosterone levels and influencing fatty acid metabolism in favor of prostaglandins that maintain normal fluid levels in the body.*

Nettle root is from a plant that has a particular affinity for nitrate-rich soil, found in most temperate regions of the world. It has a high lignan content which researchers believe may be responsible for the root's ability to bind to sex hormone binding globulin (SHBG), a key to its ability to maintain prostate health. Androgens such as testosterone and estrogen bind to SHBG. And as men age, their SHBG levels increase, making them more susceptible to this binding. Nettle root has a strong affinity for SHBG, and promotes cell health by limiting the amount of testosterone and estrogen that can bind to it. Nettle root also modulates the effects of androgens by normalizing sodium-potassium ATPase and aromatase activity in prostate tissue.*

Nettle root extract is a popular herbal preparation in Germany, and its widespread use spurred the onset of numerous clinical trials over the past 10 years. Collectively, these trials, which include double blind, placebo-controlled clinical trials on up to 5,000 patients, demonstrate the benefits of using nettle root for normalizing SHBG levels and maintaining healthy urinary function in men.*

Pygeum bark contains phytosterols (including beta-sitosterol, beta-sitosterone and campesterol), ferulic esters of long chain fatty acids, and pentacyclic triterpenes that moderate prostaglandin and prolactin metabolism in the prostate and function to normalize cholesterol levels and protein kinase c activity. Collectively these actions support healthy prostate and bladder activity in men.*

Green tea shows tremendous promise in maintaining the health of the prostate gland. Researchers at the University of California Los Angeles reported that consumption of tea polyphenols, as found in green tea, for as little as five consecutive days, causes an increase in polyphenols in prostate tissue and a reduction in levels of polyamines, both actions supporting healthy prostate tissue. This data supports recent epidemiological and laboratory studies suggesting health-promoting actions of green tea on the prostate gland.*

*THIS STATEMENT HAS NOT BEEN EVALUATED BY THE FOOD AND DRUG ADMINISTRATION.
THIS PRODUCT IS NOT INTENDED TO DIAGNOSE, TREAT, CURE OR PREVENT ANY DISEASE.

Lycopene from tomato skin is a well-researched carotenoid used to support prostate health. Compared to other known carotenoids, lycopene is considered by experts to be one of the most potent antioxidants, with its unsurpassed singlet-oxygen quenching capacity. An impressive number of clinical trials and epidemiological studies demonstrate the statistically significant association between consumption of lycopene-containing foods and prostate health.*

Tomato skin extract contains another potent antioxidant, known as myricetin. This flavonol further enhances the singlet-oxygen quenching capabilities of lycopene. When compared to consuming tomato pulp, ingestion of tomato skin extract also results in a higher absorption of carotenoids, including lycopene, that support prostate health.*

Pumpkin seed oil is a valuable source of essential fatty acids (EFAs) and zinc, which are both important to maintaining healthy prostate function.*

Researchers have identified a direct correlation between healthy prostate function and normal EFA levels in the body. EFAs represent a group of essential fats that the body is incapable of manufacturing on its own. They include the omega 3 (linolenic) and omega 6 (linoleic) fatty acids. EFAs are required constituents of every membrane in the body, playing a crucial role in maintaining the health of every living cell in the body. They maintain the fluidity of cellular membranes, aid in producing and balancing hormones, and play an essential role in managing healthy fluid levels. The body metabolizes these fatty acids into a group of components known as prostaglandins. The word prostaglandin comes from the fact that these products of fatty acid metabolism were originally found in the prostate gland (prosta - gland - in). Prostaglandins regulate every organ system in the body.*

A deficiency in zinc, blocks the essential rate-limiting enzyme Delta-6-desaturase in the transformation of EFA's into the important prostaglandins. The prostate gland has a unique characteristic of storing high levels of zinc. In fact, healthy prostate tissue contains a higher concentration of zinc than all other tissue in the body. Not surprisingly, researchers have found that the level of zinc in the prostate gland declines dramatically when it is challenged, making pumpkin seed oil, with its high levels of both EFAs and zinc, an ideal source of fat for individuals interested in maintaining healthy prostate and urinary function.*

Rosemary leaf is a natural antioxidant that helps reduce the free-radical damage that occurs with aging.*

IMPORTANT INFORMATION REGARDING PROSTATE HEALTH

The American Cancer Society and the American Urological Association recommend that men begin testing to check for prostate cancer at age 50, and up to ten years earlier for individuals at higher risk (such as African Americans, individuals with a genetic predisposition to prostate disease and smokers). In addition, the National Institute on Aging recommends that men over age 40 receive a thorough prostate exam as a part of their annual physical.

COMPLEMENTARY PHYTO-CAPS/LIQUID FORMULAS/LIQUID EXTRACTS

Saw Palmetto Liquid Phyto-Caps™, Liqui-lieve Liquid Phyto-Caps™

SAFETY EVALUATION/CONTRAINDICATIONS

Before using this product, talk with your healthcare professional if you suffer from a medical condition. Please visit www.gaiaherbs.com to obtain information regarding potential contraindications and/or side effects that may be associated with herbs found in this formula.*

KNOWN DRUG INTERACTIONS

Before using this product, talk with your healthcare professional if you take any medications. Please visit www.gaiaherbs.com to obtain information regarding any possible drug interactions that may be associated with herbs found in this formula.*

REFERENCES

Agarwal, A; Shen, H; et al. Lycopene content of tomato products: Its stability, bioavailability and in vivo antioxidant properties. J Med Food 2001; 4(1):9-15.

Agarwal, S.; Rao, A.V. Tomato lycopene and its role in human health and chronic diseases. CMAJ 2000; 163(6):739-744.

American Cancer Society. Prostate Cancer.:Overview. 2005. http://www.cancer.org/docroot/CRI/CRI 2 1x.asp?rnav=criov&dt=36. Accessed 3/14/05.

Andro M-C, Riffaud J-P. Pygeum africanum extract for the treatment of patients with benign prostatic hyperplasia: A review of 25 years of published experience. Curr Ther Res 1995;56:796 [review].

Di Silverio F et al. Effects of long-term treatment with Serenoa repens (Permixon®) on the concentrations and regional distribution of androgens and epidermal growth factor in benign prostatic hyperplasia. Prostate 1998;37:77–83.

Giovannucci, E. Tomatoes, tomato-based products, lycopene, and cancer: Review of the epidemologic literature. J Natl Cancer Inst 1999; 91(4):317-331.

Henning S. Tea polyphenols slow prostate cancer cell growth. University of California, Los Angeles, Center for Human Nutrition report at Experimental Biology 2004 Washington, DC.

Jian L et al. Protective effect of green tea against prostate cancer: a case control study in southeast China. Int J Cancer 2004 Jan1;108(1):130-5.

Molina-Jimenez MF et al. Neuroprotective effect of fraxetin and myricetin against rotenone-induced apoptosis in neuroblastoma cells. Brain Res. 2004 May 29;1009(1-2):9-16.

National Institute on Aging Age Page: Prostate Problems. 2000. http://www.niapublications.org/engagepages/Cancer_Facts_for_People_Over_50.pdf. Accessed 3/14/05.

Sartor L Prostate carcinoma and green tea: (-)epigallocatechin-3-gallate inhibits inflammation-triggered MMP-2 activation and invasion in murine TRAMP model. Int J Cancer. 2004 Dec 10;112(5):823-9.

Schiebel-Schlosser G, Friederich M. Phytotherapy of BPH with pumpkin seeds–a multicenter clinical trial. Zeits Phytother 1998;19:71–6.

Sokeland J. Combined sabal and urtica extract compared with finasteride in men with benign prostatic hyperplasia: analysis of prostate volume and therapeutic outcome. BJU Int 2000 Sep;86(4):439-442.

*THIS STATEMENT HAS NOT BEEN EVALUATED BY THE FOOD AND DRUG ADMINISTRATION.
THIS PRODUCT IS NOT INTENDED TO DIAGNOSE, TREAT, CURE OR PREVENT ANY DISEASE.

Steenkamp V. Phytomedicines for the prostate. Fitoterapia 2003 Sep;74(6):545-52.

Strauch G et al. Comparison of finasteride (Proscar®) and Serenoa repens (Permixon®) in the inhibition of 5-alpha reductase in healthy male volunteers. Eur Urol 1994;26:247–52.

Wilt T et al. Pygeum africanum for benign prostate hyperplasia. Coch Data Syst Rev 2002;(1):CD001044.

Yang YJ et al. Comparison of fatty acid profiles in the serum of patients with prostate cancer and benign prostatic hyperplasia. Clin Biochem 1999; 32(6):405-9.

Zaichick VY et al. Zinc in the human prostate gland: normal hyperplastic and cancerous. Int Urol Nephrol 1997;29(5):565-74j7

QUICK DEFENSE

Maintains a Healthy Inflammatory Response*

ALCOHOL-FREE CONCENTRATED EXTRACTS OF:

FORMULA	MG EXTRACT PER 2 CAPSULES
Echinacea root (*E. angustifolia* & *E. purpurea*)	210 mg
Andrographis leaves (*Andrographis paniculata*)	100 mg
Black Elder berries (*Sambucus nigra*)	100 mg
Ginger rhizome supercritical extract (*Zingiber* off.)	10 mg
STANDARDIZED TO FULL SPECTRUM ACTIVITY PROFILE	
℞-A Factors (Total Alkylamides from Echinacea)	10 mg

DOSAGE

Liquid Phyto-Caps: Take 2 capsules 5 times daily for 2 days at onset. Repeat if necessary.

DURATION OF USE

4 days

BEST TAKEN

At onset, with warm water

DESCRIPTION OF FORMULA

When the respiratory tract experiences airborne stress, the immune system secretes specific inflammatory hormones that have far-reaching and detrimental effects on the body. In order to preclude this effect, it is important to support the inflammatory response. Quick Defense Liquid Phyto-Caps™ contain select herbs that are critical to enhancing the body's respiratory response to environmental stressors and supporting the epithelial cells that line the respiratory system. This unique formulation utilizing patent-pending extraction methods has produced a compounded formula that has a profound impact on the body and helps to maintain a healthy inflammatory response to respiratory stress.*

Echinacea root has long been used by Native American groups to support the respiratory functions during the winter season. However, the exact function of this plant has not been clearly understood until recently. Research conducted by Gaia Herbs, along with several universities and institutions, has elucidated compounds that have restructured our understanding of how Echinacea works. These compounds, identified and concentrated by Gaia Herbs, are called "℞-A Factors", which represent the specific alkylamide fractions known as isobutylamides. These concentrated alkylamide factors found primarily in the roots of the Echinacea angustifolia and Echinacea purpurea help maintain a healthy inflammatory response. "℞-A Factors" support the tissues of the sinus and throat cavity that are exposed to air-borne stressors, and balance an acutely challenged immune system.*

Regarded as an "Elder" plant in Native American Herbalism, the Elderberry has been used collectively by various tribes as a tonic medicine and food staple to promote overall health and vitality. It compliments the Quick Defense Liquid Phyto-Caps™ formula by supporting respiratory resistance through the promotion of free-radical quenching antioxidants rich in the fruit extracts. By providing powerful antioxidant protection from free-radical airborne elements, the Elderberry prevents damage to the cellular tissues of the body and promotes overall wellness to the respiratory apparatus.*

Andrographis is a traditional medicine that has been used extensively in India, China, and Thailand to support many functions of the body. In Traditional Chinese Medicine, Andrographis is considered a "cooling" herb and was often prescribed with warming herbs such as Ginger making this addition to the formula critical to restoring balance to the body. Recent clinical studies have confirmed this herb's ability to reestablish tissue integrity during respiratory crisis. Interestingly, the clinical data illustrated the wide scope of its potency when it suggested that Andrographis promotes both antigen-specific as well non-specific immunefunctions making this plant as versatile as it is potent.*

Ginger is highly valued in many traditions, including Ayurveda, and traditional Western herbalism for its soothing properties. Ginger rhizome is one of the most powerful botanical inhibitors of 5-lipoxygenase, an enzyme responsible for the production of pro-inflammatory prostaglandins and thromboxanes. By supporting a healthy inflammatory response, Ginger promotes wellness of the mucous membranes in the sinus cavity and respiratory system during times of challenge.*

Quick Defense Liquid Phyto-Caps™ is a compounded botanical preparation that utilizes historical wisdom with modern research to enhance the body's respiratory response to environmental stressors. By supporting the epithelial cells that line the respiratory system Quick Defense Liquid Phyto-Cap™ reinforces a healthy inflammatory response and hastens quick and vital improvement.*

*Note: The intention of this information is to represent the traditional use of the individual botanicals found in these formulas and to inform the reader of any evolving scientific inquiry relevant to the formula's ingredients.

The intention of this information is to represent the traditional use of the individual botanicals found in these formulas and to inform the reader of any evolving scientific inquiry relevant to the formula's ingredients.

SAFETY EVALUATION/CONTRAINDICATIONS

Before using this product, talk with your healthcare professional if you suffer from a medical condition. Please visit www.gaiaherbs.com to obtain information regarding potential contraindications and/or side effects that may be associated with herbs found in this formula.*

KNOWN DRUG INTERACTIONS

Before using this product, talk with your healthcare professional if you take any medications. Please visit www.gaiaherbs.com to obtain information regarding any possible drug interactions that may be associated with herbs found in this formula.*

REFERENCES

Bensky K, Gamble A: Chinese Herbal Medicine Materia Medica, Seattle, 1986, Eastland Press.

Caceres DD, Hancke JL, Burgos RA, et al. Use of visual analogue scale measurements (VAS) to assess the effectiveness of standardized Andrographis paniculata extract SHA-10 in reducing the symptoms. Phytomedicine 1999;6:217-23.

Langner E, Greifenberg S, Gruenwald J. Ginger: history and use. Adv Ther 1998;15:25-44.

Mascolo N et al: J Ethnopharmacol 58(1):59-73, 1997.

Raduner S, et al. Alkylamides from Echinacea are a new class of cannabinomimetics. Cannabinoid type 2 receptor-dependent and -independent immunomodulatory effects, J Biol Chem. 2006 May 19; 281(20):14192-206.

Subauste M, Jacoby D, Richards S, Proud D: Induction of Cytokine Release and Modulation of Susceptibility to Infection by Cytokine Exposure, Johns Hopkins Asthma and Allergy Center, Baltimore, Maryland 21224-6801.

Vogel VJ: American Indian Medicine, Norman, OK, 1970, University of Oklahoma Press.

RESPIRATORY DEFENSE

Ultimate Support for Healthy Upper Respiratory Function*

ALCOHOL-FREE CONCENTRATED EXTRACTS OF:

FORMULA	MG EXTRACT PER 3 CAPSULES
Osha root (*Ligusticum porteri*)	96 mg
Garlic bulb (*Allium sativum*)	60 mg
Grindelia floral bud (*Grindelia robusta*)	33 mg
Irish Moss flakes (*Chondrus crispus*)	21 mg
Hyssop flowers (*Hyssopus* off.)	15 mg
Barberry root bark (*Berberis vulgaris*)	12 mg
Oregon Grape root (*Berberis aquifolium*)	12 mg
Goldenseal rhizome (*Hydrastis canadensis*)	12 mg
Mullein leaf (*Verbascum* spp.)	12 mg
Lobelia herb & seed (*Lobelia inflata*)	9 mg
St. John's Wort flower bud (*Hypericum perforatum*)	9 mg
Echinacea purpurea root	6 mg
Echinacea purpurea flowering top	6 mg
Echinacea angustifolia root	4.5 mg
Echinacea purpurea seed	1.05 mg

DOSAGE

Short term: 1 capsule 3-4 times daily

Long term: 1-2 capsules two to three times per day

DURATION OF USE

Short term: 5-14 days

Long term: 3-4 months

BEST TAKEN

Between meals with warm water

MAXIMIZING BENEFITS

Humans are constantly exposed to viruses and bacteria. Despite our best efforts it is almost impossible to avoid contact with at least some of these, and many people end up with what is known as the common cold. The winter months generally increase such exposures, in part because people spend more time indoors and in contact with another. However, many people who are exposed to viruses and bacteria do not develop a common cold. This is likely due to their

*THIS STATEMENT HAS NOT BEEN EVALUATED BY THE FOOD AND DRUG ADMINISTRATION. THIS PRODUCT IS NOT INTENDED TO DIAGNOSE, TREAT, CURE OR PREVENT ANY DISEASE.

immune system's defense against infection. Respiratory Defense supports the body's natural defense, by combining several healing herbs together to support healthy immune function and to maintain a healthy respiratory tract.

Osha root is another Pacific West plant that grows only in high elevation. It has an excellent reputation for promoting health in the respiratory system. It is included here because of this reputation. Scientific research does not yet exist for this valuable plant.*

Garlic bulb is mentioned in some of the oldest written records that exist, dating back to 2,600 BC in the Middle East. Its reputation in traditional cultures is vast, especially for its effect in maintaining health in the respiratory system. Studies show that garlic does help support immune function. It doesn't hurt that garlic also helps support a healthy cardiovascular system.*

Grindelia buds contain an aromatic resin that is considered to be an important tonic for the lungs. The resins specifically support the activity of mucous membranes in the respiratory tract.*

Irish Moss (actually a lichen and not a moss) is used traditionally for supporting respiratory health in European herbalism. There has been little study of this interesting lichen in modern times.*

Hyssop herb is used as a flavoring in liquors and candies, attesting to its pleasant taste. It is often used as a bath herb as well. Folk use of this pleasing plant focused on mild calming properties and gentle respiratory support. It is considered safe for children, a positive since they tend to like the taste!*

Barberry root is a bitter tonic that pharmacologically shares many properties with Goldenseal and Oregon Grape root. As one may expect of plants with closely related chemistry, the traditional use of Barberry is also similar to other berberine containing plants.*

Oregon Grape root has a history of traditional use closely resembling that of Goldenseal. It also soothes and strengthens mucous membranes and contains the alkaloid berberine, with immune stimulating properties*

Goldenseal rhizome and root is another plant native to North America. It has traditionally been used to soothe the mucous membranes. Goldenseal contains the immunostimulatory alkaloid, Berberine.*

Mullein leaf and flower are listed by the German Commission E to support a healthy respiratory tract. This vindicates its traditional use to soothe and promote health in the respiratory system.*

Lobelia herb & seed were considered by the Eclectic physicians in the late nineteenth century to be one of the most important plants. They utilized it to strengthen and relieve spasm in the respiratory system. It is surprising, given the high regard and widespread use of Lobelia, that there is so little investigation of its properties in modern research. This is likely due to the fact that in overdose it can cause nausea. Researchers likely overlooked the traditional method of giving small amounts of Lobelia in combination with other herbs to avoid the side effects while maximizing its benefits.*

St. John's Wort flower buds have been used traditionally for more than 2,000 years. It is utilized here for its harmonizing effect and for its support to nervous system health.*

It has been said that Native Americans used Echinacea to treat more conditions than any other remedy. The Eclectic medical doctors, from the first half of the last century, also praised Echinacea for its benefits to the respiratory tract. Today, modern science is beginning to support much of its established traditional use, by showing that extracts of Echinacea spp. have the ability to strengthen immune function. Research has further shown that alcohol/water extracts of Echinacea significantly enhance natural killer cell function, and have phagocytic and metabolic influence on macrophages. This simply means that Echinacea has the potential to non-specifically activate your immune system. In other words, your normal immune response is enhanced.*

Note: The intention of this information is to represent the traditional use of the individual botanicals found in these formulas and to inform the reader of any evolving scientific inquiry relevant to the formula's ingredients.

COMPLEMENTARY PHYTO-CAPS/LIQUID FORMULAS/LIQUID EXTRACTS

Short term: Echinacea Supreme Liquid Phyto-Caps™, Quick Defense Liquid Phyto-Caps™ (for optimum immune system support)

Long term: Anti-Oxidant Supreme Liquid Phyto-Caps™, Energy & Vitality Liquid Phyto-Caps™, Olive Leaf Liquid Phyto-Caps™

SAFETY EVALUATION/CONTRAINDICATIONS

Do not use during pregnancy or lactation. If a skin rash appears while taking the formula, its used should be discontinued and a physician knowledgeable in herbal medicine consulted. If nausea occurs, the formula should be taken with food. If nausea persists, the amount taken should be decreased by half. If vomiting occurs, the formula should be discontinued and a physician knowledgeable in herbal medicine should be consulted.

DRUG INTERACTIONS

Consult a physician if taking any pharmaceutical drugs.

REFERENCES

Moore M. Medicinal Plants of the Pacific West. Santa Fe: Red Crane Books, 1993.

Moore M. Medicinal Plants of the Mountain West. Santa Fe: Museum of New Mexico Press, 1979.

Carlson JH, Douglas HG. Antibiotic agents separated from the root of lace-leaved leptotaenia. J Bacteriol 1948;55:615-21.

Curtin LSM; Moore M (ed). Healing Herbs of the Upper Rio Grande: Traditional Medicine of the Southwest. Santa Fe: Western Edge Press, 1947, reprinted 1997:121-4.

Koch HP, Lawson LD (eds). Garlic: The Science and Therapeutic Application of Allium sativum L and Related Species, 2nd ed. Baltimore: Williams & Wilkins, 1996:1-24.

Reuter HD. Allium sativum and Allium ursinum: part 2. Pharmacology and medicinal application. Phytomedicine 1995;2:73-91.

Salman H, Bergman M, Bessler H, et al. Effect of a garlic derivative (alliin) on peripheral blood cell immune responses. Int J Immunopharmacol 1999;21:589-97.

Warshafsky S, Kamer RS, Sivak SL. Effect of garlic on total serum cholesterol: A meta-analysis. Ann Intern Med 1993;119:599-605.

Blumenthal M, Busse WR, Goldberg A, et al. (eds). The Complete German Commission E Monographs: Therapeutic Guide to Herbal Medicines. Austin: American Botanical Council and Boston: Integrative Medicine Communications, 1998:173.

Zgórniak-Nowosielska I, Grzybek J, Manolova N, et al. Antiviral activity of flos verbasci infusion against influenza and herpes simplex viruses. Arch Immunol Ther Exp 1991;39:103-8.

Hoffmann D. The Complete Illustrated Herbal. New York: Barnes & Noble Books, 1996:100.

Barrett B. Echinacea for upper respiratory infection: An assessment of randomized trials. HealthNotes Review of Complementary and Integrative Medicine 2000;7:211-8.

Zgórniak-Nowosielska I, Grzybek J, Manolova N, et al. Antiviral activity of flos verbasci infusion against influenza and herpes simplex viruses. Arch Immunol Ther Exp 1991;39:103-8.

Amin AH, Subbaiah TV, Abbasi KM. Berberine sulfate: Antimicrobial activity, bioassay, and mode of action. Can J Microbiol 1969:15:1067-76

(SIBERIAN) RHODIOLA ROSEA

(Rhodiola rosea)

Support for the Body's Adaptogenic Response to Stress*

ALCOHOL-FREE CONCENTRATED EXTRACTS OF:

FORMULA	MG PER 2 CAPSULES
Rhodiola Rosea root (*Rhodiola rosea*)	400 mg

STANDARDIZED TO FULL SPECTRUM ACTIVITY PROFILE

Rosavins	12 mg
Salidrosides	3.2 mg

DOSAGE
1 Liquid Phyto-Cap 2 times daily.

DURATION OF USE
3-4 months

BEST TAKEN
Between meals, with a small amount of warm water.

HISTORY

The fragrant rhodiola rosea root, also known as roseroot, has been used throughout history in Iceland, Sweden, France, Russia, and Greece. Popular with the Vikings to enhance mental and physical endurance, this revered adaptogen was included in the first Swedish Pharmacopeia. In addition, the respected Greek physician, Dioscorides, discussed the virtues of this root in his De Materia Medica discourse in the first century A.D.*

More recently, rhodiola rosea was re-discovered by a Soviet soldier in Afghanistan by the name of Dr. Zakir Ramazanov. What he discovered was that care packages from his fellow soldier's moms included this prized plant, which he found helped them and him to reduce stress and bolster mental and physical energy.*

Consequently, this root is now being studied at universities throughout the world. And what researchers are discovering is that this popular general tonic serves to promote health and vitality by supporting mental and physical endurance and encouraging overall metabolic efficiency.*

It contains an assortment of chemical constituents; the most well researched being the rosavins and salidrosides that encourage a healthy brain, immune system and hormonal balance.*

RHODIOLA AND STRESS

Rhodiola rosea reduces cortisol levels while optimizing levels of key brain chemicals involved in mood, such as serotonin and dopamine, that function together to maintain a healthy response to stress.*

When experiencing stress, in any form, the adrenal glands secrete specific hormones that have a profound effect on the body. One can imagine the adrenal glands as little hats that sit on top of the two kidneys. These hats secrete hormones such as cortisol in response to stress. Over time, as one experiences stress on a daily basis, the adrenal glands can function less optimally with respect to the secretion of these stress-related hormones. This can lead to something called adrenal stress, which means that the adrenal glands are overworked. Things such as nervousness, poor memory, cravings for sweets, weight gain, fatigue and compromised sleep are all associated with an upset in the levels of these hormones-either too much, or too little.*

Rhodiola rosea root supports the functioning of the adrenal glands and encourages a healthy response to physical, emotional and mental stress by normalizing cortisol levels and other stress-related hormones. If used regularly, it functions to enhance the body's natural resistance and adaptation to stressful influences.*

A TRUE ADAPTOGEN

Fittingly, rhodiola rosea is classified as an adaptogen, which represents a class of herbs that help the body adapt to stresses of various kinds. In order to achieve this classification, a plant must be harmless and it must have a normalizing, broad-spectrum action that brings the body back to homeostasis, particularly when under stressful influences.*

A remarkable characteristic of this herbal extract is that rhodiola rosea optimizes attention span and the capacity to learn, while at the same time encouraging a calm and relaxed emotional state.*

POSITIVE ADAPTOGEN EFFECTS OF RHODIOLA

- Supports healthy emotional levels & resistance to stress
- Helps maintain physical energy & mental alertness
- Supports normal sleep patterns & appetite
- Helps maintain healthy sexual function for men & women
- Promotes healthy cardiovascular function by helping maintain normal emotional balance

COMPLEMENTARY PHYTO-CAPS/LIQUID FORMULAS/LIQUID EXTRACTS

Adrenal Health Liquid Phyto-Caps™, Eleuthero Root Liquid Phyto-Caps™

SAFETY EVALUATION/CONTRAINDICATIONS

Do not take during pregnancy or lactation.*

KNOWN DRUG INTERACTIONS

There are no known drug interactions with this herb. Before using this product, talk with your healthcare professional if you take any medications.*

REFERENCES

Brown RP, Gerbarg PL, Ramazanov Z. Rhodiola rosea: a phytomedicinal overview. Herbalgram 2002;56:40–52.

Darbinyan V, Kteyan A, Panossian A, et al. Rhodiola rosea in stress induced fatigue - a double blind cross-over study of a standardized extract SHR-5 with a repeated low-dose regimen on the mental performance of healthy physicians during night duty. Phytomedicine 2000;7(5):365-71.

Petkov VD, Yonkov D, Mosharoff A, et al. Effects of alcohol aqueous extract from Rhodiola rosea L. roots on learning and memory. Acta Physiol Pharmacol Bulg 1986;12(1):3-16.

Spasov AA, Wikman GK, Mandrikov VB, et al. A double-blind, placebo-controlled pilot study of the stimulating and adaptogenic effect of Rhodiola rosea SHR-5 extract on the fatigue of students caused by stress during an examination period with a repeated low-dose regimen. Phytomedicine 2000;7(2):85-89.

SAW PALMETTO

(Serenoa repens)

Ultimate Support of Prostate Health*

ALCOHOL-FREE CONCENTRATED EXTRACT OF:

SAW PALMETTO	MG EXTRACT PER 2 CAPS
(*Serenoa repens*)	
Supercritical CO_2 extract	376 mg

STANDARDIZED TO FULL SPECTRUM ACTIVITY PROFILE

Fatty acids (from Saw Palmetto)	320 mg
Fatty acids (from Soy Lecithin)	300-500 mg

DOSAGE
1 liquid Phyto-Cap, 2 times daily

DURATION OF USE
4-6 months

BEST TAKEN
Between meals, with warm water

HISTORY

Saw Palmetto is a small shrub native to the Southeastern United States. Native Americans used the berries as both a food and a remedy. Saw Palmetto was official in the National Formulary from 1926-1950 and was also found in the 23rd edition of the United States Dispensatory. Whereas it fell out of favor in the United

*THIS STATEMENT HAS NOT BEEN EVALUATED BY THE FOOD AND DRUG ADMINISTRATION. THIS PRODUCT IS NOT INTENDED TO DIAGNOSE, TREAT, CURE OR PREVENT ANY DISEASE.

States, physicians in Europe continued to utilize this invaluable herb. In Germany today, it's one of the top ten herbals prescribed by physicians.*

A RELEVANT HERBAL FOR MEN

Saw Palmetto has been the focus of numerous clinical studies that have pointed toward its effectiveness in supporting proper function of the prostate. This is especially relevant for men over the age of 50, to help maintain normal function of the prostate.

One of the first double-blind studies of Saw Palmetto involved 110 patients. A significant number of subjects showed normalization in urinary and prostate health. The extract was well tolerated. An open trial with 505 subjects demonstrated similar results. After 90 days of treatment, 88% of the patients felt the therapy was effective.

Another large double-blind, randomized international study followed 1,098 men for 6 months. Saw Palmetto supported urinary flow rate and improved quality of life. The study suggested that Saw Palmetto is effective in promoting prostate health. Additionally, 6% of the men in the Saw Palmetto group felt their sexual function had improved.

A recent meta-analysis of 18 randomized trials concluded that Saw Palmetto supports urinary and prostate health, along with exerting a positive effect on sexual function.

MECHANISM OF ACTION

The mechanism of action of Saw Palmetto is not yet fully understood. As with most herbals, Saw Palmetto's effectiveness is probably the result of several differing actions. Possible explanations include inhibition of 5-alpha reductase, anti-estrogenic activity in prostate tissue, prostate volume reduction, and alpha 1-adrenergic receptor antagonism.

COMPLEMENTARY PHYTO-CAPS/LIQUID FORMULAS/LIQUID EXTRACTS

Nettle root, Saw Palmetto Supreme, Prostate Health Liquid Phyto-Caps™

SAFETY EVALUATION/CONTRAINDICATIONS

Do not use during pregnancy and lactation.

KNOWN DRUG INTERACTIONS

Consult a physician if you are taking any pharmaceutical drug.

REFERENCES

Wood HC and Osol A. United States Dispensatory, 23rd Edition. Philadelphia. JP Lippincott; 1943:971-972.

Schulz V, et al. Rational Phytotherapy. New York; Springer-Verlag; 1998: 288.

Champault G, et al. A double-blind trail of an extract of the plant serona repens in benign prostatic hyperplasia. British Journal of Clinical Pharmac. 1984;18:461-462.

Braeckman J. The extract of serenoa repens in the treatment of benign prostatic hyperplasia: A multicenter open study. Current Therapeutic Research. 1994; 55(7): 776-784.

Carraro JC, et al. Comparison of phytotherapy (permixon) with finasteride in the treatment of benign prostatic hyperplasia: a randomized international study of 1,098 patients. Prostate. 1996; 29 (4): 231-240.

Wilt TJ, et al. Saw Palmetto extracts for the treatment of benign prostatic hyperplasia: A systematic review. JAMA. 1998; 280 (18): 1604-1609.

Niederprüm HJ, et al. Testosterone 5-reductase inhibition by fatty acids from sabal serrulata fruits. Phytomedicine. 1994;1: 127-133.

DiSilverio F, et al. Evidence that serenoa repens extract displays an antiestrogenic activity in prostatic tissue of benign prostatic hypertrophy patients. European Urology 1992; 21: 309-314.

Goepel M, et al. Saw Palmetto extracts potently and noncompetively inhibit human (1- adrenoceptors in vitro. Prostate. 1999; 38:208-215.

Gerber GS, et al. Saw Palmetto (serenoa repens) in men with lower urinary tract symptoms: effects on urodynamic parameters and voiding symptoms. Urology. 1998; 51: 1003-1007.

Plosker GL and Brogden RN. Serenoa repens (permixon). A review of its pharmacology and therapeutic efficacy in benign prostatic hyperplasia. Drugs Aging. 1996; 9(5): 379-395.

Blumenthal M, et al. The Complete German Commission E Monographs: Therapeutic Guide to Herbal Medicines. Austin. American Botanical Council; 1998. Page 201.

Carilla E, et al. Binding of permixon, a new treatment for prostatic benign hyperplasia, to the cytosolic androgen receptor in rat prostate. Journal Steroid Biochem. 1984; 20: 521-523.

Sultan C, et al. Inhibition of androgen metabolism and binding by a liposterolic extract of Serenoa repens B in human foreskin fibroblasts. Journal Steroid Biochem. 1984; 20: 515-519.

SERENITY WITH KAVA KAVA

For Ultimate Support of Relaxation*

ALCOHOL-FREE CONCENTRATED EXTRACTS OF:

FORMULA	MG EXTRACT PER 3 CAPSULES
Skullcap herb (*Scutellaria lateriflora*)	60 mg
Passionflower vine (*Passiflora incarnata*)	60 mg
Kava Kava rhizome (*Piper methysticum*)	60 mg
Chamomile flowers (*Matricaria recutita*)	45 mg
Wild Oats milky seed (*Avena sativa*)	27 mg
Hops strobile (*Humulus lupulus*)	24 mg
Mugwort herb (*Artemisia vulgaris*)	15 mg
Peppermint leaf (*Mentha piperita*)	9 mg

DOSAGE
Liquid Phyto-Caps: 1 capsule, 3 times daily

DURATION OF USE
3-4 months

BEST TAKEN
Between meals, with warm water

*THIS STATEMENT HAS NOT BEEN EVALUATED BY THE FOOD AND DRUG ADMINISTRATION. THIS PRODUCT IS NOT INTENDED TO DIAGNOSE, TREAT, CURE OR PREVENT ANY DISEASE.

A SOOTHING CHARM

This calming formula works not only as a nervous relaxant, but also as a nervous system strengthener, particularly where overwork and stress play a role. Additionally, botanicals that help with anxiety and support digestion have been incorporated to ease these often seen but unwanted manifestations of stress. This formula works like a soothing charm, and has almost immediate influence.

American Skullcap was used extensively by the early Eclectic healers of the last century as a nutritive tonic and a soothing agent. It was said to be especially useful for nervous stress, particularly when manifested as "excitability, restlessness, or wakefulness". Skullcap has been brought into this formula for its specific use with nervousness from mental or physical stress. It is this highly specific use that makes Skullcap an excellent addition to this stress formula.*

Passionflower vine shares with American Skullcap its traditional use as a soothing remedy for nervous excitement and irritability. When mental worry and weariness are evident, the Passionflower is considered specific. The monograph published by Germany's Commission E lists Passionflower for use with nervous restlessness. In addition, there is some evidence to suggest that Passionflower provides support during times of anxiety.*

Kava Kava is often used for support during nervous anxiety. Used traditionally to elevate the mind and relax the body, Kava has been the subject of numerous clinical trials for the treatment of nervous anxiety.*

Chamomile flowers are considered soothing, with specific influence on digestion. Matricaria, the first of Chamomile's scientific names, comes from the root word 'matrix', meaning womb or mother. This reflects the opinion that it is particularly useful in supporting female reproductive health. A surprising amount of research exists for this botanical that is often considered mild - science being more inclined to research powerful, pharmacologically vociferous plants. It is, however, extremely reliable and is placed in this Serenity formula for its calming effect with restlessness and irritability, particularly where there is a need for support with digestion and flatulence.*

Wild Oats are considered supportive to nervous system health, specific for those individuals who experience nervous exhaustion. This use is reflective of its traditionally espoused ability to restore the "wasted elements of nerve force." Wild Oats is another plant that has received official mention by the German Commission E, in this case for (temporary) anxiety, stress, and weakness. It also is discussed as a restorative tonic.*

Hops strobiles are used traditionally for nervous irritation and wakefulness, chiefly where temporary anxiety and worry are the cause. The German Commission E monograph mentions Hops for restlessness and anxiety, as well as for enhancement of sleep function. Hops was used historically to encourage digestion and to promote healthy cerebro-spinal function. Hops serves this formula as a valued relaxing and restorative tonic.*

*THIS STATEMENT HAS NOT BEEN EVALUATED BY THE FOOD AND DRUG ADMINISTRATION.
THIS PRODUCT IS NOT INTENDED TO DIAGNOSE, TREAT, CURE OR PREVENT ANY DISEASE.

Mugwort also receives mention by the German Commission E as a calmative plant, for use with (temporary) restlessness, anxiety, and sleeplessness. Similar to a number of other plants in this formula, Mugwort promotes healthy digestion, thereby assisting with an increase in overall vitality.*

Peppermint possesses a soothing action, promotes healthy digestion, and helps to relieve intestinal bloating and flatulence. The German Commission E has stated that Peppermint supports digestion and promotes liver health.*

COMPLEMENTARY PHYTO-CAPS/LIQUID FORMULAS/LIQUID EXTRACTS

Skullcap/St. John's Wort Supreme, Melissa Supreme

KNOWN DRUG INTERACTIONS

Consult a physician if you are taking any pharmaceutical drugs.

SAFETY EVALUATION/CONTRAINDICATIONS

Do not use this product during pregnancy or lactation.

Caution: US FDA advises that a potential risk of rare, but severe, liver injury may be associated with kava-containing dietary supplements. Ask a healthcare professional before use if you have or have had liver problems, frequently use alcoholic beverages, or are taking any medication. Stop use and see a doctor if you develop symptoms that may signal liver problems, including jaundice (yellowing of the skin or whites of the eyes) and brown urine. Other nonspecific symptoms can include nausea, vomiting, light-colored stools, unexplained tiredness, weakness, stomach or abdominal pain, and loss of appetite. Not for use by persons under 18 years of age, or by pregnant or breastfeeding women. Not for use with alcoholic beverages. Excessive use, or use with products that cause drowsiness, may impair your ability to operate a vehicle or heavy equipment

REFERENCES

Blumenthal M, et al. Ed. The Complete German Commission E Monographs.Austin, TX: American Botanical Council; 1998.

Harrison T. Savage civilization. New York: Alfred A. Knopf; 1937

Anonymous. Natural anxiolytics – Kava and L.72 antianxiety formula. The American Journal of Natural Medicine. 1994; 1(2): 10-14.

Witchl M. (Bisset NG, Ed.) Herbal Drugs and Phytopharmaceuticals. Medpharm, CRC Press: Boca Raton. 1994.

Priest AW, Priest LR. Herbal medication. A clinical dispensary handbook. 1982.

Pittler MH, et al. Efficacy of Kava extract for treating Anxiety: Systematic review and meta-analysis. J Clin Psychopharmacology. 2000; 20: 84-89.

SKIN & NAIL SUPPORT

WITH GOTU KOLA AND SILICA

Supports Radiant and Vital Skin and Nails*

ALCOHOL-FREE CONCENTRATED EXTRACTS OF:

FORMULA	MG EXTRACT PER 2 CAPSULES
Triphala Powder Extract Blend consisting of: (*Emblica officinalis, Terminalia bellerica, Terminalia chebula*)	200 mg
Horsetail aerial parts (*Equisetum arvense*)	150 mg
Alfalfa aerial parts (*Medicago sativa*)	60 mg
Gotu Kola leaf & root (*Centella asiatica*)	42 mg
Yellow Dock root (*Rumex crispus*)	26 mg
Nettle leaf (*Urica dioica*)	22 mg
Burdock root (*Arctium lappa*)	17 mg
Figwort aerial parts (*Scrophularia nodosa*)	6 mg
Oregon Grape root (*Berberis aquifolium*)	5 mg
Astaxanthin	4 mg
Horsetail, Nettle & Alfalfa mineral ash	

STANDARDIZED TO FULL SPECTRUM ACTIVITY PROFILE:

Silica (from Horsetail)	50 mg
Total Triterpenoids (from Gotu Kola)	3.2 mg

DOSAGE

Liquid Phyto-Caps: 2 capsules, 2 times daily

DURATION OF USE

3-6 months

BEST TAKEN

Between meals with a small amount of warm water.

VIBRANT SKIN AND NAILS

Numerous botanicals are used to support the healthy growth and strength of skin, nails, and connective tissue. In part, the explanation for these effects has been that the plants contain minerals essential for tissue healing, such as silica. Skin health is also intimately tied with health in other systems, especially digestive, urinary, cardiovascular, lymphatic and liver. Supporting these systems indirectly encourages healthy skin. While tradition is rich with recorded uses of

*THIS STATEMENT HAS NOT BEEN EVALUATED BY THE FOOD AND DRUG ADMINISTRATION. THIS PRODUCT IS NOT INTENDED TO DIAGNOSE, TREAT, CURE OR PREVENT ANY DISEASE.

plants for skin health, several of these herbs have yet to be studied in modern clinical trials. As such, this formula is based primarily on traditional uses of the following plants.*

Triphala extract is an Ayurvedic remedy combining the fruits of three antioxidant and soothing herbs: Terminalia chebula, Terminalia bellerica, and Phyllanthus emblica. Triphala is used as a digestive tonic and to support the skin in Ayurvedic medicine.*

Horsetail herb and ash from the roasted plant contains silica in significant quantities, a nutrient important for healthy skin and nails. Horsetail is regarded as a useful tonic for connective tissue and has a mild supportive effect to the urinary system.*

Alfalfa leaf contains phytoestrogens and is also nutrient dense. It provides hormonal and nutritional support for the skin. Alfalfa appreciates wide use as a skin and hair tonic.*

Gotu Kola leaf & root have long been used to support the health of skin, hair, and nails in Asia. Numerous clinical trials have shown that Gotu Kola indeed has numerous beneficial dermatologic effects. These supporting actions include increased integrity of skin tissue, connective tissue maintenance, increased formation of connective tissue structural components, and increased keratization of the skin. Additionally, Gotu Kola supports capillary strength and circulation. Finally, Gota Kola is shown to be supportive for the liver.*

Yellow Dock root (Rumex crispus) has a long history of maintaining skin health. It supports skin and nails by optimizing digestion. It also supports lymphatic and liver function. This helps by reducing the toxins processed out through the skin.*

Nettle leaf and its ash are phytonutrient and mineral dense. Nettle was used traditionally to support healthy hair and skin. It is also used for supporting healthy joints, and as a mild tonic to the urinary system.*

Burdock root is a popular food in Japan, known as Gobo. It has similar properties and uses to Yellow Dock. It has also been used topically for maintaining hair health.*

Figwort herb is an alterative and astringent herb historically used to soothe and support the health of skin and mucosal membranes.*

Oregon Grape root is considered a useful tonic for the entire digestive tract, and has indirect benefits for maintaining healthy skin. Topically, it shows promise in double-blind trials for supporting skin health. This is probably related to its soothing and immuno-modulating benefits.*

Astaxanthin is an antioxidant carotenoid. This ingredient also enjoys some scientific research. It appears to help protect the skin and have other supportive benefits. It may also maintain normal growth patterns of skin cells and regulate the immune system.*

Alfalfa ash is a highly prized mineral rich food, and by special processing delivers key nutrients to the formula such as silica, calcium, potassium and zinc in order to enhance skin and hair integrity.*

COMPLEMENTARY PHYTO-CAPS/LIQUID FORMULAS/LIQUID EXTRACTS

Liver Health Liquid Phyto-Caps™, Milk Thistle/Yellow Dock Supreme, Red Clover Supreme

SAFETY EVALUATION/CONTRAINDICATIONS

Do not take during pregnancy or lactation.

KNOWN DRUG INTERACTIONS

Please consult a physician if you are taking any pharmaceutical drugs.

REFERENCES

Felter HW, Lloyd JU. King's American Dispensatory 2 vols., 18th ed. Portland OR: Eclectic Medical Publications, 1898, 1983.

Weiss RF. Herbal Medicine. Gothenburg, Sweden: Ab Arcanum, 1988.

Geller CA. Skin therapies using herbs. 1995 Gaia Symposium Proceedings: Naturopathic Herbal Wisdom. 35-39.

Wiesenauer M, Lüdtke R. Mahonia aquifolium in patients with psoriasis vulgaris--an intraindividual study. Phytomedicine 1996;3:231-5.

Maher TJ. Astaxanthin continuing education module. New Hope Institute of Retailing. August 2000:1-8.

Lemmo EA. Silica: The Mineral Building Block That Promotes Healthy Bone and Connective Tissue and Helps Prevent Premature Aging and Cardiovascular and Alzheimer's Diseases. New Canaan, CT: Keats Publishing, 1998.

Moore M. Medicinal Plants of the Pacific West. Santa Fe: Red Crane Books, 1993.

Blumenthal M, Busse WR, Goldberg A, et al. (eds). The Complete German Commission E Monographs: Therapeutic Guide to Herbal Medicines. Austin: American Botanical Council and Boston: Integrative Medicine Communications, 1998.

Kartnig. Clinical Applications of Centella asiatica (L.) Urb. Herbs Spices Med Plants. 1988; 3: 146-73.

Kapoor. Handbook of Ayurvedic Medicinal Plants. FL: CRC, 1990.

Murray, M. The Healing Power of Herbs. CA. Prima, 1995.

Belcaro, et. al. Improvement of Capillary Permeability in Patients with Venous Hypertension After Treatment with TTFCA. Angiology. 1990; July, 533-40.

Nadkarni AK, Nadkarni KM. Indian Materia Medica. Bombay: Popular Prakashan, 1976.

Kurashige M, Okimasu E, Inoue M, Utsumi K. Inhibition of oxidative injury of biological membranes by astaxanthin. Physiol Chem Phys Med N M R 1990;22:27-38.

Hoffman D. The Holistic Herbal. Scotland: Findhorn Press, 1986.

SOUND SLEEP

Ultimate Support for Refreshing and Revitalizing Sleep*

ALCOHOL-FREE CONCENTRATED EXTRACTS OF:

FORMULA	MG EXTRACT PER 2 CAPSULES
Valerian root (*Valeriana officinalis*)	150 mg
GABA (Gamma aminobutyric acid)	106 mg
L-glycine	106 mg
Kava Kava root (*Piper methysticum*)	26 mg
Passionflower vine (*Passiflora incarnata*)	18 mg
California Poppy (*Eschscholzia californica*)	16 mg
Skullcap herb (*Scutellaria lateriflora*)	12 mg
Hops strobile (*Humulus lupulus*)	12 mg

DOSAGE

Liquid Phyto-Caps: 2 capsules with a small amount of warm water

DURATION OF USE

3-4 months

BEST TAKEN

1 hour before bed

FORMULA FOR HEALTHY SLEEP

This formula brings together a number of herbal plants that are recognized for their beneficial application in addressing difficulty with sleep. This compound works to reduce the anxiety, irritability, restlessness, physical tension, and worry that one will often see associated with occasional sleeplessness. This compound may also be used at times when nervous excitement and anxiety affect normal and healthy sleep function.

Valerian root has reportedly been used since around the time of Christ to induce sleep. Today, the highly respected German Commission E notes its use for restlessness and nervous disturbances of sleep. The World Health Organization (WHO) also suggests its use as a sleep-promoting herb, stating that it is often used in the treatment of occasional nervous excitement and disturbances of sleep, when associated with anxiety. This has been further suggested by other sources.*

GABA & L-glycine have been included in this formula due to the benefits reported by the highly respected clinician, Dr. Bill Mitchell, ND. In combination, they are reputed to possess a mild calming quality that supports the overall function of this formula.*

*THIS STATEMENT HAS NOT BEEN EVALUATED BY THE FOOD AND DRUG ADMINISTRATION. THIS PRODUCT IS NOT INTENDED TO DIAGNOSE, TREAT, CURE OR PREVENT ANY DISEASE.

Kava Kava is well known for its relaxing effect. Used traditionally to elevate the mind and relax the body, it is said that when consuming Kava, you "feel friendly" and "cannot hate." Numerous clinical trials have supported the use of Kava for the treatment of nervous anxiety. In fact, the German Commission E approves Kava for 'conditions of nervous anxiety, stress and restlessness'! Kava is used here to address the stress and anxiety that can often prevent someone from obtaining deep, restful sleep.*

Passionflower is another example of a plant that has traditionally been reported to induce sleep by its calming or quieting influence. It has also traditionally been used to support the nervous system. Passionflower has been approved by the highly regarded European Scientific Co-operative on Phytotherapy (ESCOP) for "tenseness, restlessness and irritability with difficulty in falling asleep."*

California poppy has received wide acknowledgement from a number of respected clinicians for use as a mild sleep aid. One highly respected practitioner from Europe states that California poppy is "altogether gentle, more in the direction of establishing equilibrium."*

American Skullcap was used by the Eclectic physicians of the last century as a tonic and support to the nervous system. It was said to be especially useful for nervous conditions manifesting with "excitability, restlessness, or wakefulness." Skullcap is included here for its specific use with nervousness from mental or physical exhaustion.*

Hops strobiles are used traditionally for nervous irritation and wakefulness, chiefly where anxiety and worry are the cause. The German Commission E monograph mentions Hops for restlessness and anxiety, as well as disorders of sleep. Hops was also used historically to stimulate digestion and to tonify cerebro-spinal function. Hops serves this formula as a valued relaxing and restorative tonic.*

COMPLEMENTARY PHYTO-CAPS/LIQUID FORMULAS/LIQUID EXTRACTS

Adrenal Health Liquid Phyto-Caps™, Serenity with Kava Kava Liquid Phyto-Caps™, Valerian Root Liquid Phyto-Caps™

SAFETY EVALUATION/CONTRAINDICATIONS

Do not use this product during pregnancy or lactation

Caution: US FDA advises that a potential risk of rare, but severe, liver injury may be associated with kava-containing dietary supplements. Ask a healthcare professional before use if you have or have had liver problems, frequently use alcoholic beverages, or are taking any medication. Stop use and see a doctor if you develop symptoms that may signal liver problems, including jaundice (yellowing of the skin or whites of the eyes) and brown urine. Other nonspecific symptoms can include nausea, vomiting, light-colored stools, unexplained tiredness, weakness, stomach or abdominal pain, and loss of appetite. Not for use by persons under 18 years of age, or by pregnant or breastfeeding women. Not

*THIS STATEMENT HAS NOT BEEN EVALUATED BY THE FOOD AND DRUG ADMINISTRATION.
THIS PRODUCT IS NOT INTENDED TO DIAGNOSE, TREAT, CURE OR PREVENT ANY DISEASE.

for use with alcoholic beverages. Excessive use, or use with products that cause drowsiness, may impair your ability to operate a vehicle or heavy equipment

KNOWN DRUG INTERACTIONS

Consult a physician if you are taking any prescription drugs.

REFERENCES

Valpiani C. Valeriana officinalis. Journal of the Australian Traditional Medicine Society. 1995;1(2):57-62.

Houghton PJ. The Scientific Basis for the Reputed Activity of Valerian. J. Pharm. Pharmacol. 1999;51:505-512.

Blumenthal M, et al. Ed. The Complete German Commission E Monographs.Austin, TX: American Botanical Council; 1998.

Brown D. Valerian: Clinical Overview - Phytotherapy Review & Commentary. Townsend Letter for Doctors. 1995:150151.

Sherman, JA The complete botanical prescriber. Self Published, 1993. Pg. 101.

Miller JG, Murray WJ. Herbal Medicinals: A Clinician's Guide. New York: Pharma Prod Press, 1998. Pg. 222.

Weiss RF. Herbal Medicine. Beaconsfield: Beaconsfield Pub, 1988.

Harrison T. Savage civilization New York: Alfred A. Knopf; 1937

Anonymous. Natural anxiolytics – Kava and L.72 antianxiety formula. The American Journal of Natural Medicine. 1994; 1(2): 10-14.

Witchl M. (Bisset NG, Ed.) Herbal Drugs and Phytopharmaceuticals. Medpharm, CRC Press: Boca Raton. 1994.

Priest AW, Priest LR. Herbal medication. A clinical dispensary handbook. 1982.

Mitchell W. Foundations of Natural Therapeutics – Biochemical Apologetics of Naturopathic Medicine. Tempe, Arizona. Southwest College Press. 1997. Pg. 265.

Mitchell W. Plant Medicine. Seattle, Wa: Self-published; 2000. Pg. 14-15. Pg. 124.

ST. JOHN'S WORT

(Hypericum perforatum)

Ultimate Support for Emotional Well-Being*

ALCOHOL-FREE CONCENTRATED EXTRACT OF:

ST. JOHN'S WORT FLOWER BUDS	MG EXTRACT PER 3 CAPS
(*Hypericum perforatum*)	540 mg

STANDARDIZED TO FULL SPECTRUM ACTIVITY PROFILE

Hypericins	2.7mg

DOSAGE
1 liquid Phyto-Cap, 3 times daily

DURATION OF USE
4-6 months

BEST TAKEN
Between meals, with warm water

HISTORY

St. John's Wort is a perennial herb with bright yellow flowers. It can be found growing wild in many parts of the world. This precious herb has an extensive history of use. In the 1st century AD, Dioscorides utilized St. John's Wort to heal and soothe the skin and to manage body temperature. During the 19th and 20th centuries Eclectic physicians used the aerial parts of the herb to support nervous system health.

NUMEROUS CLINICAL TRIALS

St. John's Wort is an established prescription in Europe. Numerous clinical trials have confirmed its efficacy. Several placebo-controlled studies were conducted in the early 1990's. In a multi-center, double-blind study, 72 patients were randomized into two treatment groups. One group received 300 mg St. John's Wort three times a day, and the other group received a placebo. Significant improvement was seen in 80% of patients after 4 weeks of study.

Another multi-center, double-blind trial with 105 subjects evaluated St John's Wort. Subjects received either St. John's Wort or a placebo. At the end of the four-week study period substantial improvements were seen in the St. John's Wort group. There were no notable side effects.

*THIS STATEMENT HAS NOT BEEN EVALUATED BY THE FOOD AND DRUG ADMINISTRATION. THIS PRODUCT IS NOT INTENDED TO DIAGNOSE, TREAT, CURE OR PREVENT ANY DISEASE.

A meta-analysis of 23 randomized clinical trials including a total of 1757 subjects was conducted in 1996. After reviewing the trials the authors concluded that St. John's Wort was significantly more effective than a placebo.*

MECHANISM OF ACTION

As with most botanicals, the effects of St. John's Wort are probably the combination of differing modes of action. Early research suggested that St. John's Wort was a monoamine oxidase (MAO) inhibitor. However, later research showed that no relevant MAO inhibition could be shown. The researchers concluded that the effects could not be explained in terms of MAO inhibition alone. Possible mechanisms include inhibition of synaptic uptake of serotonin, norepinephrine, and dopamine, L-glutamine and GABA uptake inhibition, and serotonin uptake inhibition by elevating free intracellular sodium.

COMPLEMENTARY PHYTO-CAPS/LIQUID FORMULAS/LIQUID EXTRACTS

Adrenal Health Liquid Phyto-Caps™, Phyto-Proz Supreme Liquid Phyto-Caps™, Kava Kava root Liquid Extract

SAFETY EVALUATIONS / CONTRAINDICATIONS

Do not use during pregnancy or lactation.

KNOWN DRUG INTERACTIONS

Consult a physician if taking any pharmaceutical drugs.

St. John's Wort appears to be an inducer of the metabolic pathway cytochrome P450. Therefore it should be used with caution with any drug that is metabolized via the cytochrome P450 pathway. This includes protease inhibitors for HIV (indinavir, amprenivir), transplant rejection (cyclosporine, rapamycin), heart disease (digoxin), seizure (phenobarbitol) medication, and other pharmaceuticals. However, it is important to note that certain foods such as grapefruit inhibit the cytochrome P450 pathway. Cruciferous vegetables such as broccoli and cabbage are P450 inducers.

REFERENCES

Felter HW and Lloyd JU. King's American Dispensatory. Portland, Oregon. Eclectic Medical Publications; 1983: 1038-1039. (originally published in 1898).

Hänsgen KD, et al. Multi center double blind study examining the antidepressant effectiveness of the Hypericum extract LI 160. Journal of Geriatric Psychiatry and Neurology. 1994; 7: s15-s18.

Harrer G and Sommer H. Treatment of mild/moderate depressions with hypericum. Phytomedicine. 1994; 1:3-8.

Linde K, et al. St John's wort for depression- an overview and meta-analysis of randomized clinical trials. BMJ. 1996; 313:253-258.

Phillip M, et al. Hypericum extract versus imipramine or placebo in patients with moderate depression: randomized multicentre study of treatment for 8 weeks. BMJ. 1999; 319: 1534-1539.

Brenner R, et al. Comparison of an extract of hypericum (LI 160) and sertraline in the treatment of depression: a double-blind, randomized pilot study. Clinical Therapeutics. 2000; 22(4): 411-419.

Schrader E. Equivalence of St. John's Wort extract (ZE 117) and fluoxetine: a randomized, controlled study in mild to moderate depression. Int Clin Psychopharmacol. 2000; 15(2): 61-68.

Woelk H. Comparison of St. Johns's wort and imipramine for treating depression: randomized controlled trial. BMJ. 2000; 321: 536-539.

Suzuki O, et al. Inhibition of monoamine oxidase by hypericin. Planta Medica. 1984; 50: 272-274.

Bladt S and Wagner H. Inhibition of MAO by fractions and constituents of Hypericum extract. Journal of Geriatric Psychiatry and Neurology. 1994; 7: s57-s59.

Theide HM and Walper A. Inhibition of MAO and COMT by Hypericum extracts and hypericin. Journal of Geriatric Psychiatry and Neurology.1994; 7: s54-s56.

Muller WE, et al. Hyperforin represents the neurotransmitter reuptake inhibiting constituent of hypericum extract. Pharmacopsychiatry. 1998; 31(suppl. 1): 16-21.

Wonnemann M, et al. Inhibition of synaptosomal uptake of 3H-L-glutamate and 3H-GABA by hyperforin, a major constituent of St John's wort: the role of amiloride sensitive sodium conductive pathways. Neuropsychopharmacology. 2000; 23(2): 188-197.

Singer A, et al. Hyperforin, a major antidepressant constituent of St. john's wort, inhibits serotonin uptake by elevating free intracellular Na +1. J Pharmacol Exp Ther. 1999; 290(3): 1363-1368.

Blumenthal M, et al. The Complete German Commission E Monographs: Therapeutic Guide to Herbal Medicines. Austin. American Botanical Council; 1998: 214-215.

Schulz V, et al. Rational Phytotherapy. New York; Springer-Verlag; 1998: 50-65.

Breidenbach TH, et al. Drug interaction of St. John's Wort with ciclosporin. Lancet. 2000;255:1912.

Henny JE. Risk of drug interactions with St. John's Wort. JAMA. 2000; 283(13): 1679.

McIntyre M. A review of the benefits, adverse events, drug interactions, and safety of St. John's Wort (Hypericum perforatum): The implications with regard to the regulation of herbal medicine. Journal of Alternative and Complementary Medicine. 2000; 6(2): 115-124.

STRESS RESPONSE

Supports Healthy Adrenal Function*

ALCOHOL-FREE CONCENTRATED EXTRACTS OF:

FORMULA	MG EXTRACT PER 2 CAPSULES
Rhodiola root (*Rhodiola rosea*)	200 mg
Ashwagandha root and leaf (*Withania somnifera*)*	100 mg
Schizandra berry (*Schizandra chinensis*)	100 mg
Wild Oats (*Avena sativa*)	100 mg
Holy Basil E.T.O.H. (*Ocimum sanctum*)	100 mg
Holy Basil Supercritical Extract (*Ocimum sanctum*)	50 mg

*Ingredient is protected under US Patent Nos. 6,153,198 and 6,713,092

STANDARDIZED TO FULL SPECTRUM ACTIVITY PROFILE

Withanolide glycosides (from Ashwagandha)	8 mg
Rosavins (from Rhodiola root)	6 mg
Salidrosides (from Rhodiola root)	1.6 mg

DOSAGE

Liquid Phyto-Caps: 2 capsules, 2 times daily

DURATION OF USE

3 months

BEST TAKEN

After meals, with warm water

DESCRIPTION OF FORMULA

Stress Response enhances the body's physiologic response to stress. Stress is defined as any situation or condition that causes undue physical, emotional and/or mental strain on the body. When one experiences stress, in any form, the adrenal glands secrete specific hormones that have a profound effect on the body. One can imagine the adrenal glands as little "hats" that sit on top of the kidneys. These hats secrete hormones such as cortisol and DHEA in response to stress. Over time, as one experiences stress on a daily basis, the adrenal glands can function less optimally, secreting unhealthy levels of these stress-related hormones. Overworking of the adrenal glands can lead to something called adrenal stress. Nervousness, poor memory, difficulty with concentration and decision-making, cravings for sweets, weight gain and compromised sleep are all associated with failure to maintain healthy levels of these two hormones.

The Stress Response formula can have a profound influence on the body, helping to maintain a healthy response to stress by supporting the adrenal glands and nourishing the nervous system. Select herbs within the formula contain compounds recognized for their ability to support the health and function of the adrenal glands and maintaining normal secretion levels of key stress-related hormones such as cortisol.*

Rhodiola rosea root supports the functioning of the adrenal glands and encourages a healthy response to physical, emotional and mental stress by normalizing cortisol levels and other stress-related hormones. If used regularly, it enhances the body's natural resistance and adaptation to stressful influences. Rhodiola rosea root is classified as an adaptogen, which represents a class of herbs that help the body adapt to stresses of various kinds. In order to achieve this classification, a plant must be harmless and must have a normalizing, broad-spectrum action that supports homeostasis, particularly when under stressful influences.*

Holy Basil has long been used in Ayurvedic medicine to support a healthy response to stress, nourish the mind and elevate the spirit. Revered by Ayurvedic practitioners as "the incomparable one," this herb's documented actions on the body date back thousands of years. Today, we know that holy basil contains a variety of constituents, including eugenol, camphor, caryophyllene, ursolic acid, luteolin and apigenin that function collectively to normalize stress hormones and enhance adrenal function. The properties inherent in this herb make it ideally suited for helping to support a healthy adrenal system and stress response.*

Ashwaghanda, often referred to as "Indian Ginseng," is a common herb used in Ayurvedic medicine (from India) to support mental and physical vitality and stamina. It contains steroidal compounds and additional chemical constituents that advance the body's natural resistance and adaptation to stressful influences. Ashwaghanda also supports mental endurance, promotes total metabolic efficiency and encourages an overall sense of well-being.*

Schizandra berries provide powerful antioxidant protection, particularly from free radicals and other toxins in the environment that may cause cellular damage. Regarded as a popular adaptogenic agent, schizandra berries are unique in that they hold a remarkable blend of five distinct flavor properties collectively serving to promote overall health and vitality. Namely, bitter, sweet, sour, salty and hot. Schizandra berries function to enhance the body's natural resistance and adaptation to stressful influences, support mental endurance and promote overall metabolic efficiency.*

Wild Oats milky seed contains numerous compounds that promote a vital nervous system while working to ease temporary nervous stress, weakness, and exhaustion.*

COMPLEMENTARY PHYTO-CAPS/LIQUID FORMULAS/LIQUID EXTRACTS

Rhodiola Rosea Liquid Phyto-Caps™, Astragalus Supreme Liquid Phyto-Caps™

*THIS STATEMENT HAS NOT BEEN EVALUATED BY THE FOOD AND DRUG ADMINISTRATION.
THIS PRODUCT IS NOT INTENDED TO DIAGNOSE, TREAT, CURE OR PREVENT ANY DISEASE.

SAFETY EVALUATION/CONTRAINDICATIONS

Before using this product, talk with your healthcare professional if you suffer from a medical condition. Please visit www.gaiaherbs.com to obtain information regarding potential contraindications and/or side effects that may be associated with herbs found in this formula.*

KNOWN DRUG INTERACTIONS

Before using this product, talk with your healthcare professional if you take any medications. Please visit www.gaiaherbs.com to obtain information regarding any possible drug interactions that may be associated with herbs found in this formula.*

REFERENCES

Brown RP, Gerbarg PL, Ramazanov Z. Rhodiola rosea: a phytomedicinal overview. Herbalgram 2002;56:40–52.

Chiu PY et al. In vivo antioxidant action of a lignan-enriched extract of Schisandra fruit and an anthraquinone-containing extract of Polygonum root in comparison with schisandrin B and emodin. Planta Med. 2002 Nov;68(11):951-6.

Darbinyan V et al. Rhodiola rosea in stress induced fatigue - a double blind cross-over study of a standardized extract SHR-5 with a repeated low-dose regimen on the mental performance of healthy physicians during night duty. Phytomedicine 2000;7(5):365-71.

Darbinyan V, Kteyan A, Panossian A, et al. Rhodiola rosea in stress induced fatigue - a double blind cross-over study of a standardized extract SHR-5 with a repeated low-dose regimen on the mental performance of healthy physicians during night duty. Phytomedicine 2000;7(5):365-71.

Davis JM et al. Effects of oat beta-glucan on innate immunity and infection after exercise stress. Med Sci Sports Exerc. 2004 Aug;36(8):1321-7.

Dhuley JN.Adaptogenic and cardioprotective action of ashwagandha in rats and frogs. J Ethnopharmacol. 2000 Apr;70(1):57-63.

Hoffmann D. Oats. http://www.healthy.net/scr/Article.asp?Id=1592 [Accessed March2, 2005].

Kelly GS. Rhodiola rosea: a possible plant adaptogen. Altern Med Rev 2001;6:293-302.

Kucinskaite A, Briedis V, Savickas A.[Experimental analysis of therapeutic properties of Rhodiola rosea L. and its possible application in medicine].[Article in Lithuanian]. Medicina (Kaunas). 2004;40(7):614-9.

Maslova LV et al. [The cardioprotective and antiadrenergic activity of an extract of Rhodiola rosea in stress]. [Article in Russian]. Eksp Klin Farmakol 1994;57(6):61-3.

Petkov VD et al. Effects of alcohol aqueous extract from Rhodiola rosea L. roots on learning and memory. Acta Physiol Pharmacol Bulg 1986;12(1):3-16.

Spasov AA et al. A double-blind, placebo-controlled pilot study of the stimulating and adaptogenic effect of Rhodiola rosea SHR-5 extract on the fatigue of students caused by stress during an examination period with a repeated low-dose regimen. Phytomedicine 2000;7(2):85-89.

Vats V, Yadav SP, Grover JK. Ethanolic extract of Ocimum sanctum leaves partially attenuates streptozotocin-induced alterations in glycogen content and carbohydrate metabolism in rats. Ethnopharmacol. 2004 Jan;90(1):155-60.

THYROID SUPPORT

Ultimate Support for Metabolic Enhancement*

ALCOHOL-FREE CONCENTRATED EXTRACTS OF:

FORMULA	MG EXTRACT PER 2 CAPSULES
L-Tyrosine	300 mg
Schizandra berry (*Schizandra chinensis*)	156 mg
Coleus root (*Coleus forskholii*)	154 mg
Kelp fronds (*Laminaria digitata*)	130 mg
Ashwagandha, Av. root (*Withania somnifera*)	120 mg
Bladderwrack fronds (*Fucus vesiculosis*)	56 mg

STANDARDIZED TO FULL SPECTRUM ACTIVITY PROFILE

Iodine (from seaweed)	0.3 mg

DOSAGE
1 Liquid Phyto-Cap, 2 times daily

DURATION OF USE
4-6 Months

BEST TAKEN
Between meals, with warm water

DESCRIPTION OF FORMULA
The thyroid gland is one of the most important regulators of metabolism, its effect reaching throughout the body. It is in turn regulated by the two master glands of the endocrine system, the pituitary and the hypothalamus. The thyroid gland produces hormones (known as thyroid hormones) from the amino acid tyrosine and from iodine. Since the thyroid can affect practically every cell in the body in a wide variety of ways, normal thyroid function is essential to health.

Lack of energy, inability to concentrate, mood fluctuation, dry skin and hair loss, weight gain, and many other seemingly unrelated problems may indicate a need for thyroid support.

The Thyroid Support formula is designed to help maintain healthy thyroid gland function and metabolism.*

L-Tyrosine is a central component of thyroid hormones. Adequate tyrosine levels help maintain normal thyroid function. Further, tyrosine is required for the

*THIS STATEMENT HAS NOT BEEN EVALUATED BY THE FOOD AND DRUG ADMINISTRATION.
THIS PRODUCT IS NOT INTENDED TO DIAGNOSE, TREAT, CURE OR PREVENT ANY DISEASE.

synthesis of important neurotransmitters like epinephrine, norepinephrine and dopamine, all of which can become depleted during stressful events.*

Schizandra berries are unique in that they hold a remarkable blend of five distinct flavor properties. Namely, bitter, sweet, sour, salty and hot. They also contain an array of active constituents including schizandrins, schizandrols, schizandrers, schisantherins, and others, collectively referred to as lignans. These substances work together to enhance and protect overall cellular vitality. As a group, the varying actions associated with the Schizandra berry maintain healthy nerve, liver, lung and adrenal gland function. Accordingly, this berry serves as a valuable general tonic that encourages overall health and stamina, and improves one's natural ability to tolerate both physical and emotional stress. Likewise, Schizandra offers antioxidant protection and enhances healthy memory, mental clarity, energy levels, coordination and endurance. In addition, Schizandra may enhance the liver's cleansing capabilities and encourage healthy hormonal metabolic efficiency.*

Coleus forskholii is a mint family herb that contains forskolin, a compound that works directly on the heart muscle and on blood vessels to optimize blood flow throughout the cardiovascular system. Forskolin also helps to maintain healthy fat metabolism and facilitates thyroid and immune system health.*

Kelp is very similar to Bladderwrack, and is a potent source of trace minerals, iodine, and phytochemical constituents that help to maintain gastrointestinal and thyroid health and support normal metabolic function.*

Ashwagandha, often referred to as "Indian Ginseng," is a common herb used in Ayurvedic medicine (from India) to enhance mental and physical vitality and stamina. It contains natural steroidal compounds and additional chemical constituents that advance the body's natural resistance and adaptation to stressful influences. As well, Ashwagandha supports mental endurance, promotes total metabolic efficiency and encourages an overall sense of well-being.*

Bladderwrack is a select species of seaweed with a long history of use for maintaining thyroid function and maintaining a healthy body weight. It is recognized as a natural source of magnesium, iron, zinc, potassium and other minerals. Likewise, this nutritive tonic contains iodine, an essential substrate for the thyroid hormone. Bladderwrack also contains important phytochemicals that work synergistically to support healthy metabolism. For example, it is comprised of complex carbohydrates (alginates) that support healthy digestive function and the elimination of toxic waste. Further, it contains the chemical fucoidin, recognized for enhancing blood flow and maintaining healthy blood. This marine algae may also help to support healthy glucose metabolism.*

COMPLEMENTARY PHYTO-CAPS/LIQUID FORMULAS/LIQUID EXTRACTS

Metabolic Support Liquid Phyto-Caps™

*THIS STATEMENT HAS NOT BEEN EVALUATED BY THE FOOD AND DRUG ADMINISTRATION.
THIS PRODUCT IS NOT INTENDED TO DIAGNOSE, TREAT, CURE OR PREVENT ANY DISEASE.

SAFETY EVALUATION/CONTRAINDICATIONS

Do not use during pregnancy or lactation. If symptoms of excessive thyroid activity (restlessness, anxiety, palpitations, or diarrhea) occur, the formula should be discontinued and a physician should be consulted. This formula should not be used by those with Hyperthyroidism, Hashimoto's thyroiditis, or Graves' disease. Use with caution and seek the advice of a qualified healthcare professional if you have high or low blood pressure. This formula may also exacerbate acne due to its iodine content, and prolonged ingestion may reduce iron absorption.*

KNOWN DRUG INTERACTIONS

This formula should be used with caution in combination with drugs that inhibit blood clotting and platelet aggregation including but not limited to warfarin (Coumadin®), heparin, clopidogrel (Plavix®), pentoxifylline (Trental®), and aspirin. Additionally, this formula may interact with diuretics (due to sodium content), lithium (by increasing hypothyroid effects), barbiturates and thyroid hormone therapy.*

REFERENCES

Archana R, Namasivayam A. Antistressor Effect of Withania somnifera. J Ethnopharmacol. Jan1999;64(1):91-3.

Boone K. Withania – The Indian Ginseng and Anti-aging Adaptogen. Nutrition and Healing. Jun1998;5(6):5-7.

Bruneton J. Pharmacognosy Phytochemistry Medicinal Plants. Paris: Lavoisier Publishing, 1995:44-47.

Budd M. Mild hypothyroidism--the missed diagnosis. Int J Alt Compl Med 1998;16:25-27.

Ellingwood F. American Materia Medica, Pharmacognosy and Therapeutics 11th ed. Sandy, OR: Eclectic Medical Publications, 1919:382-3.

Felter HW. Eclectic Materia Medica, Pharmacology and Therapeutics. Sandy, OR: Eclectic Medical Publications, 1922:381.

Hoffmann D. The Complete Illustrated Herbal. New York: Barnes & Noble Books, 1996:94.

Jain S, Shukla SD, Sharma K, Bhatnagar M. Neuroprotective Effects of Withania somnifera Dunn. in Hippocampal Sub-regions of Female Albino Rat. Phytother Res. Sep2001;15(6):544-8.

Kubo S, et al. Effect of Gomisin A (TJN-101) on Liver Regeneration. Planta Med. Dec1992;58(6):489-92.

Lamela M, et al. Hypoglycemic activity of several seaweed extracts. J Ethnopharmacol. Nov1989; 27(1-2):35-43.

Lamela M, Vázquez-Freire MJ, Calleja JM. Isolation and effects on serum lipid levels of polysaccharide fractions from Fucus vesiculosus. Phytother Res 1996;10(suppl):S175-6.

Leung AY, Foster S. Encyclopedia of Common Natural Ingredients Used in Food, Drugs, and Cosmetics, 2d ed. New York: John Wiley & Sons, 1996, 469–72.

Lindner E, et al. Positive Inotropic and Blood Pressure Lowering Activity of a Diterpene Derivative Isolated from Coleus forskohli: Forskolin. Arzneim-Forsch/Drug Res. 1978;28:284-89.

Maeda S, et al. Effects of Gomisin A on Liver Functions in Hepatotoxic Chemicals-treated Rats. Jpn J Pharmacol. Aug1985;38(4): 347-53.

*THIS STATEMENT HAS NOT BEEN EVALUATED BY THE FOOD AND DRUG ADMINISTRATION.
THIS PRODUCT IS NOT INTENDED TO DIAGNOSE, TREAT, CURE OR PREVENT ANY DISEASE.

McGuffin M, Hobbs C, Upton R, et al. American Herbal Product Association's Botanical Safety Handbook. Boca Raton, FL: CRC Press, 1997, 104.

Mills SY. Out of the Earth: The Essential Book of Herbal Medicine. Middlesex, UK: Viking Arkana, 1991:514-6

Mishra LC, Singh BB, Dagenais S. Scientific Basis for the Therapeutic Use of Withania somnifera (Ashwagandha): A Review. Altern Med Rev. Aug2000;5(4):334-46.

Murray M, Pizzorno J. Encyclopedia of Natural Medicine. Rocklin, CA: Prima Publishing, 1991:386-90.

Neri DF, Wiegmann D, Stanny RR, et al. The effects of tyrosine on cognitive performance during extended wakefulness. Aviat Space Environ Med 1995;66:313-9.

Newall CA, et al. Herbal Medicines: A Guide for Health Care Professionals. London: The Pharmaceutical Press;1996:124-126.

Ohtaki Y, et al. Deoxycholic Acid as an Endogenous Risk Factor for Hepatocarcinogenesis and Effects of Gomisin A, a Lignan Component of Schizandra Fruits. Anticancer Res. Mar1996;16(2):751-55.

Panda S, Kar A. Withania somnifera and Bauhinia purpurea in the Regulation of Circulating Thyroid Hormone Concentrations in Female Mice. J Ethnopharmacol. Nov1999;67(2):233-9.

PDR for Herbal Medicines, 2nd ed. Montvale, NJ: Medical Economics Company; 2000:107.

Schulick P. Herbal Therapy from the Sea. 1993.

Scudder JM. Specific Medication and Specific Medicines. Sandy, OR: Eclectic Medical Publications,1890, 1985:116.

Seamon KB, Daly JW. Forskolin: A unique diterpene activator of cAMP-generating systems. J Cyclic Nucleotide Res 1981;7:201-24.

Seamon KB, et al. Forskolin: Its Biological and Chemical Properties. In: Advances in Cyclic Nucleotide and Protein Phosphorylation Research. vol. 20. New York: Raven Press;1986:1-150.

Shiota G, et al. Rapid Induction of Hepatocyte Growth Factor mRNA after Administration of Gomisin A, a Lignan Component of Shizandra Fruits. Res Commun Mol Pathol Pharmacol. Nov1996;94(2):141-46.

Upton R, ed. Ashwagandha root (Withania somnifera): Analytical, quality control, and therapuetic monograph. American Herbal Pharmacopoeia 2000;April:1-25.

Willenborg DO, Parish CR. Inhibition of allergic encephalomyelitis in rats by treatment with sulfated polysaccharides. J Immunol 1988;140:3410-5.

TURMERIC SUPREME

Maintains Healthy

Joint, Heart, Cardiovascular and Liver Function*

ALCOHOL-FREE CONCENTRATED EXTRACTS OF:

FORMULA	MG PER 1 CAPSULE
Turmeric rhizome ETOH Extract (*Curcuma longa*)	330 mg
Turmeric rhizome Supercritical Extract (*Curcuma longa*)	60 mg

STANDARDIZED TO FULL SPECTRUM ACTIVITY PROFILE

BIOACTIVITY PER 1 CAPSULE	MG ACTIVITY
Tumerones from super critical extract	39 mg
Curcumins from ETOH extract	36 mg

DOSAGE

1 Liquid Phyto-Cap™ 1 time daily.

DURATION OF USE

3 weeks and then as needed

BEST TAKEN

After meals, with a small amount of warm water.

Although Turmeric is most familiar as a primary ingredient in traditional curry, Turmeric's popularity extends far beyond the reach of the culinary and has fascinated researchers worldwide. Gaia Herbs Turmeric Supreme combines two unique extraction techniques to create a whole-plant standardized extract representing the most complete Turmeric supplement available today.

HISTORY

Turmeric is one of the most widely used herbs in the east and has been used extensively in Ayurveda and Traditional Chinese Medicine. Traditional Ayurveda used Turmeric for body systems including the stomach, liver, as well as topically for minor wounds. Its effectiveness is still appreciated by many today. In fact, in India, there is a Turmeric medicated "Band-Aid" to assist in the recovery of minor abrasions.*

MECHANISM OF ACTION

Although Turmeric is known for its beautiful and ornate floral presentation most medical curiosities focus on the under-ground parts called rhizomes. Within these dense fibrous root structures are a treasure chest of nutritional compounds. The most studied belong to a group of compounds called curcuminoids. In particular, modern science has focused its efforts on a compound called curcumin. Curcumin

*THIS STATEMENT HAS NOT BEEN EVALUATED BY THE FOOD AND DRUG ADMINISTRATION. THIS PRODUCT IS NOT INTENDED TO DIAGNOSE, TREAT, CURE OR PREVENT ANY DISEASE.

is a yellow pigment found in the rhizomes that are responsible for its bright color. In the National Library of Medicine, there are over 160 studies dedicated to this compound and interest does not seem to be waning. In fact, at the time of this writing, the United States National Institutes of Health are conducting 4 clinical trials using Turmeric for pancreatic cancer, multiple myeloma, Alzheimer's, and colorectal cancer. Although, no conclusions have been published the degree of interest within the medical community is apparent.*

Most researchers agree that the basic mechanism of action within Turmeric is its potent antioxidant action. Curcuminoids seem to scavenge for damaging particles in the body known as "free-radicals". Although free radicals are a normal by-product of our metabolism, in excess amounts they can negatively alter cell membranes and even cause cell death. Free-radicals can lead to severe health challenges downstream and have been studied for their impact on everything from arthritis, inflammation, heart disease to cancer. Researchers worldwide have recognized Turmeric as one of the most potent free-radical quenchers available in the plant world. *

Gaia Herbs has created a full-spectrum extract utilizing water, food-grade alcohol, and super-critical CO_2 to deliver the most potent extract available in the market. Each capsule contains Certified Organic Turmeric concentrated to the free-radical scavenging Curcuminoids for the most potent activity.

COMPLEMENTARY PHYTO-CAPS/LIQUID FORMULAS/LIQUID EXTRACTS

Infla-Profen Liquid Phyto-Caps™, Anti-Oxidant Supreme Liquid Phyto-Caps™, Hawthorn Supreme Liquid Phyto-Caps™, Liver Support Liquid Phyto-Caps™

SAFETY EVALUATION/CONTRAINDICATIONS

Turmeric is well tolerated though should be avoided by people with history of gallstones.

KNOWN DRUG INTERACTIONS

This herb should be used with caution in combination with drugs that inhibit blood clotting and platelet aggregation including but not limited to warfarin (Coumadin®), heparin, clopidogrel (Plavix®), pentoxifylline (Trental®), and asprin.

REFERENCES

Fetrow CW, Avila JR. Professional's Handbook of Complementary & Alternative Medicines. 1st ed. Springhouse, PA: Springhouse Corp., 1999.

Mills S, Bone K. The Essential Guide to Herbal Safety. St. Louis MO : Elsevier, Inc, 2005.

Surh YJ. Anti-tumor promoting potential of selected spice ingredients with antioxidative and anti-inflammatory activities: a short review. Food Chem Toxicol 2002; 40:1091-7.

URINARY SUPPORT

Supports Healthy Functioning of the Urinary System*

ALCOHOL-FREE CONCENTRATED EXTRACTS OF:

FORMULA	MG EXTRACT PER 2 CAPSULES
Uva Ursi solid extract (*Arctostaphylos uva ursi*)	370 mg
Pipsissewa leaf (*Chimaphila umbellata*)	92 mg
Coptis rhizome (*Coptis chinensis*)	50 mg
Echinacea Supreme (*Echinacea purpurea* aerial parts, *Echinacea purpurea* root, *Echinacea purpurea* seed)	30 mg
Usnea lichen (*Usnea* spp.)	14 mg

DOSAGE

2 Liquid Phyto-Caps every 1-2 hours

DURATION OF USE

1-2 weeks

BEST TAKEN

Between meals with a small amount of warm water.

DESCRIPTION OF FORMULA

Urinary Support promotes a healthy urinary system. This formula optimizes circulation and accordingly promotes normal tone within the urinary tract. Additionally, it restores and enhances immune system function, particularly within the kidneys and urinary tract. Both the traditional use of these plants and modern day scientific inquiry provide the basis for this formulation.*

Uva Ursi leaf comes from a North American shrub long respected by many Native American tribes. Uva Ursi supports health and optimal immune protection in the tissues of the urinary tract and kidneys. The constituent arbutin is associated with maintaining health and proper immune protection in the urinary tract, but must have an alkaline environment to be effective. Hence, it is advisable to avoid acidic foods, including acidic fruits and juices, while taking this herb, to ensure maximum efficacy.*

Pipsissewa herb is native to the eastern coast of North America and a traditional urinary tract tonic. Like Uva Ursi, Pipsissewa contains arbutin. Pipsissewa helps to maintain urinary tract and prostate gland health, and promotes fluid balance.

Chinese Coptis rhizome is one of several plants containing immune supportive alkaloids. The most researched of these alkaloids is berberine. Coptis contains others including coptisine. These alkaloids have been shown to support the body's natural non-specific immune response. It is also shown to increase blood flow to the spleen, resulting in a second mechanism that enhances the body's non-specific immune response. Additionally, this herb supports kidney function by promoting the healthy excretion of urine.*

Echinacea enhances normal immune function, particularly by ensuring healthy non-specific immune function. For example, Echinacea supports the function of white blood cells that swallow up, obliterate and then clean up organisms. Its effects extend to the urinary tract, providing immune protection for healthy kidney and urinary tract tissue.*

Usnea lichen, otherwise known as Old Man's Beard, contains a variety of lichen acids and other constituents that work synergistically to promote mucous membrane health and digestive health. Specific lichen acids, such as usnic acid, have a bitter quality that may function to protect the body.*

COMPLEMENTARY PHYTO-CAPS/LIQUID FORMULAS/LIQUID EXTRACTS

Cranberry Concentrate Liquid Phyto-Caps™, Dandelion Root and Leaf, Nettle Leaf, and Echinacea/Goldenseal Supreme.

SAFETY EVALUATION/CONTRAINDICATIONS

Do not take during pregnancy or lactation. The urine may harmlessly turn brown while taking this formula. Foods that acidify the urine may interfere with efficacy of the formula. Do not take Urinary Support if you have liver disease, any kidney disorder, renal failure, gastrointestinal irritation, diabetes, infertility, or peptic ulcer disease. Use with caution if you have cystitis. Do not use this formula long-term (more than 3 consecutive weeks).*

KNOWN DRUG INTERACTIONS

Drugs that acidify the urine may interfere with the efficacy of the formula. Do not administer simultaneously with tetracycline, codeine, atropine, and/or Cardec DM® (doses of each should be separated by at least one hour). This formula should be used with caution in combination with diuretics such as Triamterene, Thiazide diuretics, Spironolactone, and Loop diuretics.*

REFERENCES

Amin AH, Subbaiah TV, Abbasi KM. Berberine sulfate: Antimicrobial activity, bioassay, and mode of action. Can J Microbiol 1969;15:1067-76.

Blumenthal M, et al. ed. The Complete German Commission E Monographs: Therapeutic Guide to Herbal Medicines. Trans. S. Klein. Boston, MA: American Botanical Council, 1998.

Blumenthal M, Goldberg A, Brinckmann J (eds). Herbal Medicine Expanded Commission E Monographs. Newton, MA: Integrative Medicine Communications, 2000.

Brinker F, Formulas for Healthful Living. Sandy, OR: Eclectic Medical Publications, 1995, pg. 145,

Brinker F. Herb Contraindications and Drug Interactions. 2nd ed. Sandy, OR: Eclectic Medical Publications, 1998.

Gruenwald J, et al. PDR for Herbal Medicines. 1st ed. Montvale, NJ: Medical Economics Company, Inc., 1998.

Hobbs C. Usnea: The Herbal Antibiotic; and other Medicinal Lichens. Santa Cruz: Botanica Press, 1990.

Jahodar L, Jilek P, Paktova M, Dvorakova V. Antimicrobial effect of arbutin and an extract of the leaves of Arctostaphylos uva-ursi in vitro. Cesk Farm 1985;34:174-8.

Larsson B, Jonasson A, Fianu S. Prophylactic effect of UVA-E in women with recurrent cystitis: a preliminary report. Curr Ther Res Clin Exp 1993;53:441-3.

Lis-Balchin M, Hart S, Simpson E. Buchu (Agathosma betulina and a. crenulata, Rutaceae) essential oils: Their pharmacological action on guinea-pig ileum and antimicrobial activity on microorganisms. J Pharm Pharmacol 2001;53:579-82.

McGuffin M, et al., ed. American Herbal Products Association's Botanical Safety Handbook. Boca Raton, FL: CRC Press, 1997, pg. 43, 212.

Melchart D, Linde K, Worku F, et al. Immunomodulation with Echinacea--a systematic review of controlled clinical trials. Phytomedicine 1994;1:245-54 [review].

Newall CA, Anderson LA, Philpson JD. Herbal Medicine: A Guide for Healthcare Professionals. London, UK: The Pharmaceutical Press, 1996.

Simpson D. Buchu--South Africa's amazing herbal remedy. Scott Med J 1998;43:189-91.

Sun D, Abraham SN, Beachey EH. Influence of berberine sulfate on synthesis and expression of Pap fimbrial adhesin in uropathogenic Escherichia coli. Antimicrob Agents Chemother 1988;32(8):1274-7.

von Frohne D. Investigations into questions of the urinary disinfectant effects of uva ursi extract. Planta Med 1970;18:1-25.

VALERIAN ROOT

(Valeriana officinalis)

For Ultimate Support of Restful Sleep*

ALCOHOL-FREE CONCENTRATED EXTRACT OF:	
VALERIAN ROOT	**MG EXTRACT PER 3 CAPS**
(*Valeriana* off.)	200 mg

STANDARDIZED TO FULL SPECTRUM ACTIVITY PROFILE	
Valerenic acids (from Valerian)	1.8 mg

DOSAGE
2 Liquid Phyto-Caps, 1 hour before bedtime

DURATION OF USE
4-6 months

BEST TAKEN
With warm water

HISTORY

Valerian is a perennial herb with a lengthy tradition of use in supporting normal sleep. The root (rhizome) was official in the United States Pharmacopeia from 1820-1936 and in the National Formulary from 1888-1946. Valerian is still used extensively to promote healthy sleep in Germany, France, Belgium, and Switzerland.*

ENHANCED SLEEP QUALITY

Difficulty sleeping under normal conditions can be manifested as one or more of the following: inability to fall asleep (> 30 minutes) upon retiring; intermittent waking after falling asleep; or early morning awakenings. Numerous clinical studies have substantiated the efficacy of Valerian root to promote relaxation and maintain healthy sleep cycles.*

One of the earliest studies was a placebo-controlled double-blind trial of 128 subjects. Participants received 400 mg of Valerian extract, a Valerian combination, or a placebo, one hour before bedtime. Subjects felt that they had a significant improvement in sleep quality and in time to fall asleep. Valerian had no detectable "hangover" effect the next morning. However, some subjects who took the Valerian formula reported morning sleepiness.*

A recent randomized, double blind, placebo-controlled study was conducted with 16 patients. Those persons taking the Valerian extract had improvements in sleep structure and sleep perception. An interesting finding was that fewer side effects were experienced with Valerian than with the placebo (3 vs. 18).*

Valerian contains a variety of compounds that likely function collectively to encourage relaxation and a healthy sleep cycle, improve one's natural ability to endure both physical and emotional stress, and support optimal nervous system health.*

COMPLEMENTARY PHYTO-CAPS/LIQUID FORMULAS/LIQUID EXTRACTS

Kava Kava Liquid Phyto-Caps™, Sound Sleep Liquid Phyto-Caps™, Valerian/Poppy Supreme, Skullcap/St. John's Wort Supreme

SAFETY EVALUATIONS / CONTRAINDICATIONS

Do not use during pregnancy and lactation. Do not drive or operate dangerous machinery after taking Valerian. Adverse reactions, such as excitability, insomnia, headaches, uneasiness and/or drowsiness and tiredness may occur on occasion. If you use this product for an extended period, it is wise to taper doses slowly rather than suddenly stopping.*

KNOWN DRUG INTERACTIONS

Valerian may potentiate the effects and adverse reactions associated with alcohol, barbiturates, benzodiazepines and other drugs with sedative actions. This herb may not have been studied sufficiently to determine its interactions with other medications. Before using Valerian, talk with your healthcare professional if you take any medications.*

REFERENCES

Blumenthal M, et al. The Complete German Commission E Monographs: Therapeutic Guide to Herbal Medicines. Austin. American Botanical Council; 1998.

Donath F, et al. Critical evaluation of the effect of valerian extract on sleep structure and sleep quality. Pharmacopsychiatry. 2000; 33 (2): 47-53.

Dorn M. [Efficacy and tolerability of baldrian versus oxazepam in non-organic and non-psychiatric insomnia]. Forsch Komplementarmed Klass Naturheilkd 2000; 7(2) 79-84. [article in German]

Hendriks H, et al. Central Nervous Depressant Activity of Valerenic Acid in the Mouse. Planta Med. Feb1985;(1):28-31.

Hobbs C. Valerian: a literature review. Herbalgram. 1989; 21:19-34.

Houghton PJ. The Biological Activity of Valerian and Related Plants. J Ethnopharmacol. 1988;22(2):121-42.

Houghton PJ. The scientific basis for the reputed activity of valerian. J. Pharm. Pharmacol. 1999; 51: 505-12, 519-526.

Leathwood PD, et al. Aqueous extract of valerian root (Valeriana officinalis L.) Improves sleep quality in man. Pharmacology Biochemistry and Behavior. 1982; 17: 65-71.

Ortiz JG, et al. Effects of Valeriana officinalis extracts on [3H] flunitrazepam binding, synaptosomal [3H] GABA uptake, and hippocampal [3H] GABA release. Neurochemical Research. 1999; 24 (11): 1373-1378.

Santos MS, et al. Synaptosomal GABA Release as Influenced by Valerian Root Extract--Involvement of the GABA Carrier. Arch Int Pharmacodyn Ther. 1994;327(2):220-31.

Santus MS, et al. The amount of GABA present in aqueous extracts of valerian is sufficient to account for [3H] GABA release in synaptosomes. Planta Medica 1994; 60: 475-476.

Upton R, editor. Valerian Root, Valeriana officinalis: Analytical, Quality Control, and Therapeutic Monograph. Santa Cruz, CA. American Herbal Pharmacopeia; 1999.

Wagner J. et al. Beyond benzodiazepines: Alternative pharmacologic agents for the treatment of insomnia. The Annals of Phamacotherapy. 1998; 32: 680-691.

VISION ENHANCEMENT

Anti-Oxidant Support for Healthy Vision and Eye Function*

ALCOHOL-FREE CONCENTRATED EXTRACTS OF:

FORMULA	MG EXTRACT PER 2 CAPSULES
Bilberry berry (*Vaccinium myrtillus*)	50 mg
Grape seed (*Vitis vinifera*)	20 mg
Lutein	10 mg
Astaxanthin	2 mg

STANDARDIZED TO FULL SPECTRUM ACTIVITY PROFILE

Anthocyanidins (from Bilberry)	12.5 mg
Polyphenols (from Grape seed)	1.9 mg

DOSAGE
Liquid Phyto-Caps: 1 capsule, 2 times daily

DURATION OF USE
3-4 months or longer

BEST TAKEN
With food, particularly containing some type of healthy fat such as olive oil.

DESCRIPTION OF FORMULA

Everyone wants to protect and even optimize his or her vision. The eyes undergo numerous challenges, however, that threaten optimal vision. Most people are familiar with constant strain of use. This can be exacerbated by insufficient light (particularly natural light), flickering fluorescent lights, and computer screens. This strain is believed to contribute to the common visual challenges we face.*

Free-radical excess is another serious problem for the eyes; it can discourage proper function in the eyes. Not only do the eyes have to handle the usual free radical burden resulting from normal metabolism by healthy cells, but also free radicals that are introduced in the diet, from the air, and in the water. Additionally, the ultraviolet portion of sunlight bathes and challenges the eyes, causing further damage. Luckily there are several herbals that can help compensate for all these challenges and thus help maintain healthy eyes.*

Bilberry is rich in anthocyanosides, flavonoids, oligomeric proanthocyanidins and other phytochemicals that promote blood vessel integrity and enhance microcirculation, particularly to the eyes. Bilberry also helps to maintain ocular health by protecting the eyes from the effects of environmental stressors. Likewise, this fruit offers potent antioxidant protection in the retina, which can be susceptible to oxidative insults over time.*

Grape seed extract offers a potent source of proanthocyanidins, powerful antioxidants with the unique ability to cross the blood-brain barrier, offering optimal protection to the brain and eyes from destructive elements in the environment. Grape seed proanthocyanidins help to maintain the structure and function of retinal tissue by supporting healthy circulation, maintaining the integrity of blood vessels around the eye structure, and reducing eye strain that is associated with the normal aging process.*

Lutein is a carotenoid related to beta-carotene. Large studies have suggested that lutein is a protective antioxidant for the eyes. Lutein is best absorbed when taken with a fatty meal.*

Astaxanthin is another carotenoid. It acts as an antioxidant in the retina, similar to lutein.*

COMPLEMENTARY PHYTO-CAPS/LIQUID FORMULAS/LIQUID EXTRACTS

Anti-Oxidant Supreme Liquid Phyto-Caps™, Bilberry Leaf

SAFETY EVALUATION/CONTRAINDICATIONS

Do not take during pregnancy and lactation. Use with caution and seek the advice of a qualified healthcare professional if you have a hemorrhagic disorder.*

KNOWN DRUG INTERACTIONS

This formula should be used with caution in combination with drugs that inhibit blood clotting and platelet aggregation including but not limited to warfarin (Coumadin®). The herbs in this formula have not been studied extensively to determine their interactions with other medications.*

REFERENCES

Bombardelli E, Morazzoni P. Vitis vinifera L. Fitoterapia 1995;66:291-317.

Brown D. Herbal Prescriptions for Health and Healing. Roseville, CA: Prima Health, 2000:47-54.

Brown L, Rimm EB, Seddon JM, et al. A prospective study of carotenoid intake and risk of cataract extraction in US men. Am J Clin Nutr 1999;70:517-24.

Chasan-Taber L, Willett WC, Seddon JM, et al. A prospective study of carotenoid and vitamin A intakes and risk of cataract extraction in US women. Am J Clin Nutr 1999;70:509-16.

Corbe C, Boissin JP, Siou A. Light vision and chorioretinal circulation. Study of the effect of procyanidolic oligomers (Endotelon). J Fr Ophtalmol 1988;11:453-60.

Cunio L. Vaccinium myrtillus. Australian J Med Herbalism 1993;5:81-85.

Fromantin M. OPC in the treatment of capillary weakness and retinopathy in diabetics. Méd Int 1981;16:432-4.

Leung AY, Foster S. Encyclopedia of Common Natural Ingredients Used in Food, Drugs and Cosmetics 2nd ed. New York: John Wiley & Sons Inc., 1996:84-5.

Murray M. Bilberry (Vaccinium myrtillus). Am J Nat Med 1997;4:18-22.

Muth ER, Laurent JM, Jasper P. The effect of bilberry nutritional supplementation on night visual acuity and contrast sensitivity. Alt Med Rev 2000;5:164-73.

Roodenburg AJC, Leenen R, van het Hof KH, et al. Amount of fat in the diet affects bioavailability of lutein esters but not of alpha-carotene, beta-carotene, and vitamin E in humans. Am J Clin Nutr 2000;71:1187-93.

Vérin MMP, Vildy A, Maurin JF. Therapeutic essay: Retinopathy and OPC. Bordeaux Med 1978;11:1467-73.

Weiss RF. Herbal Medicine. Gothenberg, Sweden: Ab Arcanum and Beaconsfield: Beaconsfield Publishers Ltd, trans. Meuss AR, 1985:101-2.

Yarnell E. Review of clinical trials on oligomeric proanthocyanidins. HealthNotes Review of Complementary and Integrative Medicine 1999;6:92-4.

WOMEN'S LIBIDO

For the Enhancement of Libido*

ALCOHOL-FREE CONCENTRATED EXTRACTS OF:

FORMULA	MG EXTRACT PER 3 CAPSULES
Suma root (*Pfaffia paniculata*)	75 mg
Chuchuhuasi bark (*Maytenus macrocarpa*)	45 mg
Tribulus bark (*Tribulus terrestris*)	42 mg
Damiana leaf (*Turnera diffusa*)	39 mg
Sarsaparilla root (*Smilax regelii*)	39 mg
Horny Goat Weed (*Epimedium grandiflorum*)	39 mg
Wild Oats milky seed (*Avena sativa*)	24 mg
Ginger rhizome, Supercritical CO_2 Extract (*Zingiber* off.)	12 mg
Blue Vervain (*Verbena hastata*)	12 mg

DOSAGE

Liquid Phyto-Caps: 1 capsule, 3 times daily

DURATION OF USE

2-3 months

BEST TAKEN

Between meals, with warm water

*THIS STATEMENT HAS NOT BEEN EVALUATED BY THE FOOD AND DRUG ADMINISTRATION.
THIS PRODUCT IS NOT INTENDED TO DIAGNOSE, TREAT, CURE OR PREVENT ANY DISEASE.

A LONG-LASTING APPROACH

This powerful formula helps restore a woman's libido where it has become lessened, or altogether lost. Any long-lasting approach to libido support must include an effective strategy for building nervous system reserve. No stimulants have been used here. To drive an already exhausted physiology with stimulants is counterproductive. The primary focus of this formula is simple nervous system support.*

Often, individuals who live in modern society become stressed beyond the natural bounds of a healthy physiology. Regardless of the origin of the stress, the effects may very well be the same – nervous exhaustion, and sexual disinterest. In this formula we bring together powerful nervous system tonics that are also known to support sexual performance and/or desire.*

Suma is known traditionally for use in the promotion of normal sexual function. Its benefits as a tonic have lead it to be commonly known as Brazilian Ginseng. Suma's indigenous name is Para Todo, meaning "for everything." Reports also suggest that Suma and its related species have been used as aphrodisiacs for some 300 years.*

Chuchuhuasi and its related species have found long traditional application with matters relating to sexual performance. It is a tonic that strengthens a wide array of digestive processes. It is present in this formula, primarily for its noted tonic effect, and for its reputation for enhancing performance.*

Tribulus is reported to be a folkloric medicine used to support the cardiovascular system and healthy vision. It has also been used traditionally as an aphrodisiac. A small number of in-vitro studies have leant support to this traditional use as an aphrodisiac, suggesting that protodiosin (an isolated constituent of Tribulus) can promote healthy sexual activity (in animals).*

Damiana is reported to be a tonic used in traditional cultures as an aphrodisiac. In fact, the plant was formally given the species name, aphrodisiaca. It is a tonic that is said to support sexual function in both women and men, specifically where sexual weakness and debility are associated with nervousness and despondency. In the tradition of physiomedicalism, Damiana is considered to be an aphrodisiac, with particular influence as a trophorestorative (builds nervous strength). At least one scientific study with animals supports its use for sexual performance.*

Sarsaparilla is an alterative (blood purifier) that is also known for its normalizing activity. Liver support is also noted. Sarsaparilla is included in this performance formula for its tonifying influence combined with its ability to support healthy metabolism.*

Epimedium is better known by its common name, Horny Goat Weed. As such a name might imply, this plant is considered an aphrodisiac. Traditionally, it is also used as a tonic. In Traditional Chinese Medicine, Epimedium is known to encourage sexual desire and activity.*

Wild Oats are present here for the same reason that they appear in our Male Libido formula – for their valued influence on nervous system health. This plant is often used with complaints of the digestive system where there is also temporary physical weakness and fatigue. Wild Oats may also be used as nourishment.*

Ginger is a well-known herbal food. Traditionally, Ginger has long been used during menstruation. It is included in this Women's Libido formula for its traditional use as an aphrodisiac.*

Blue Vervain is another example of a plant remedy that is traditionally used to support normal menstruation. Species related to Verbena hastata are reported to have influence over the nervous system. Blue Vervain is both calming and building to the nervous system. Such influence over the nervous system has lead to its use with stress.*

Note: The intention of this information is to represent the traditional use of the individual botanicals found in these formulas and to inform the reader of any evolving scientific inquiry relevant to the formula's ingredients.

COMPLEMENTARY PHYTO-CAPS/LIQUID FORMULAS/LIQUID EXTRACTS

Adrenal Health Liquid Phyto-Caps™, Phyto-Proz Liquid Phyto-Caps™

SAFETY EVALUATION/CONTRAINDICATIONS

Do not use this product during pregnancy or lactation. Women with hormone sensitive conditions such as breast, uterine or ovarian cancer, endometriosis, and uterine fibroids should consult a qualified healthcare professional before using this formula due to its potential estrogenic effects.

KNOWN DRUG INTERACTIONS

Consult a physician if you are taking any prescription drugs.

REFERENCES

Agricultural Research Service. Dr. Duke's Phytochemical and Ethnobotanical Databases: Ethnobotanical uses Turnera Diffusa. Online. Internet. [8/23/00]. Available WWW:http://www.ars-grin.gov/cgi-bin/duke/ethnobot.pl

Priest AW, Priest LR. Herbal medication. A clinical dispensary handbook. 1982. Pg. 80.

Arletti R, et al. Stimulating property of Turnera diffusa and Pfaffia paniculata extracts on the sexual-behaviour of male rats. Psychopharmacology. 1999;143(1):15-19.

Walker M. Medical Journalist Report of Innovative Biologics. Townsend Letter for Doctors. 1998; Nov: 18-22.

Agricultural Research Service. Dr. Duke's Phytochemical and Ethnobotanical Databases: Ethnobotanical uses Epimedium grandiflorum. Online. Internet. [8/30/00]. Available WWW: http://www.ars-grin.gov/cgi-bin/duke/ethnobot.pl

Blumenthal M, et al. Ed. The Complete German Commission E Monographs. Austin, TX: American Botanical Council; 1998. Pg. 356.

NAPRALERT Search results for Maytenus ilicifolia (ethnomedical information). Program for Collaborative Research in the Pharmaceutical Sciences College of Pharmacy, University of Illinois at Chicago. September 15, 1994.

Agricultural Research Service. Dr. Duke's Phytochemical and Ethnobotanical Databases: Ethnobotanical uses Maytenus ilicifolia. Online. Internet. [8/30/00]. Available WWW: http://www.ars-grin.gov/cgi-bin/duke/ethnobot.pl

Schwontkwoski D. Herbs of the Amazon: Traditional and common uses. Salt Lake City: Science Student Braintrust Pub, 1993.

Easterling J. Traditional uses of rainforest botanicals. Self Published. Pg. 20.

Willard T. Wild Rose Scientific Herbal. Wild rose College of Natural Healing; Alberta; 1991.

Bisset NG. Herbal Drugs and Phytopharmaceuticals. Ann Arbor. CRC Press;1994.

Schulick P. Ginger, common spice or wonder drug. Herbal Free Press, Vermont. USA.

Newmark TM, Schulick P. Beyond Aspirin. Prescott, Az. HOHM Press. 2000. Pg. 244.

Qureshi S, et al. Studies on herbal aphrodisiacs used in Arab system of medicine. Am J Chin Med. 1989;17(1-2):57-63.

Agricultural Research Service. Dr. Duke's Phytochemical and Ethnobotanical Databases: Ethnobotanical uses Pfaffia tuberosa. Online. Internet. [8/30/00]. Available WWW: http://www.ars-grin.gov/cgi-bin/duke/ethnobot.pl

NAPRALERT Search results for Pfaffia paniculata (ethnomedical information). Program for Collaborative Research in the Pharmaceutical Sciences College of Pharmacy, University of Illinois at Chicago. November 4, 1994.

Felter H, Lloyd JU. King's American Dispensatory. Portland. Eclectic Medical Publications; 1983.

WHOLE BODY DEFENSE

Maintains a Healthy Inflammatory Response*

ALCOHOL-FREE CONCENTRATED EXTRACTS OF:

FORMULA	MG EXTRACT PER 2 CAPSULES
Echinacea aerial parts fresh juice (*E. purpurea*)	500 mg
Astragalus root (*Astragalus membranaceus*)	150 mg
Larch gum (*Larix occidentalis*)	100 mg
Maitake PD Fraction (*Grifola frondosa*)	6 mg
STANDARDIZED TO FULL SPECTRUM ACTIVITY PROFILE	
Total Polysaccharides and Glycoproteins	50 mg
℞-P Factors – Echinacea Polysaccharides from fresh juice	10 mg

DOSAGE

Liquid Phyto-Caps: Take 1 capsule with a small amount of warm water 2 times daily between meals.

DURATION OF USE

3 months

BEST TAKEN

Between meals, with warm water

DESCRIPTION OF FORMULA

Living in today's caustic environment can be a burden to our already active immune system. In response to this dilemma, Gaia Herbs, Inc. has singled out the most highly selected herbs from across the globe that enhance the body's long-term immune system response to environmental stressors. As a result, the unique formula created in Whole Body Defense enhances the vital force of our immune system while simultaneously supplying the body with free-radical quenching antioxidants.*

Echinacea root has a long and honored history by Native American groups and was once considered by many tribes as "a remedy for more ailments than any other plant". Even at the turn of the century, Eclectic Physicians used it widely for skin disruptions, respiratory complaints, and as a general antiseptic. However, until recently, the exact function of this plant had not yet been clearly understood. Thanks to the NIH-NCCAM research grant bestowed to the Gaia Herbs Research

*THIS STATEMENT HAS NOT BEEN EVALUATED BY THE FOOD AND DRUG ADMINISTRATION. THIS PRODUCT IS NOT INTENDED TO DIAGNOSE, TREAT, CURE OR PREVENT ANY DISEASE

Lab, a select group of compounds have now been elucidated that are responsible for understanding how Echinacea works. Utilizing a patent-pending extraction method, a new set of compounds have now been whole-plant standardized and are known as "Px-P Factors" which collectively represent the polysaccharides and glycoprotein fractions. The "Px-P Factors" in Whole Body Defense support the phagocytic activity of macrophage cells while also promoting healthy levels of interferon. In doing so, these compounds deliver a powerful preventative action and supply a naturally healthy immune response.*

Astragalus membranaceus has been used for centuries in Traditional Chinese Medicine to tonify "chi" which translates into English as 'life force' or 'life energy'. Astragalus was popularly used historically as an immune enhancing tonic to prevent susceptibility to the "cold". Several studies have confirmed its ability to bolster the activity of our immune system by encouraging normal levels of natural killer cells and interferon production. By fortifying the immune system our body is better suited to tolerate the harsh environment of the winter season.*

Arabinogalactans are an important water-soluble polysaccharide found in plants such as carrots, radishes, tomatoes, pears, and Echinacea to name a few. Whole Body Defense includes a specific group of arabinogalactans found exclusively in the coniferous tree the western larch (Larix occidentalis). Larch arabinogalactans are actually a mixture of several different arabinogalactans which research has suggested may have immune-enhancing activity. In fact, some studies have shown that it has a positive effect on the levels of interferon, interleukin-1 and interleukin-6 as well as stimulating phagocytosis and natural killer cell activity.*

Indigenous to northeastern Japan, Maitake mushrooms typically grow at the foot of Oak trees in clusters that resemble fluttering butterflies. This resemblance led the Japanese to refer to this type of mushroom as Maitake, which means "dancing mushroom." Maitake's primary use within traditional Chinese and Japanese medicine centers around its ability to enhance the immune system. In particular, this mushroom includes a beta-glucan polysaccharide known as grifolan. Grifolan is credited for rousing macrophages, natural killer cells, interleukin-1 and -2, and T-cells within the immune system.*

With today's toxic environment our immune system is in need for a vital, direct, and efficacious botanical support. In order to strengthen our long-term health and biochemical responses to environmental stressors it has become wise to supplement our diet with herbal tonics. Whole Body Defense is formulated to enhance the vital force of our immune system utilizing age-old wisdom and modern-day scientific extraction techniques to deliver a potent herbal immune-supporting formula.*

*Note: The intention of this information is to represent the traditional use of the individual botanicals found in these formulas and to inform the reader of any evolving scientific inquiry relevant to the formula's ingredients.

COMPLEMENTARY HERBS/FORMULAS

Anti-Oxidant Supreme Liquid Phyto-Caps™, Maitake Defense Liquid Phyto-Caps™

SAFETY EVALUATION/CONTRAINDICATIONS

Before using this product, talk with your healthcare professional if you suffer from a medical condition. Please visit www.gaiaherbs.com to obtain information regarding potential contraindications and/or side effects that may be associated with herbs found in this formula.*

KNOWN DRUG INTERACTIONS

Before using this product, talk with your healthcare professional if you take any medications. Please visit www.gaiaherbs.com to obtain information regarding any possible drug interactions that may be associated with herbs found in this formula.*

BIBLIOGRAPHY

Bensky K, Gamble A: Chinese Herbal Medicine Materia Medica, Seattle, 1986, Eastland Press.

Ellingwood F, Lloyd JU: American Materia Medica, Therapeutics and Pharmacognosy, 2nd Ed., Portland, 1983, Eclectic Medical Publications.

Han DW, Xu RL, Yeoung SCS: Abst Chin Med 2(1):105-134, 1998.

Hauer J, Anderer FA. Mechanism of Stimulation of Human Natural Killer Cytotoxicity by Arabinogalactan from Larix occidentalis. Can Immunology, Immunotherapy 1993; 36:237-44.

McGuffin M, Hobbs C, Upton R, Goldberg A, eds. American Herbal Products Association's Botanical Safety Handbook. Boca Raton, FL: CRC Press, LLC 1997.

Turner RB, Riker DK, Gangemi JD: Antimicrob Agents Chemother 44(6):1708-1709, 2000.

Vogel VJ: American Indian Medicine, Norman, OK, 1970, University of Oklahoma Press.

*THIS STATEMENT HAS NOT BEEN EVALUATED BY THE FOOD AND DRUG ADMINISTRATION.
THIS PRODUCT IS NOT INTENDED TO DIAGNOSE, TREAT, CURE OR PREVENT ANY DISEASE

Index

D

E

F

G

H

N

O

P

Q

R